KS3 Maths Progress

Confidence • Fluency • Problem-solving • Progression

ONE

Series editors:
Dr Naomi Norman • Katherine Pate

ALWAYS LEARNING

PEARSON

Published by Pearson Education Limited, Edinburgh Gate, Harlow, Essex, CM20 2JE.

www.pearsonschoolsandfecolleges.co.uk

Text © Pearson Education Limited 2014
Typeset by Tech-Set Ltd, Gateshead
Original illustrations © Pearson Education Limited 2014
Cover illustration by Robert Samuel Hanson
Index by Indexing Specialists (UK) Ltd

The rights of Nick Asker, Lynn Byrd, Andrew Edmondson, Bobbie Johns, Catherine Murphy and Katherine Pate to be identified as authors of this work have been asserted by them in accordance with the Copyright, Designs and Patents Act 1988.

First published 2014

17 16 15 14
10 9 8 7 6 5 4 3 2 1

British Library Cataloguing in Publication Data
A catalogue record for this book is available from the British Library

ISBN 978 1 447 96229 8

Printed in Italy by Lego S.p.A

Acknowledgements
The publisher would like to thank the following for their kind permission to reproduce their photographs:

Alamy Images: Derek Croucher 203, Tony Hobbs 144, Travel Pictures 154; **DK Images:** Peter Anderson 59; **Fotolia.com:** butenkow 224, Kara 110, Val Thoermer 151; **Getty Images:** Stu Forster 141; **Pearson Education Ltd:** Jon Barlow 121; **Plainpicture Ltd:** photocake. de 11; **Shutterstock.com:** Aleksandrs Samuilovs 113, D. Hammonds 14, Dmitry Kalinovsky 115, leungchopan 233, Monkey Business Images 118, Natalia Barsukova 169, pedrosala 226, Roobcio 66; **SuperStock:** Cultura Limited 256; **Thinkstock:** Belinda Pretorius 69, Kevin Snair 62, mariakraynova 64; **Veer / Corbis:** adriano77 1, Anastasia Tepikina 208, Andresr 229, Arrixx 45, BestPhotoStudio 41, Comaniciu Dan Dumitru 95, Corepics 149, cynoclub 6, darrenbaker 172, decisiveimages 199, Galyna Andrushko 250, herreid 29, hinnamsaisuy 178, _human 43, jarih 205, Karin Lau 125, Kudrin Ruslan 201, Maridav 89, Matthew Maloney 9, Melinda Fawver 196, Michael Bednarek 32, Monkey Business Images 3, 86, 236, oliopi 260, steve100 253, stillfx 181, stockphotos 38, 147, stokkete 92, Tom Gowanlock 231, Tom Wang 175, wayoutwest 35, zmkstudio 123; **www.imagesource.com:** Corbis Super RF 139

All other images © Pearson Education

Every effort has been made to trace the copyright holders and we apologise in advance for any unintentional omissions. We would be pleased to insert the appropriate acknowledgement in any subsequent edition of this publication.

CONTENTS

KS3 Maths Progress

Confidence • Fluency • Problem-solving • Progression

Pedagogy at the heart – This new course is built around a unique pedagogy that's been created by leading mathematics educational researchers and Key Stage 3 teachers. The result is an innovative learning structure based around 10 key principles designed to nurture confidence and raise achievement.

Pedagogy – our 10 key principles

- Fluency
- Mathematical Reasoning
- Multiplicative Reasoning
- Problem Solving
- Progression

- Concrete-Pictorial - Abstract (CPA)
- Relevance
- Modelling
- Reflection (metacognition)
- Linking

Progression to Key Stage 4 – In line with the 2014 National Curriculum, there is a strong focus on fluency, problem-solving and progression to help prepare your students' progress through their studies.

Stretch, challenge and support – Catering for students of all abilities, these Student Books are structured to deliver engaging and accessible content across three differentiated tiers, each offering a wealth of worked examples and questions, supported by key points, literacy and strategy hints, and clearly defined objectives.

Within each unit:

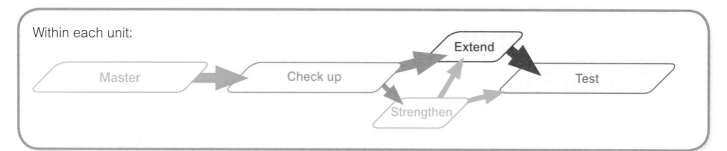

Master → Check up → Strengthen / Extend → Test

Differentiated for students of all abilities:

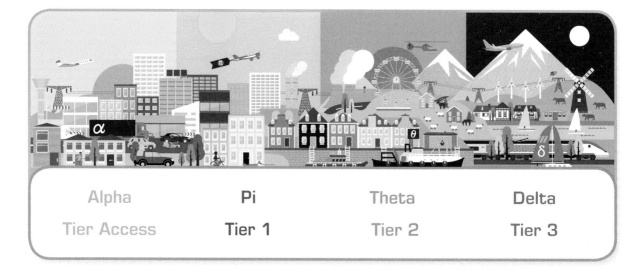

Alpha	Pi	Theta	Delta
Tier Access	Tier 1	Tier 2	Tier 3

Progress with confidence!

This innovative Key Stage 3 Maths course embeds a modern pedagogical approach around our trusted suite of digital and print resources, to create confident and numerate students ready to progress further.

Help at the front-of-class – **ActiveTeach Presentation** is our tried and tested service that makes all of the Student Books available for display on a whiteboard. The books are supplemented with a range of videos and animations that present mathematical concepts along a concrete - pictorial - abstract pathway, allowing your class to progress their conceptual understanding at the right speed.

Learning beyond the classroom – Focussing on online homework, **ActiveCourse** offers students unprecedented extra practice (with automarking) and a chance to reflect on their learning with the confidence-checker. Powerful reporting tools can be used to track student progression and confidence levels.

Easy to plan, teach and assess – Downloadable **Teacher Guides** provide assistance with planning through the Schemes of Work. Lesson plans link both front-of-class **ActiveTeach Presentation** and **ActiveCourse** and provide help with reporting, functionality and progression. Both **Teacher Guides** and **ActiveTeach Presentation** contain the **answers** to the Student Book exercises.

Teacher Guides include **Class Progression Charts** and **Student Progression Charts** to support formative and summative assessment through the course.

Practice to progress – KS3 Maths Progress has an extensive range of practice across a range of topics and abilities. From the **Student Books** to write-in **Progression Workbooks** through to **ActiveCourse**, there is plenty of practice available in a variety of formats whether for in the classroom or for learning at home independently.

For more information, visit
www.pearsonschools.co.uk/ks3mathsprogress

Welcome to KS3 Maths Progress student books!

Confidence · Fluency · Problem-solving · Progression

Starting a new course is exciting! We believe you will have fun with maths, at the same time nurturing your confidence and raising your achievement.

Here's how:

At the end of the *Master* lessons, take a *Check up* test to help you decide to *Strengthen*, or *Extend* your learning. You may be able to mark this test yourself.

Choose only the topics in *Strengthen* that you need a bit more practice with. You'll find more hints here to lead you through specific questions. Then move on to *Extend*.

Extend helps you to apply the maths you know to some different situations. *Strengthen* and *Extend* both include *Enrichment* or *Investigations*.

When you have finished the whole unit, a *Unit test* helps you see how much progress you are making.

Clear *Objectives*, showing what you will cover in each lesson, are followed by a *Confidence* panel to boost your understanding and engage your interest.

Have a look at *Why Learn This?* This shows you how maths is useful in everyday life.

Improve your *Fluency* – practise answering questions using maths you already know.

The first questions are *Warm up*. Here you can show what you already know about this topic or related ones…

…before moving on to further questions, with *Worked examples* and *Hints* for help when you need it.

Your teacher has access to Answers in either ActiveTeach Presentation or the Teacher Guides.

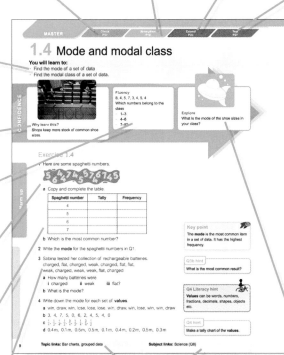

Topic links show you how the maths in a lesson is connected to other mathematical topics. Use the *Subject links* to find out where you might use the maths you have learned here in your other lessons, such as science, geography and computing.

Explore a real-life problem by discussing and having a go. By the end of the lesson you'll have gained the skills you need to start finding a solution to the question using maths.

STEM and Finance lessons

Context lessons expand on *Real, STEM* and *Finance* maths. Finance questions are related to money. STEM stands for Science, Technology, Engineering and Maths. You can find out how charities use maths in their fundraising, how engineers monitor water flow in rivers, and why diamonds sparkle (among other things!)

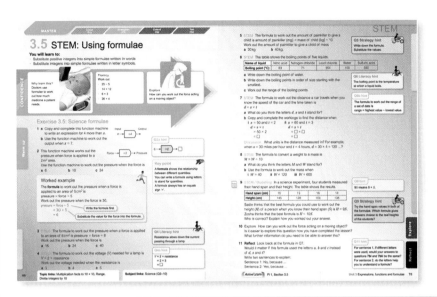

You can improve your ability to use maths in everyday situations by tackling *Modelling, Reasoning, Problem-solving* and *Real* questions. *Discussions* prompt you to explain your reasoning or explore new ideas with a partner.

Some questions are tagged as *Finance* or *STEM*. These questions show how the real world relies on maths. Follow these up with whole lessons that focus on how maths is used in the fields of finance, science and technology.

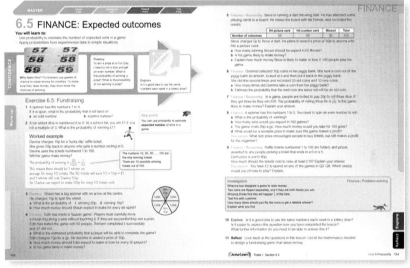

As well as hints that help you with specific questions, you'll find *Literacy hints* (to explain some unfamiliar terms) and *Strategy hints* (to help with working out).

At the end of each lesson, you get a chance to *Reflect* on how confident you feel about the topic.

Your teacher may give you a Student Progression Chart to help you see your progression through the units.

Further support

You can easily access extra resources that tie in to each lesson – look for the ActiveLearn icon on the lesson pages for ActiveCourse online homework links. These are clearly mapped to lessons and provide fun, interactive exercises linked to helpful worked examples and videos.

The Progression Workbooks, full of extra practice for key questions will help you reinforce your learning and track your own progress.

Enjoy!

1.1 Tables and pictograms

You will learn to:
- Find information from tables and pictograms.

CONFIDENCE

Why learn this?
Tables make it easy to understand a large amount of data.

Fluency

△ △ ○ ○ △ ○ △ △ △

- Which is the most common shape?
- How many more triangles than circles?
- How many shapes altogether?

Explore
How can a table show the number of children in students' families?

Exercise 1.1

Warm up

1 The table shows the number of girls and boys in a class.

Student	Number
girls	13
boys	17
Total	30

a How many girls are there?

b How many more boys than girls are there?

> **Q1b hint**
>
> Boys
>
> | 17 |
> | 13 |
>
> Girls ?

2 STEM / Real The table shows the number of faults on cars that were tested for their MOT.

Number of faults	Number of cars
0	8
1	12
2	10
3	8
4	6

a How many cars had 2 faults?

b How many cars had more than 2 faults?

c How many cars were tested altogether?

d What was the most common number of faults?

e How many cars passed the MOT?

> **Q2 Literacy hint**
>
> Cars over three years old must pass an MOT test each year to make sure that they are safe. MOT stands for Ministry of Transport.

> **Q2e hint**
>
> If a car passed the test, would it have any faults?

Topic links: Probability

3 This **pictogram** shows the numbers of text messages Kayleigh sent.

Numbers of texts sent

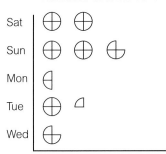

Key: ⊕ represents 4 texts

a How many texts do these represent?

i ⊟ ii ◿

b Copy and complete the table to show the number of texts she sent each day.

c On which day did she send the most messages?

d How many messages did she send at the weekend?

e How many messages did she send altogether?

Day	Messages
Sat	
Sun	
Mon	2
Tue	
Wed	

Key point

A **pictogram** uses pictures to show **data**. The **key** shows what each picture represents.

Q3 Literacy hint

Data is a set of information.

Q3e Literacy hint

'Altogether' means 'add them all up'.

4 Real This pictogram shows the shoe sizes of some Year 9 boys.

Y9 boys' shoe sizes

a How many boys have shoe size 7?

b What is the most common shoe size?

c How many boys have shoe size bigger than 7?

d How many boys have shoes smaller than size 8?

e Five boys have size $7\frac{1}{2}$. Draw the pictures to show this.

Key: represents 2 boys

Q4c hint

	size 8	size 9	size 10
	10	3	1

5 Explore How can a table show the number of children in students' families?

Is it easier to explore this question now you have completed the lesson?

What further information do you need to be able to answer this?

6 Reflect

a For each statement A, B and C, choose a score.

1 – always yes   2 – sometimes yes   3 – never

A I try hard at maths.

B I am calm in maths lessons.

C I am good at maths.

b Did you score 2 or 3 for any of the statements?

If so, discuss with a classmate what you might do to try to score 1.

Q6a hint

Write A, B or C. Put your score beside each letter.

Explore

Reflect

1.2 Bar charts

You will learn to:

- Find information from bar and bar-line charts
- Display data using bar and bar-line charts.

Why learn this?
School outfitters record the uniform sizes they sell each week so they can order enough stock.

Fluency
15 students walk to school.
8 students cycle.
How many more students walk than cycle?

Explore
How do TV news reports show data?

CONFIDENCE

Exercise 1.2

Warm up

1 What steps do these scales go up in?

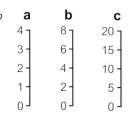

a
4
3
2
1
0

b
8
6
4
2
0

c
20
15
10
5
0

Worked example

The **bar chart** shows some students' favourite takeaway shops.

Key point
A **bar chart** uses bars of equal width to show data.

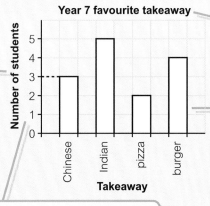

Look across to find the number of students who chose Chinese.

The title says what the chart is about.

The bars are the same width. They have equal width gaps between them.

The vertical axis shows the number of students. The numbers go up in steps of 1.

a How many students chose each takeaway?
3 Chinese, 5 Indian, 2 pizza, 4 burger
b How many more students chose a burger than a pizza?
4 − 2 = 2 students
c How many students are there altogether?
3 + 5 + 2 + 4 = 14 students

Add up the numbers for each takeaway.

Discussion What does the tallest bar show?

2 The **bar chart** shows the e-reader covers sold by a shop.

a How many blue covers were sold?

b More red covers were sold than blue covers. How many more?

c How many covers were sold altogether?

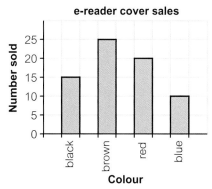

e-reader cover sales

3 Real The table shows the homes of some Year 7 students.

Copy and complete the bar chart.

Discussion Does it matter how you colour in the bars?

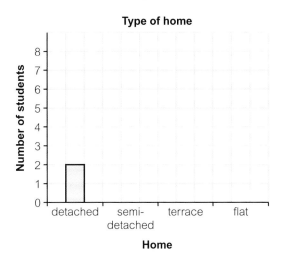

Type of home	Number of students
detached house	2
semi-detached house	8
terraced house	6
flat	4

Q3 hint

Make the bars the same width. Put spaces between the bars. Give your chart a title.

Investigation **Problem-solving**

1 Make a table similar to that in Q3 using data for students in your class.

2 Enter the data into a **spreadsheet**.

3 Use the spreadsheet to draw a bar chart.

Literacy hint

A **spreadsheet** is a computer program that processes data.

4 The **bar-line chart** shows the number of goals scored by a school hockey team in its matches.

Key point

A **bar-line chart** uses lines instead of bars.

Q4b hint

Write the number of matches for each number of goals.
In 3 matches the team scored 0 goals, in 5 matches…, etc.
Then add up the numbers of matches.

a How many times did the team score 3 goals?

b Work out the total number of matches that the team played.

c The team has one final match to play. What is the most likely number of goals it will score?

Q4c hint

Which number of goals is most common?

5 The table shows the number of texts Marrit sent one week.

Day	Sun	Mon	Tue	Wed	Thu	Fri	Sat
Number of texts	12	4	2	6	8	10	10

Copy and complete this bar-line chart for the data.

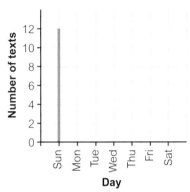

Q5 hint

Give your chart a title.

6 Reasoning What is missing from this bar chart?

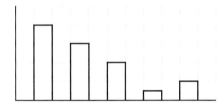

7 Explore How do TV news reports show data?
Is it easier to explore this question now you have completed the lesson? What further information do you need to be able to answer this?

8 Reflect Sometimes in maths you have to read a lot.
   a How hard is it to read maths questions?
   Choose one of these.
   A always hard   **B** sometimes hard   **C** never hard
   b Discuss these questions with a classmate.
      i What makes maths questions hard to read sometimes?
      ii If you find it hard to read a maths question, what could you do?

1.3 Grouped data

You will learn to:
- Organise data using a tally chart
- Understand and use frequency tables
- Understand and draw a grouped bar chart.

Why learn this?
Scientists group data when recording animals' birth weights.

Fluency
What is the most common value in each set of data?
- 3, 8, 9, 9, 5, 4
- 1, 6, 5, 5, 3, 6, 7, 6
- 334, 338, 343, 334, 383

Explore
How could you show the number of star jumps Year 7 students can do in 30 seconds?

Exercise 1.3

1 The table shows the days Year 7 students were born on.

Day	Number of students
Sunday	6
Monday	9
Tuesday	11
Wednesday	8
Thursday	9
Friday	10
Saturday	7
Total	

a How many students were born
  i on a Wednesday
  ii at the weekend
  iii on a weekday?
b How many students are there altogether?

2 This **tally chart** shows how some Year 7 students travel to school.

Method of travel	Tally
bicycle	||||
car	卌 卌 ||||
walk	卌 卌 卌 |||
bus	
other	|||

a How many students cycle to school?
b How many walk to school?
c 21 students travel by bus. Draw the **tally** marks for this.
d A student is picked from Year 7. What is the most likely way they travel to school?

Key point

You can record data in a **tally chart**.
Use a **tally** mark | for each value.
Group tally marks in 5s like this 卌

3 Yuri counted the food items in students' lunch boxes.

6, 7, 5, 6, 5, 8, 6, 4, 5, 5, 7, 6, 5, 6, 4, 7, 6, 5, 6, 4

a Copy the **frequency table**. Tally the numbers in the table.
Fill in the **frequency** column.

Food items	Tally	Frequency
4		
5		
6		
7		
8		
Total		

Key point

The **frequency** is the number of times something happens.
A **frequency table** gives the frequency for each item.

Q3a hint

Work along the row of numbers. Point to one number at a time and make a tally mark.

b How many lunch boxes had 4 food items?

c Which numbers are missing?

   i 7 lunchboxes had ____ items.

   ii 6 lunchboxes had ____ items.

d What is the most common number of items in a lunch box?

e How many lunch boxes did Yuri count? How did you work it out?

Investigation   Reasoning

1 Find a 6-sided pencil. Use a pen to label two sides with A, two with B and two with C.

2 a Roll the pencil 30 times.

   b Record the letter on the top side in this tally chart.

Result	Tally	Frequency
A		
B		
C		
Total		

Key point

A **frequency diagram** is like a bar chart.

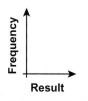

3 Draw a **frequency diagram**.

4 Was there a most common result? If yes, what was it?

---

4 An engineer's toolbox contains drills with these sizes (in mm).

7   10   4   12   2   5   4   9   3   18   6   15

The engineer records the sizes in this **grouped frequency table**.

Drill size (mm)	Tally	Frequency
1–5		
6–10		
11–15		
16–20		

Key point

Data is sometimes put into **groups** or **classes**, such as, 1–5, 6–10, 11–15, …
The group 1–5 includes 1, 2, 3, 4 and 5.
A **grouped frequency table** gives the frequency for each group.

a Which **class** contains

   i a 7 mm drill   **ii** a 10 mm drill?

b Copy the table. Tally the drill sizes in the table. Fill in the frequency column.

c How many drills are in the **group** 11–15 mm?

d Draw a bar chart for the data.

5 **Problem-solving** Fleur asked some students how many coins they had on them.
The grouped bar chart shows her results.

Numbers of coins

Number of coins	Number of students
0–2	6
3–5	
6–8	
9–11	
12–14	

a What values are included in the group 6–8 coins?

b How many students had 9–11 coins on them?

c Which group has the highest frequency?

d Copy and complete the grouped frequency table.

e One of the students had 10 coins. Write the class their number of coins belongs to.

f How many students had 9 or more coins?

g Input the table from part **d** into a spreadsheet. Use the spreadsheet to draw a bar chart.

Discussion Can you tell from the table how many classmates had 7 coins?

Q5f hint

Which groups include students with 9 or more coins?

6 Patrick investigated the numbers of books students owned.
He recorded his results in a grouped frequency table.

a Which group has the highest frequency?

b i Copy the axes.

Numbers of books	Frequency
0–4	8
5–9	12
10–14	6
15–19	6
20–24	2
25–29	2

Q6a hint

Which class has the highest number of students?

Q6b hint

Give your chart a title.

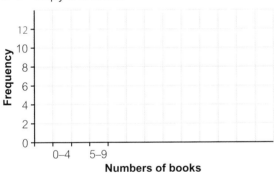

Numbers of books

ii Draw a grouped frequency diagram for the data.

7 **Explore** How could you show the number of star jumps Year 7 students can do in 30 seconds?
Look back at the maths you have learned in this lesson.
How can you use it to answer this question?

8 **Reflect**

a Say the word 'frequency' aloud.

b Are these statements hard to read? If yes, then ask a teacher to help you.
Q3 began, 'Yuri counted the food items in students' lunch boxes'.
Point to the frequency table in Q3.
The frequency tells you the number of times there are 4, 5, 6, 7 or 8 items in a lunch box.

c Look at Q4, Q5 and Q6 with a classmate.
For each question, say and complete this sentence.
'The frequency tells you the number of times there are…'

Q8c hint

Look at how each question begins, then look at its frequency table.

1.4 Mode and modal class

You will learn to:
- Find the mode of a set of data
- Find the modal class of a set of data.

Why learn this?
Shops keep more stock of common shoe sizes.

CONFIDENCE

Fluency
8, 4, 5, 7, 3, 4, 5, 4
Which numbers belong to the class
- 1–3
- 4–6
- 7–9?

Explore
What is the mode of the shoe sizes in your class?

Exercise 1.4

Warm up

1 Here are some spaghetti numbers.

a Copy and complete the table.

Spaghetti number	Tally	Frequency
4		
5		
6		
7		

b Which is the most common number?

2 Write the **mode** for the spaghetti numbers in Q1.

3 Sabina tested her collection of rechargeable batteries.
charged, flat, charged, weak, charged, flat, flat, weak, charged, weak, weak, flat, charged

a How many batteries were
   i charged   **ii** weak   **iii** flat?

b What is the mode?

4 Write down the mode for each set of **values**.

a win, draw, win, lose, lose, lose, win, draw, win, lose, win, win, draw

b 3, 4, 7, 5, 0, 6, 2, 4, 5, 4, 0

c $\frac{1}{4}, \frac{1}{2}, \frac{1}{4}, \frac{1}{2}, \frac{3}{4}, \frac{1}{2}, \frac{1}{4}, \frac{3}{4}, \frac{1}{2}$

d 0.4m, 0.1m, 0.5m, 0.5m, 0.1m, 0.4m, 0.2m, 0.5m, 0.3m

Key point
The **mode** is the most common item in a set of data. It has the highest frequency.

Q3b hint
What is the most common result?

Q4 Literacy hint
Values can be words, numbers, fractions, decimals, shapes, objects etc.

Q4 hint
Make a tally chart of the **values**.

5 Jackson drew this bar chart to show his classmates' favourite cold drinks.
What is the mode?
Discussion Which two drinks should the school canteen stock most of?

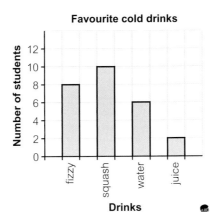

Favourite cold drinks

Q5 hint

Which drink did most students choose?

Worked example

Students ran laps around their playing field for charity.
The table shows the laps they ran.

Laps	Frequency
1–3	5
4–6	2
7–9	6
10–12	4

Look for the class with the highest frequency.

Find the modal class.

The modal class is 7–9 laps.

Write the class.

Key point

The **modal class** is the class or group with the highest frequency.

6 **STEM** Sue recorded the lengths of newts for a wildlife survey.

Length (mm)	Frequency
41–60	9
61–80	11
81–100	6
101–120	2
121–140	1

  a What is the **modal class** for the length?

  b One newt was 93 mm long. Which class is this in?

  Discussion Sue says that the mode is 11. What has she done wrong?

7 **Real** A rugby club played 32 games.
The bar chart shows their scores.

  a What is the modal class of scores?

  b In how many games did the club score between 20 and 39?

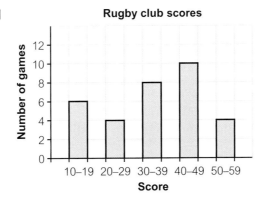

Rugby club scores

Q7b Strategy hint

Which bar(s) do you need to look at?

8 **Explore** What is the modal shoe size in your class?
Is it easier to explore this question now you have completed the lesson? What further information do you need to be able to answer this?

9 **Reflect** Copy and complete these sentences.
To find the mode from a bar chart you look for _____
To find the mode from a table you look for _____

Q9 hint

Look back at what you did to answer Q5.

Explore

Reflect

1.5 Range and median

You will learn to:
- Find the range and median of a set of data
- Compare sets of data using their range, mode and median.

Why learn this?
Football fans can use the range, median and mode to compare teams.

Fluency
- Order these numbers from smallest to largest.
  8, 12, 4, 7, 9, 7
- What is the difference between 7 and 12?

Explore
Compare the goals scored by the top and bottom teams in the Premier League.

Exercise 1.5

1 Find the number that is halfway between

   a 4 and 10   **b** 20 and 30

   c 16 and 24   **d** 7 and 8

   e 12 and 13.

2 Find the mode for each set of data.

   a 5, 2, 8, 4, 4, 3, 9

   b 50, 20, 40, 10, 20, 60, 20, 30, 50, 10

   c 0.1, 0.6, 0.3, 0.1, 0.8, 0.1

   d 0, 1, 1, 0, 0

3 Order the values from smallest to largest. Work out their **range**.

   a 7, 9, 3, 12, 10

   b 8, 3, 15, 6, 2, 12, 6

   c 70, 20, 20, 40, 100

   d 21, 50, 17

   e 250, 150, 400, 300, 350, 250, 200

4 Here are the number of press-ups done by some Year 7 students.
12, 8, 5, 7, 2, 3, 6, 5, 6, 2, 5

   a Work out the range.

   b Find the mode.

5 Work out the range and mode for each data set.

   a 6 cm, 4 cm, 8 cm, 8 cm, 5 cm, 4 cm, 8 cm, 7 cm

   b 25 g, 27 g, 20 g, 22 g, 20 g, 23 g, 23 g, 22 g, 26 g, 20 g

   c 100 mm, 300 mm, 500 mm, 400 mm, 200 mm, 300 mm, 500 mm, 100 mm, 300 mm

   d 65°, 50°, 55°, 60°, 55°, 70°, 50°, 70°, 50°, 55°, 50°

Q1a hint

Count in to the middle.

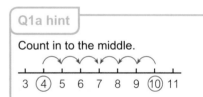

Key point

The **range** shows how spread out a set of data is.

$$\text{range} = \text{largest value} - \text{smallest value}$$

Q3 hint

largest value = ☐
smallest value = ☐
range = ☐ − ☐

Q4a hint

First order the values from smallest to largest.

Q5 hint

Don't forget to write the units in your answers.

Worked example

Find the **median** of 8, 3, 15, 6, 2, 12, 6.

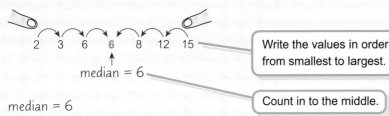

Write the values in order from smallest to largest.

Count in to the middle.

median = 6

Key point

The **median** is the middle value when the data is written in order.

6 Finance These are the prices paid for video games on an internet auction site.
£4, £5, £7, £12, £13, £14, £19, £21, £22

   a Work out the range.

   b Find the median.

7 Write each set of data in order, from smallest to largest.
Then find the median.

   a 5 cm, 2 cm, 7 cm, 4 cm, 4 cm

   b 17, 12, 16, 15, 15, 18, 11, 16, 12

   c 20 g, 70 g, 50 g, 30 g, 75 g, 15 g, 55 g

8 Find the median for each set of test results.
The first has been done for you.

   a 4, 7, 7, 8, 9, 10

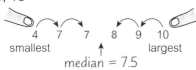

Key point

For a data set with an even number of items there are two middle values. The median is halfway between them.

Q8 hint

Write the numbers in order first.

   b 20, 20, 30, 40, 50, 60, 90, 90

   c 10, 5, 7, 10, 3, 4

   d 14 km, 7 km, 18 km, 12 km, 16 km, 11 km, 13 km, 15 km

   e 16 m*l*, 10 m*l*, 10 m*l*, 12 m*l*, 18 m*l*, 20 m*l*

   Discussion Is the median always one of the values?

9 The number of children in the families of some Year 7 students are
3, 1, 2, 1, 1, 2, 1, 2, 6, 1, 1, 2, 2, 1
Find the median.
Discussion What do you notice about the median for this set of values?

10 Competitors in highland games have to throw a heavy object over a bar.
These are the heights of the bars for successful throws, in feet, for two teams.
Team 1: 15, 13, 14, 12, 13, 12, 11, 13
Team 2: 11, 16, 12, 11, 14, 11, 12, 10

   a i Work out the range for each team.
     ii Which team has the bigger range?

   b i Write down the mode for each team.
     ii Which team has the higher mode?

Key point

You can compare two sets of data using the range and mode.

11 Real Darren and Miriam each take 10 shots at a basketball hoop. Here are their results.

Darren: 5   6   7   6   7   7
Miriam: 9   1   6   4   2   9

Key point

You can also compare two sets of data using the range and the median.

a i Work out the median scores.

ii Who has the better median score?

b i Work out the range of their scores.

ii Who has the smaller range?

Discussion Who would you pick for your basketball team based on the median and range?

Investigation 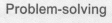   Problem-solving

1 Choose any row, column or complete diagonal from the grid.

	1st	2nd	3rd	4th	5th	6th
A	4	7	2	6	5	1
B	10	0	3	5	2	9
C	4	3	3	7	2	8
D	5	1	0	4	0	10
E	3	9	1	1	1	8
F	5	0	9	10	2	6

2 Work out the range and median.

3 Repeat steps 1 and 2 for five more sets of numbers.

4 Find a row with range 6.

5 Which column has a median of 2?

6 Which diagonal has the highest range?

---

12 Explore Compare the goals scored by the top and bottom teams in the Premier League.

Is it easier to explore this question now you have completed the lesson? What further information do you need to be able to answer this?

13 Reflect Look back at the worked example and read the question carefully.

a Discuss with a classmate.

i Is the worked example picture helpful? Why?

ii Are the comments to the right of the worked example helpful? Why?

b Copy and complete this sentence.

Worked examples are helpful because _____

MASTER

Check
P17

Strengthen
P19

Extend
P23

Test
P27

1.6 Mean

You will learn to:
• Calculate the mean of a set of data.

Why learn this?
When buying a smartphone, you might want to know the mean time between charges.

Fluency
5, 2, 2, 2, 9
Find
• the mode
• the median
• the total.

Explore
How long do smartphone batteries last between charges?

Exercise 1.6

1 Work out the total of
   a 12, 34, 17, 42, 18
   b 6, 1, 12, 5, 11, 4, 10, 9
   c 110, 220, 90, 180, 140, 170, 200, 210, 220, 140

> **Q1a hint**
>
> Add the numbers:
> 12 + 34 + 17 + 42 + 18
> Press the = key to show the total.

2 Work out
   a 22 ÷ 5   **b** 45 ÷ 6   **c** 364 ÷ 13   **d** 160 ÷ 25

3 Share
   a £36 between 4 people
   b 24 cards between 6 people
   c 42 sweets between 7 people.

4 5 members of a paintball team have these numbers of paintballs.
8, 4, 9, 3, 1
   a How many paintballs do they have altogether?
   b They share the paintballs equally.
     How many does each player have?

Worked example

Find the **mean** of 2, 2, 6, 4, 1.

total = 15

| 2 | 2 | 6 | 4 | 1 | 5 values |

| 3 | 3 | 3 | 3 | 3 | 15 ÷ 5 = 3 |

> Add up the values.

total = 2 + 2 + 6 + 4 + 1 = 15
mean = total ÷ number of values = 15 ÷ 5 = 3
mean = 3

> There are 5 values so divide the total by 5.

> **Key point**
>
> Mode and median are both averages. They show a typical value for a set of data.
> The **mean** is another **average**.

Warm up

5 Work out the mean for each set of values.

  a 1, 2, 5, 6

  b 4, 6, 8, 10

  c 2, 1, 6, 3, 3, 5, 2, 4, 1, 3

  d 20p, 20p, 30p, 30p, 50p

  e 5m, 2m, 8m, 2m, 10m, 6m

  f 13kg, 6kg, 29kg, 20kg, 7kg, 22kg, 15kg

  Discussion Look at your answers. Does the mean have to be one of the values?

Q5a hint

Enter 1 + 2 + 5 + 6
Press the = key to give the total.
Enter ÷ 4
Press the = key to give the mean.

6 Real A business recorded employees' days off sick last year.

  2   8   0   5   1   0   3   0   12   4

  Work out the mean.

  Discussion Can you ignore values that are 0 when working out the mean?

7 4 children brought these numbers of sparklers to a party.

  8   15   9   12

  a What is the mean number of sparklers?

  b They shared the sparklers equally. How many sparklers did each child get?

8 4 girls have these numbers of charms on their bracelets.

  9, 6, 7, 4

  a Work out the mean number of charms.

  b Reasoning Can they share their charms equally?

9 A bag contains potatoes weighing 120g, 150g, 100g, 130g, 120g, 130g.

  Work out the mean weight.

Q9 hint

Remember to include the units in your answer.

10 8 students collected these amounts of money for a sponsored walk.

  £5, £8, £4, £6, £4, £3, £2, £12

  Work out the mean amount collected.

11 7 students went out for a meal. The meals cost

  £4.50, £5, £6.50, £6, £9, £4.50, £6.50

  Work out the mean cost of the meals.

12 In a science lesson some students measured their heights.

  152cm, 140cm, 152cm, 150cm, 145cm, 139cm, 143cm, 147cm

  Work out

  a the mode

  b the median

  c the mean

  d the range.

13 Players at a chess tournament won these numbers of games.

5, 2, 4, 0, 9, 4, 6, 4, 3, 8

Work out

a the mode

b the median

c the mean

d the range.

14 A school tested the performance of some BMX bicycles.
The results show the times to complete a course.

Time (min)	17	14	16	17	18	15	18	22	16

a Find the mean time to complete the BMX course.

b Work out the range.

Discussion Is there a mode?

Investigation   Reasoning

1 Work out the mean of the numbers 2, 2, 3, 3, 5.

2 a Add 1 to each of the numbers. Work out the mean again.

  b Compare the mean with Q1. What do you notice?

3 a What do you think will happen to the mean if you add 1 to the numbers in Q2?

  b Work out the mean. Were you right?

4 What would happen if you added 2 to the numbers in Q3? Try it and see.

5 Add your own number to the numbers in Q1. Work out the mean.

6 Copy and complete the rule.

  If you add a number to each value, the mean _____

---

15 Explore How long do smartphone batteries last between charges?
Is it easier to explore this question now you have completed the lesson?
What further information do you need to be able to answer this?

16 Reflect Sophia writes

Finding the mean:

Step 1: Count the values (for example, 1, 2, 9 is 3 values)

Write down Sophie's step 2.

Write down Sophie's step 3.

Compare your steps with others in the class.

> **Q16 hint**
>
> Look back at how you found the mean in this lesson.
> For each step, describe and then show what you do (for example, using 1, 2, 9...).

1 Check up

Log how you did on your Student Progression Chart.

Tables

1 The table shows the minimum daily temperatures in July.

a On how many days was the minimum temperature 12 °C?

b What was the lowest temperature in July?

c What was the most common minimum temperature?

d On how many days was the minimum temperature less than 12 °C?

e On how many days was the temperature recorded?

Temperature (°C)	Days
10	2
11	5
12	4
13	7
14	6
15	6
16	1

2 Some students chose their favourite big cat.

Big cat	Tally	Frequency
lion		12
tiger	☓ ll	
cheetah	llll	
leopard	☓ l	
jaguar	☓	

a How many students chose 'jaguar'?

b Which cat was chosen by 7 students?

c Twelve students chose 'lion'. Complete the tally marks for 12.

d Which big cat was most popular?

3 Copy this table. Complete it for this set of data.
5, 11, 3, 8, 4, 12, 10, 2, 5, 12, 7, 2, 6, 1

Group	Tally	Frequency
1–3		
4–6		
7–9		
10–12		

Charts

4 This pictogram shows the dental appointments made for some patients.

a How many appointments are for cleaning?

b How many appointments are for dentures?

c There are 11 appointments for fillings.
Draw pictures to show 11 appointments.

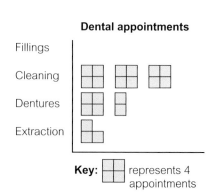

Dental appointments

Key: ▦ represents 4 appointments

5 The bar chart shows the medals received by 4 countries at the 2012 Olympics.

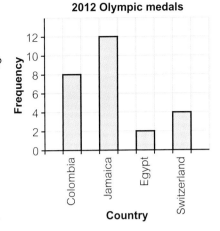

2012 Olympic medals

   a How many medals did Colombia win?
   b Colombia won more medals than Switzerland. How many more?
   c Which country won the most medals?
   d How many medals were won altogether by these countries?

6 Farhat counted the letters in each word on a page.

Letters	Frequency
1–2	10
3–4	25
5–6	20
7–8	10

   a How many words on the page had 3 or 4 letters?
   b Write down the modal class.
   c Copy and complete the bar chart.

Averages and range

7 Look at this set of data.   6, 5, 8, 0, 2, 2, 12
   a Work out the range.   **b** Write down the mode.
   c Find the median.   **d** Calculate the mean.

8 The table shows the distances, in kilometres, that some Year 7 students live from their school.

Distance from school (km)	2	1	5	1	3	2	1	5

   a Work out the range.   **b** Write down the mode.
   c Find the median.   **d** Calculate the mean.

   Here is some information about distances Year 8 students live from school.
   range = 7 km   mode = 2 km   median = 1.5 km
   e Which year group has the bigger range of distances?
   f Which year group lives the greater median distance from school?

9 How sure are you of your answers? Were you mostly
   😞 Just guessing   😐 Feeling doubtful   🙂 Confident
   What next? Use your results to decide whether to strengthen or extend your learning.

Challenge

10 a Write down three numbers with mode 8.
   b Write down three numbers with range 2.
   c Write down three numbers with median 5.

11 The bar-line chart shows the number of brothers of students in a Year 7 class.
   a What is missing from the chart?
   b 12 students do not have any brothers.
      Copy and complete the chart.

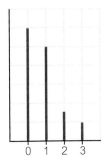

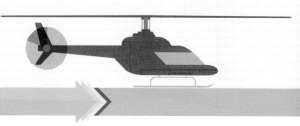

1 Strengthen

You will:

• Strengthen your understanding with practice.

Tables

1 Write down the numbers for these tallies.

a |||| b ̶|̶|̶|̶|̶ ̶|̶|̶|̶|̶ || c ̶|̶|̶|̶|̶ |||

2 Here are some coloured buttons.

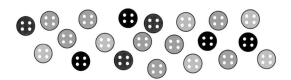

a Copy the table.

Colour	Number of buttons
red	
blue	
green	
black	

b Count each colour. Write the number in the table.

c Which is the most common colour?

d How many buttons are there altogether?

e Add up all the numbers in the table.

f What do you notice about your answers to **d** and **e**?

3 A quilt is made using coloured squares.
The table shows the number (frequency)
of squares of each colour.
Write down the missing word or number.

Colour	Frequency
red	15
blue	12
green	4
yellow	9

a There are ☐ blue squares.

b 9 squares are _____ .

c The most common colour is ____ .

d There are ☐ more blue squares than green squares.

e There are ☐ squares in total?

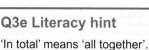

Q3e Literacy hint

'In total' means 'all together'.

4 Scarlett won these prizes in a video game.
$50, $20, $20, $100, $50, $100, $20, $20, $20, $50

a Copy the tally chart and frequency table.

Prize	Tally	Frequency (number of prizes)
$20		
$50		
$100		

b Copy the list of prizes. Cross off the first prize in the list.
Make a tally mark in the table. Do this for all the prizes.

c Count up the tally marks for each prize.
Write the number in the Frequency column.

d Which prize did Scarlett win most often?

Charts

1 Sakura drew a pictogram of the types of chocolate in a box.

   a Look at the key. Draw the symbols for

      i 2 chocolates

      ii 4 chocolates

      iii 1 chocolate.

   b How many milk chocolates are there?

   c How many white chocolates are there?

   d Copy and complete this table.

Chocolate	Frequency
milk	
white	
nut	
fruit	

   e Which is the most common chocolate?

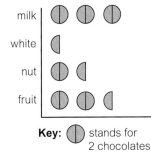

Chocolates in a box

Key: stands for 2 chocolates

Q1a iii hint

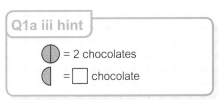

◐ = 2 chocolates

◖ = ☐ chocolate

2 The bar chart shows Year 7 students' favourite activities at a leisure centre.

   a How many students chose swimming?

   b Which is the most popular activity?

   c **i** How many students chose bowling?

      ii How many students chose cinema?

      iii How many more students chose bowling than cinema?

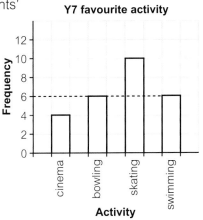

Y7 favourite activity

Q2a hint

Follow the dotted line to the Frequency axis.

Q2b hint

Which activity was chosen by the most students?

Q2c iii hint

☐ – ☐ = ☐

3 Year 8 students chose these activities as their favourite pastime.

Activity	Frequency
cinema	12
bowling	8
skating	4
swimming	6

   a Copy and complete the bar chart to represent all the data in the table.

   b Give your bar chart a title.

Activity

4 The bar-line chart shows the belt weights of some scuba divers.

   a How many belts weigh 7 kg?

   b Which belt weight is used by 2 divers?

   c Write down the **modal weight**.

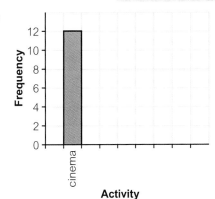

Scuba divers' belt weights

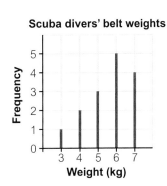

Q4c Literacy hint

The **modal weight** is the most common weight. It is another way of saying the mode.

Q4c hint

Make sure you write down the weight (kg) and not its frequency.

5 Natalie recorded the number of Likes on her Facebook posts.
0, 1, 1, 2, 2, 3, 3, 4, 5, 5, 5, 7, 7, 8, 9, 11, 12, 12, 13
She started this grouped frequency table.
5 posts have 0, 1 or 2 Likes.

a How many posts have 3–5 Likes?

b Copy and complete the grouped frequency table.

c Find the modal class.

d Copy and complete this bar chart for her data.

Likes	Frequency (number of posts)
0–2	5
3–5	
6–8	
9–11	
12–14	

Natalie's Facebook Likes

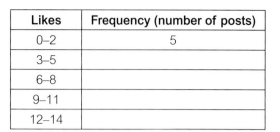

Q5a hint

The group or class 3 to 5 can be written 3–5.
It includes the values 3, 4 and 5.

Q5c hint

Which class has the highest frequency?

Averages and range

1 Write down the mode of this set of data.
5, 4, 0, 5, 4, 0, 2, 4

Q1 hint

Mode = **m**ost common

2 a These snacks were bought from a vending machine.
drink, biscuits, crisps, chocolate, drink, crisps,
chocolate, biscuits, crisps, crisps, drink
Write down the mode.

b The prices of the snacks are
80p, 40p, 50p, 60p, 80p, 50p, 60p, 40p, 50p, 50p, 80p
Write down the mode.

Q2b hint

Don't forget to write the units (p for pence).

3 Some Year 7 students counted the number of items in their pencil cases.
4, 2, 11, 5, 8, 13, 6

a Which is the smallest value?

b Which is the largest value?

c Work out the range.

Q3c hint

range = largest value − smallest value

4 Work out the range for each set of data.

a 8, 4, 8, 5, 9, 7

b 11, 6, 9, 0, 14, 4, 8

c 25 cm, 100 cm, 60 cm, 20 cm, 50 cm

d 14 kg, 20 kg, 17 kg, 15 kg, 15 kg, 17 kg, 19 kg, 15 kg

Q4a hint

Find the smallest and largest numbers first.

5 a The diagram shows some crayons arranged in order of size.
Write down the length of the middle crayon.

b Another set of crayons have these lengths.
5 cm, 5 cm, 8 cm, 9 cm, 9 cm.
Find the median.

Q5b hint

Median is the middle value when they are in order.

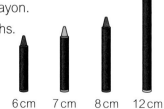

4 cm   6 cm   7 cm   8 cm   12 cm

6 The diagram shows some pencils arranged in order of size.

   a **i** Write down the lengths of the middle two pencils.

     ii Find the median length of the pencils.

   b Another set of pencils have these lengths.
10 cm, 12 cm, 12 cm, 16 cm, 17 cm, 17 cm
Find the median.

9 cm   9 cm   12 cm 14 cm 14 cm 16 cm

Q6a ii hint

The median is halfway between the two middle lengths.
Draw a number line to find halfway between two numbers.

12 cm ☐ 14 cm

7 **a** Write these values in order, from smallest to largest.
7, 3, 6, 4, 10, 7, 4

   b Find the median value.

   c Work out the median of the values 8, 3, 0, 5, 9, 2, 1.

   d Work out the median of the values 26, 20, 25, 28, 21, 23.

Q7a hint

7, ~~4~~, 6, ~~3~~, 10, 7, ~~4~~
3, 4, 4,
Cross off the smallest number and write it down.

8 Angela says the median of 5, 3, 7, 4, 1 is 7 because it is the middle number. Is she correct? Explain.

Q7c hint

Write the numbers in order first.

9 Follow these steps to arrange these counters in 4 equal piles.

   a Collect them together. $1 + 3 + 6 + 2 = \square$

   b Share them into 4 piles. $\square \div 4 = \square$

Q7d hint

There are two middle values.

10 Look at these values.   12, 4, 6, 0, 8

   a Use your calculator to add up the values.

   b How many values are there?

   c Work out the mean.

Q10b hint

Make sure you count the 0 value.

11 Work out the mean of these values.

   a 4, 2, 1, 5   **b** 8, 5, 0, 2, 8, 9, 1, 7

   c 4, 2, 5, 8, 6   **d** 13, 28, 0, 24, 19, 14, 18, 24, 16, 14

Q10c hint

Divide the total by the number of values.
$\square \div \square = \square$
The answer is a decimal.

Enrichment

1 **a** Write the ages of all the children in your family, including cousins.

   b Work out the

     i range   **ii** mode   **iii** median.

   c How many children are younger than the median age?

2 **a** **i** Look at this old saying: 'Early to bed and early to rise makes a man healthy, wealthy and wise.'
Count the letters in each word and complete the table.

     ii Find the modal class.

     iii Draw a bar chart of the data.

Words	Tally	Frequency
Fewer than 3		
3–4		
5–6		
more than 6		

   b Do you think the groups are sensible? How could you change it to make it clearer?

3 **Reflect** In these lessons you have worked out the mode, median, range and mean of values.

   a Which do you find the easiest to work out?

   b Which do you find the hardest to work out?

   c Compare your answers to parts **a** and **b** with a classmate.

1 Extend

You will:
- Extend your understanding with problem-solving.

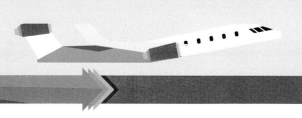

1 Here is some information about the numbers of photos Gareth uploaded.

Facebook	Flickr	Instagram	Tumblr
50	25	20	35

Draw a pictogram to show the data.

Discussion How did you decide on the best symbol to use?

2 Some Year 7 boys were asked what they like reading the most.

Fiction	Graphic novels	Non-fiction	Magazines
30	25	20	15

a Find the mode.

b Use a computer or draw by hand a bar chart to represent the data.

3 **Problem-solving** The range of the sizes of these rings is 12.
What size is the smallest ring?

26

4 **Problem-solving** The modal number of matches in these boxes is 20.

How many matchboxes could contain 20 matches?

5 This bar chart shows the number of road accidents on a road for 7 months.

a In which month were there 5 road accidents?

b In which month were there no road accidents?

c Write down the range of accidents over the 7 months.

d A 20 mph speed limit was introduced at the beginning of May. There was one road accident in May. Do you think the 20 mph speed limit made a difference?

Q5a hint

The bar height is halfway between 4 and 6 on the scale.

Q5c hint

Look at the vertical axis.

Subject links: Computing (Q2), Science (Q6, Q15), Geography (Q8, Q18), PE (Q11, Q14)

6 STEM Jason recorded the pulse rate (beats **per** minute, bpm) of some classmates.
82, 94, 96, 90, 77, 100, 84, 90, 90, 87, 100, 92, 80, 86, 79, 102, 92, 83, 99, 71

Q6 Literacy hint

Per means 'for every'.

Pulse rate (bpm)	Tally	Frequency
70–79		
80–89		
90–99		
100–109		

a Copy and complete the grouped tally chart.
b Work out the frequency for each class.
c What is the modal class?

Q6c hint

Your answer will be a class.

7 Reasoning This chart shows the tools hired from a DIY shop during a month.
a How many sanders were hired?
b How many more ladders than generators were hired?
c What is the mode?

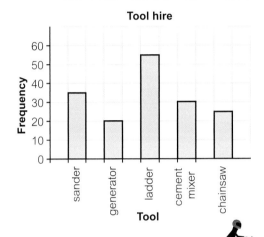

Tool hire

8 Real a A weather station forecast these maximum daily temperatures (°C) in Poole.
20, 22, 19, 19, 16, 18, 17, 18, 17, 17
  i Work out the range.   **ii** Find the mode.
b The actual temperatures for these days are shown below.
18, 21, 20, 16, 16, 13, 15, 13, 11, 13
  i Work out the range.   **ii** Find the mode.
c Compare the actual temperatures with the forecast temperatures using
  i the range   **ii** the mode.

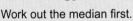

Q8c Strategy hint

The range for the forecast temperatures is _____ than for the actual temperatures.

9 Problem-solving A troop of scouts were awarded these numbers of badges.
12, 4, 8, 3, 5, 8, 5
How many scouts received more than the median number of badges?

Q9 Strategy hint

Work out the median first.

10 All the students in a Year 7 group did star jumps for 30 seconds. The grouped frequency table shows the results.

Star jumps	Frequency
20–24	3
25–29	9
30–34	10
35–39	7
40–44	2

a Find the modal class.
b How many students are in the Year 7 group?
c How many students did fewer than 25 star jumps?
d Darren did 27 star jumps. Which class contains his result?
e Draw a bar chart for the data.
Discussion Would you expect similar results for a class in Year 5?

11 The grouped bar chart shows the points scored by a rugby team.

a Find the modal class.

b In how many games did the team score

   i 19 points or less

   ii 40 points or more?

c Make a grouped frequency table for the data.

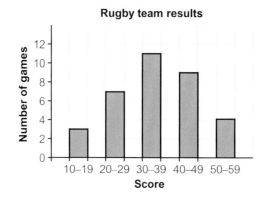

Rugby team results

Q11b ii hint

Look at the last two bars.

12 a A 10-sided dice has sides numbered 0–9. What is the largest number you can make using two 10-sided dice?

b Copy the tally chart.

Dice number	Tally	Frequency
0–19		
20–39		
40–59		

Q12a hint

These two dice show the number 27.

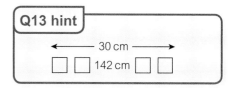

c Roll one dice, then the other, 25 times. Read the first dice, then the second to make a new number. Record the results in the tally chart.

d Find the modal class.

Q12c hint

A 0 and a 5 make 5.
A 4 and a 7 make 47.

13 Reasoning Uran measured the heights of 5 of her friends.
Each friend had a different height.
The median height is 142 cm. The range of the heights is 30 cm.
Could each statement be true or is it false?

A Two friends are taller than 142 cm.

B One friend is 30 cm taller than another friend.

C The tallest person is 142 cm + 30 cm.

Q13 hint

14 Problem-solving / Reasoning Runners took these times, in minutes, in a race.
20, 18, 20, 19, 21, 16, 54

a One of the runners pulled a muscle. Which time do you think was hers? Why?

b Work out the range, mode, median and mean.

15 STEM / Reasoning In 2013, the numbers of dragonflies in different areas were
40, 25, 95, 50, 40, 20, 40, 25, 60, 50

a Find the range and median in 2013.

In 2014, the numbers of dragonflies in these areas were
60, 10, 35, 20, 15, 40, 70, 100, 0, 25

b Find the range and median in 2014.

c Compare the ranges.

d Compare the medians.

Discussion Describe the change in dragonfly population between 2013 and 2014.

16 Finance A busker received these coins for a song.

2p, 10p, 5p, £1, 10p, 5p, 1p, 50p, 10p, 20p, 10p, 2p, 2p, 20p, 2p, 10p, 20p, 20p, 1p, 5p, 10p

a Find the

    i range   **ii** mode   **iii** median   **iv** mean

b Make a frequency table for the data.

c How much money did the busker receive altogether?
Give your answer in £ and p.

17 Reasoning Runners gave two designs of trainers a score out of 20.

Design A   19, 2, 12, 6, 16, 20, 1, 10

Design B   14, 15, 15, 17, 16, 18, 16, 17

Which design would you recommend and why?

> **Q17 hint**
> Compare the ranges and the medians.

18 STEM / Real **a** Here are the wind speeds (in **knots**) of the Atlantic hurricanes in 2010.

85, 115, 125, 135, 115, 105, 70, 75, 85, 65, 85

    i Work out the median wind speed.

    ii Work out the range of the wind speeds.

b Here are the wind speeds (knots) of the Atlantic hurricanes in 2011.
105, 120, 70, 65, 120, 80, 100

    i Work out the median wind speed.

    ii Work out the range of wind speeds.

c **Reasoning** Compare the wind speeds of hurricanes in 2010 and 2011. Write a sentence for the median and a sentence for the range.

> **Q18 Literacy hint**
> A **knot** is the unit used to measure the speed of ships and wind. It is about 1 mile per hour.

19 Reasoning **a** Work out the mean of the numbers 6 and 10.

b What is the number halfway between 6 and 10?

c Copy and complete the sentence.
The ____ of two numbers is halfway between them.

d Use the mean to find the number halfway between

    i 12 and 20   **ii** 30 and 70   **iii** 7 and 23   **iv** 5 and 10.

Investigation   **Problem-solving / Reasoning**

1 The mode of the three whole numbers 2, ☐ and ☐ is 2. Their range is 3. Find the two missing numbers.

2 The median of the three whole numbers 3, ☐ and ☐ is 5. Find two possible missing numbers.

3 The range of the five numbers 4, ☐, ☐, ☐ and ☐ is 5. The median is 6. Find some possible missing numbers.

Discussion What methods did you use to answer each question?

---

20 Reflect Look back at the questions you answered in these Extend lessons.

a Which question was easiest?

b Which question was hardest?

c Compare your answers to **a** and **b** with a classmate.
Discuss your choices.

> **Q20 hint**
> Write down the question number.

Reflect

1 Unit test

Log how you did on your Student Progression Chart.

 1 The table shows the blood types of people who gave blood at a donor centre.

a How many people have blood type B?

b How many more people have type O than type B?

c Which is the most common blood type?

d How many people gave blood?

Blood type	Number of people
A	40
B	11
O	45
AB	4

2 The pictogram shows the favourite treats of some dogs.

a How many dogs like biscuits best?

b How many dogs like bones best?

c 11 dogs like rawhide best. Draw symbols to show this.

d How many dogs are there altogether?

Dog treats

Key: ⊕ stands for 4 dogs

3 May recorded the silver coins that her friends had brought to school.

~~10p~~, ~~5p~~, ~~20p~~, ~~20p~~, ~~5p~~, ~~10p~~, ~~10p~~, ~~10p~~, ~~20p~~, ~~10p~~, 5p, 10p, 5p, 20p, 10p, 50p, 10p, 5p, 20p, 5p, 5p, 10p, 50p, 10p, 10p

She crossed off the ones she recorded in this tally chart.

Coin	Tally	Frequency
5p	||	
10p	||||	
20p	|||	
50p		

a Copy and complete the tally chart.

b Find the mode.

c Which coin has a frequency of 5?

d A coin fell on the floor. Which type of coin is it most likely to be?

4 The table shows the top maths grades of a school.

Grade	Frequency
4	10
5	20
6	30
7	70
8	50
9	30

a How many students got a grade 8?

b How many students got a grade 6 or lower?

c Find the mode.

d Copy and complete the bar-line chart.

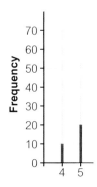

5 Look at this set of data.   2, 7, 5, 6, 4, 0, 2
  a Write down the mode.
  b Work out the range.
  c Work out the median.

6 A doctor recorded the number of breaths some patients took in 1 minute.
  a How many patients took 10 to 12 breaths?
  b Jasmine took 17 breaths in 1 minute. Which class contains this value?
  c Find the modal class.
  d How many patients took more than 15 breaths in a minute?

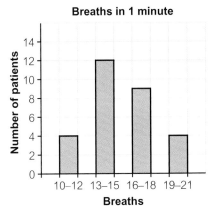

Breaths in 1 minute

7 Some camera batteries were tested.
  a After a full charge, Brand A batteries lasted these times,
    in hours.
    5, 9, 4, 8, 11, 8, 7, 8
    i Work out the range.
    ii Write down the mode.
    iii Find the median.
    iv Calculate the mean.
  b Brand B batteries had these results.
    range = 3   mode = 6   median = 7
    i Which brand of battery has the smaller range of times?
    ii Which brand of battery lasted the greater modal time?

Challenge

8

2	5	2	3	4
5	2	1	4	1
3	5	2	3	1
1	3	4	1	5
4	5	4	3	2

  a Find a row, column or diagonal where
    i the mode is 3
    ii the median is 4
    iii the range is 2
    iv the mean is 3.
  b Work with a classmate. One of you secretly chooses a row,
    column or diagonal. Find its range, mode and median.
    Ask your partner to tell you which one you picked.

Q8b hint

Give your partner one clue at a time.
For example
1st clue: the range is 4
2nd clue: the numbers are in a column
3rd clue: the median is 3

9 Reflect
  a Write down a word that describes how you feel
    • before a maths test
    • during a maths test
    • after a maths test.
    Beside each word, draw a face to show if it is a good 😊 or a bad 😟 feeling.
  b Discuss with a classmate what you could do to change 😟 feelings to
    😊 feelings.

Q9 hint

You might choose one of these
words, or a different word: OK,
worried, excited, happy, focused,
panicked, calm.

Reflect

2.1 Adding

You will learn to:
- Add numbers together in different ways
- Round to the nearest 10
- Approximate before adding.

CONFIDENCE

Why learn this?
Adding skills can be used to keep score in a game.

Fluency
- Work out
  7 + 8
  3 plus 9
  7 more than 5
  the total of 9 and 8.
- How many hundreds, tens and units in 743?

Explore
How can you quickly work out how much more money you need to make £1?

Exercise 2.1

Warm up

1 Work out
  a 5 plus 8
  b 9 more than 6
  c 10 + 30
  d 80 + 50

2 a Write 4 pairs of numbers that add to 10.
  b Write 3 numbers that add to 10.

3 Work out
  a 20 + 30 + 10
  b 50 + 20 + 60
  c 40 + 70 + 50
  d 50 + 60 + 70

4 Write the next three numbers in each **sequence**.
  a 3, 5, 7, 9, ☐, ☐, ☐
  b 2, 7, 12, 17, ☐, ☐, ☐
  c 4, 11, 18, 25, ☐, ☐, ☐

5 Add each pair of numbers together in your head.
  a 17 + 22
  b 32 + 43
  c 37 + 33
  d 69 + 75

6 Find the **sum** of 26, 42 and 62.
  Discussion Does it matter what order you add the numbers?

Q3a hint

Add the first two numbers. Then add the third number to your total.

Key point

A number **sequence** is a set of numbers that follow a rule.

Q4a hint

What is being added on each time?

$$+\square +\square$$
3, 5, 7, 9, ...

Q5a hint

Split the numbers into tens and units.
17 + 22 = 10 + 20 + 7 + 2

Q6 Literacy hint

The **sum** is all the numbers added together.

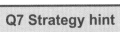

7 Work out the total of each set of numbers.
 a 4, 6, 5, 3, 1, 1
 b 1, 2, 4, 3, 6, 2
 c 6, 3, 4, 1, 7, 5
 d 5, 3, 5, 0, 2, 1

Q7 Strategy hint
Look for pairs or sets of numbers that make 10.

Worked example

What do you need to add to 53 to make 100?

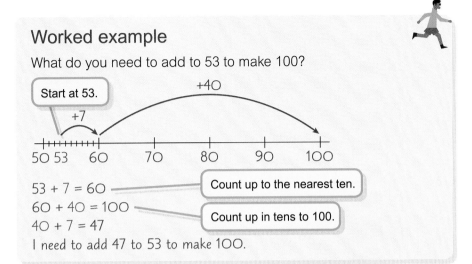

Start at 53.

+7

+40

50 53 60   70   80   90   100

53 + 7 = 60 —— Count up to the nearest ten.
60 + 40 = 100 —— Count up in tens to 100.
40 + 7 = 47
I need to add 47 to 53 to make 100.

8 Write down the number you need to add to make 100.
 a 26
 b 78
 c 3
 d 39
 e 94

Worked example

Work out 67 + 48 using the **column method**.

```
  67
+ 48
————
```
Set out the numbers in columns.
Line up the units with units, and the tens with tens.

Key point
In the **column method** you write the numbers in the calculation in their place value columns.

```
  67
+ 48
————
   5
  1
```
Start in the units column. Add the numbers together (7 + 8 = 15)
Put the 5 in the units column and carry the ten. Write the ten as a 1 underneath the tens column.

```
  67
+ 48
————
 115
  1
```
Next add the tens (6 tens + 4 tens) and add the ten carried over. This makes 11 tens.

9 Work out these additions using the column method.
 a 53 + 28
 b 78 + 84
 c 123 + 258
 d 571 + 346
 e 361 + 27
 f 162 + 89

Q9e hint
```
  361
+  27
————
```

10 The table gives the numbers of girls and boys attending some concerts.
Work out the total number of people at each concert.

Concert	Girls	Boys
A	327	48
B	799	816
C	624	358

11 Dave's computer game has 9 levels. The bar chart shows how many times he has reached each level.

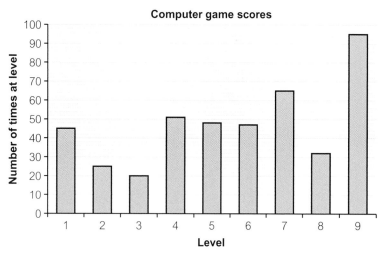

Computer game scores

a Which level has Dave reached most often?
b Which levels has he reached more than 50 times?
c How many times has he reached level 8 or higher?

12 Round each number to the nearest 10.
    a 37   b 84   c 98   d 65
    e 124   f 263   g 297   h 135

13 Use **approximation** to **estimate** these sums.
    a $48 + 47 \approx$
    b $57 + 58 \approx$
    c $87 + 101 \approx$
    d $123 + 48 \approx$
    Discussion Work out the exact answers to Q13 parts **a** and **d**.
    How close are your estimates?

14 Explore How can you quickly work out how much more money you need to make £1?
Look back at the maths you have learned in this lesson.
How can you use it to answer this question?

15 Reflect Point to any hint in this lesson.
Read the hint and the question it belongs to.
Now do the same for three other hints in this lesson.
Which hint is the most helpful?
Discuss with a classmate what makes this hint helpful.

Key point

To **round** to the nearest 10, find the multiple of 10 that the number is closest to.
Look at the digit in the Units column.
If the digit is less than 5, round down.
If the digit is 5 or more, round up.

Q12a hint

Is 37 closer to 30 or 40?

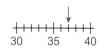

Q12e hint

Is 124 closer to 120 or 130?

Key point

An **approximation** is a number that is not exact. It is close enough for it to be useful though. Use approximations to **estimate** the answer to calculations.
$\approx$ means 'approximately equal to'.

Q13 hint

Round each number to the nearest ten. Then add them together.

Explore

Reflect

2.2 Subtracting

You will learn to:
- Subtract numbers in different ways
- Approximate before subtracting.

Why learn this?
Darts players use subtraction to work out their score after each round.

Fluency
- Work out
  10 − 6 = ☐
  110 − ☐ = 3
  20 − 14 = ☐
- Round to the nearest ten
  54   96   135

Explore
How can you quickly work out your change from £1?

Exercise 2.2

1 a Subtract 3 from 9.

  b Find the difference between 8 and 5.

  c In a choir there are 7 men and 20 women. How many more women are there than men?

  d Take away 7 from 8.

2 Work out

  a 30 − 10

  b 80 − 40

  c 70 − 20

  d 90 − 50

3 Find the next three numbers in each sequence.

  a 28, 25, 22, 19, ☐, ☐, ☐

  b 71, 65, 59, 53, ☐, ☐, ☐

  c 54, 48, 42, 36, ☐, ☐, ☐

> **Q3a hint**
> What is being subtracted each time?
>
>
> 28,   25,   22,   19,   ...

Worked example

Find the difference between 16 and 43.

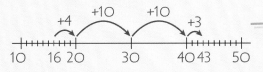

4 + 10 + 10 + 3 = 27

43 − 16 = 27

> Using a number line start at the lower number (16).
> Count up to the next number of tens (20).
> Count up to the number of tens in the higher number (40).
> Count on to the higher number (43).

> You have counted 4, then 10, then 10, then 3.

> To find the difference you subtract.

Warm up

4 Find the difference between each pair of numbers.
  a 18 and 25   **b** 67 and 72
  c 37 and 53   **d** 96 and 105
  e 67 and 134   **f** 185 and 217
  g 248 and 482   **h** 1035 and 845

Q4d hint

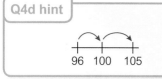

5 Work out
  a 96 − 42
  b 64 − 23
  c 77 − 33
  d 66 − 29
  e 94 − 58
  f 73 − 39

Q5a hint

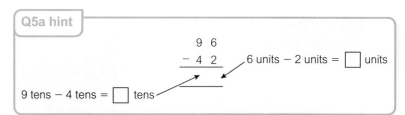

9 tens − 4 tens = ☐ tens

6 units − 2 units = ☐ units

6 In your head, subtract each number
  from 100.
  a 15   **b** 58
  c 87   **d** 49
  e 92   **f** 64

Q5d hint

The second number has more units than the first number. Split one of the tens in the first number into 10 units.

7 Use approximation to estimate these calculations.
  a 87 − 56 ≈   **b** 73 − 37 ≈
  c 145 − 64 ≈   **d** 186 − 82 ≈

Q6a hint

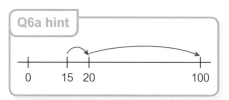

Worked example

Use the column method to work out 392 − 165.

```
  3 9 2
− 1 6 5
───────
```
Write the larger number on top.

Start with the units column.
You can't subtract 5 from 2 because this gives a negative answer.

```
  3 ⁸9̷ ¹2
− 1 6 5
───────
      7
```
Take a ten from the 9 tens to make 8 tens and 12 units.
12 − 5 = 7

```
  3 ⁸9̷ ¹2
− 1 6 5
───────
  2 2 7
```
Now look at the tens column and the hundreds column.

Check: 400 − 170 = 230, which is close to 227

Round each number to the nearest ten and subtract.

Q7 hint

Round each number to the nearest ten and then subtract.

Discussion Why do you think this is
called the column method?

8 Complete these calculations using the column method.
  Use approximation to check that your answers are reasonable.
  a 438 − 347   **b** 264 − 139
  c 381 − 193   **d** 436 − 257
  e 175 − 58   **f** 231 − 86

Q8c hint

```
  ²3̷ ¹⁷4̷ ¹1
−   1 9 3
─────────
        8
```
You can't subtract 9 from 7. Split one of the 3 hundreds into 10 tens.

9 **Reasoning** Samia needs to subtract 37 from 54.
  She can't subtract 7 from 4, so she subtracts 4 from 7.
  Will she get the right answer? Explain how you know.

Q9 hint

```
  5 4
− 3 7
─────
```

10 The chart shows the languages that students at a school chose to learn.

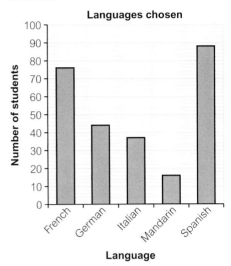

a How many more students chose French than German?

b How many more students would have to choose Spanish to make the total 100?

c What was the difference between the numbers of students choosing the most popular and least popular languages?

11 A newsagent uses a table to show the number of papers she needs to order each day.
Unfortunately she spills her drink all over the form and some numbers get washed away.
What are the missing numbers?

Q11 hint

For *The Gleaner* on Monday work out
45 + 21 + 0 = ☐
87 − ☐ = ☐

	Monday	Tuesday	Wednesday	Thursday	Friday	Saturday
The Daily Bugle	45		38	42	36	43
The Gleaner		36		39	41	36
Morning Sun	21	26	29		27	
The Chronicle	0	0	0	0		0
Total papers	87	79	82	87	122	104

12 Explore How can you quickly work out your change from £1?
Look back at the maths you have learned in this lesson.
How can you use it to answer this question?

13 Reflect Jacqueline is talking about adding and subtracting using the column method.
She says, 'You put the digits in place-value columns: hundreds, tens, units. That is the same for adding and subtracting. 'You put the larger number on top for subtracting. It doesn't matter for adding. That is different.'
Discuss with a classmate things that are the same and things that are different when adding and subtracting using the column method.

Q13 hint

Look at the second worked examples in lessons 2.1 and 2.2 to help you.

2.3 Multiplying

You will learn to:
- Multiply numbers
- Recognise multiples
- Recognise square numbers
- Find roots of square numbers on a calculator.

Why learn this?
Knowing how to multiply smaller numbers is essential for multiplying bigger numbers.

```
1×2=2
2×2=4
3×2=6
4×2=8
5×2=10
6×2=12
7×2=14
8×2=16
9×2=18
10×2=20
```

Fluency
Work out
- 2 × 3
- 2 × 5
- 1 × 6

Explore
How many ways can you arrange 48 chairs in equal rows?

Exercise 2.3

1 Copy and complete these sequences.
- **a** 2, 4, 6, 8, ☐, ☐, ☐
- **b** 3, 6, 9, 12, ☐, ☐, ☐
- **c** 6, 12, 18, 24, ☐, ☐, ☐

2 Double these numbers.
- **a** 6
- **b** 10
- **c** 8
- **d** 5

3 Double these numbers.
- **a** 15
- **b** 42
- **c** 51
- **d** 84
- **e** 68
- **f** 92

4 Work out
- **a** 3 × 4
- **b** 5 × 2
- **c** 4 × 1
- **d** 2 × 4
- **e** 4 × 5
- **f** 5 × 3

Key point
Doubling is the same as ×2 (multiplying by 2).

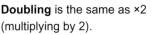

Q3a hint
Split the number into tens and units.

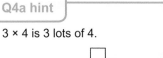

Q4a hint
3 × 4 is 3 lots of 4.

5 Work out

   a 6 × 4

   b 6 × 7

   c 9 × 3

   d 8 × 6

   e 7 × 8

   f 9 × 7

Q5 Strategy hint

Learn your times tables so that you don't have to work them out each time.

Key point

A **multiple** is a number that is in a times table.

5 × 2 = 10

10 is a multiple of 5 and a multiple of 2

6 Look at these numbers.

23	18	8	9	
25				12
16	14	10	6	

Which of the **multiples** in the box are multiples of

   a 2

   b 4

   c 3

   d 5

   e 3 and 4?

Q6a hint

Which numbers in the box are in the 2 times table?

Q6e hint

Look at your answers to parts **b** and **c**. Which number is a multiple of 3 and a multiple of 4?

7 Osman is playing a board game.

He moves a counter the number shown when he rolls a dice.

He throws a 4 five times in a row.

How far does he move altogether?

Discussion Is this easier to answer using addition or multiplication?

8 Problem-solving Football stickers come in bags of 6 regular stickers and 1 shiny sticker.

Simon buys 5 bags of stickers.

   a How many shiny stickers does he get?

   b How many regular stickers does he get?

   c How many stickers does he get altogether?

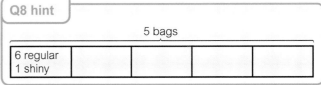

Q8 hint

5 bags

6 regular
1 shiny

9 Reasoning Desheeta buys 6 bags of sweets with 3 sweets in each.

Ahmed buys 3 bags of sweets with 6 sweets in each.

   a Which of these sentences is true?

     A Desheeta has more sweets than Ahmed.

     B Ahmed has more sweets than Desheeta.

     C Desheeta and Ahmed have the same number of sweets each.

   b Explain how you know.

10 Danny and Marita are selling boxes of cupcakes.

Danny sells 4 boxes with 8 cupcakes in each box.

Marita sells 6 boxes with 6 cupcakes in each box.

Who sells more cupcakes? How do you know?

11 Reasoning / Problem-solving There are 16 students in a class.

They need to get into groups of 3.

   a Is this possible?

   b What size groups will work exactly?

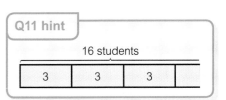

Q11 hint

16 students

| 3 | 3 | 3 | |

12 Work out

   a 5^2

   b 6^2

   c 12^2

   d 20^2

13 Reasoning **a** Which of the numbers in the box are square numbers?

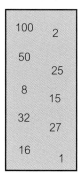

100	2
50	
	25
8	
	15
32	
	27
16	
	1

   b How do you know?

14 Write down the first ten square numbers.

15 Find the **square root** of each number using a calculator.

   a 64

   b 4

   c 81

   d 49

   e 289

   f 3136

> **Q15a hint**
>
> Press the $\sqrt{}$ key, enter 64, then press $=$.

16 **Explore** How many ways can you arrange 48 chairs in equal rows?
Look back at the maths you have learned in this lesson.
How can you use it to answer this question?

17 **Reflect**

   a Which times tables are you good at?

   b Which times tables are you not so good at?

   c Learn one fact from a times table you are not so good at.
Tell a classmate the fact you have learned.
Ask your classmate to test you on that fact tomorrow and the next day.

   d Once you are confident you know that fact, choose another and repeat step **c** above.

Explore

Reflect

> **Key point**
>
> To find the square of a number you multiply the number by itself.
> For example, 3 squared = 3 × 3 = 9.
> You write 3 squared as 3^2.

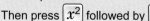

> **Q12 Strategy hint**
>
> To work out a **square number** on your calculator, type in the number to be squared.
> Then press $\boxed{x^2}$ followed by $\boxed{=}$.

> **Q13 Strategy hint**
>
> Start with 1 × 1 = 1. Is this square number in the box? Next try 2 × 2 and continue up to 10 × 10.

> **Q14 hint**
>
> The first square number is $1^2 = 1$.
> The second square number is $2^2. = \square$

> **Key point**
>
> A **square root** is a number that is multiplied by itself to produce a given number. Finding the square root is the inverse of squaring.
> 3 × 3 = 9, so $\sqrt{9} = 3$, where $\sqrt{}$ means square root.

> **Q17c hint**
>
> You could choose the 7 times table.
> You could learn 7 × 6 = 42.

2.4 Dividing

You will learn to:
- Divide one number by another
- Use times tables to help you divide
- Use approximation to estimate division calculations.

Why learn this?
Being able to divide helps you to share out equally.

Fluency
- Share 8 sweets equally between 2 people.
- Share 12 biscuits equally between 2 people.

Explore
How many ways can you share £1 equally using coins?

Exercise 2.4

1 Double these numbers.
- **a** 3
- **b** 7
- **c** 12
- **d** 23

2 Work out
- **a** 3×4
- **b** 5×4
- **c** 3×8
- **d** 5×7

3 Use the 2 times tables to answer these.
- **a** $3 \times 2 = 6$ $6 \div 2 = \square$
- **b** $10 \times 2 = \square$ $\square \div 2 = \square$
- **c** $4 \times 2 = \square$ $\square \div 2 = \square$
- **d** $5 \times 2 = \square$ $\square \div 2 = \square$

4 Halve each number.
- **a** 16
- **b** 2
- **c** 28
- **d** 32
- **e** 50
- **f** 64

5 Copy the sentences. Fill in the gaps.
- **a** Double 11 is 22, so half of 22 is $\square$.
- **b** Double 20 is 40, so half of 40 is $\square$.
- **c** Double 14 is $\square$, so half of $\square$ is 14.
- **d** Double $\square$ is 42, so half of 42 is $\square$.

Q3a hint
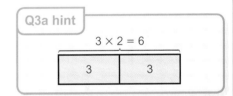

Key point
Halving is the same as $\div 2$ (dividing by 2).

Q4a hint
Split the number into tens and units.

Q5 hint
Halving is the **inverse** of doubling.

Q5 Literacy hint
An **inverse** operation is the opposite operation.

Worked example

Work out $12 \div 4$.

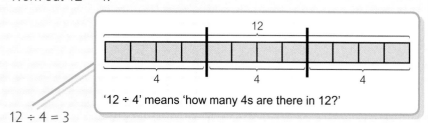

'$12 \div 4$' means 'how many 4s are there in 12?'

$12 \div 4 = 3$

6 Work out
   a $15 \div 5$ **b** $18 \div 6$
   c $24 \div 3$ **d** $28 \div 4$
   e $18 \div 3$ **f** $28 \div 7$

Discussion How does $3 \times 6 = 18$ help you to work out $18 \div 3$ and $18 \div 6$?

7 Use the multiplication facts to work out the divisions.
   a $3 \times 8 = 24$, so $24 \div 3 = \square$
   b $5 \times 7 = 35$, so $35 \div 5 = \square$
   c $6 \times 8 = 48$, so $48 \div 8 = \square$
   d $3 \times 9 = 27$, so $27 \div 9 = \square$

8 Daniel has 36 old coins in his collection.
He wants to display them in cases that contain 4 coins each.
How many cases will he need?

Q6a hint

	15	
5	5	5

Q7 hint

Dividing is the inverse of multiplying.
$3 \times 4 = 12$
$\qquad 12 \div 4 = 3$
$\qquad 12 \div 3 = 4$

Q8 hint

	36	
4	4	

Worked example

Work out $14 \div 4$.

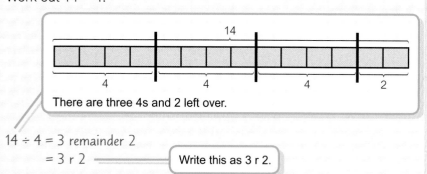

There are three 4s and 2 left over.

$14 \div 4 = 3$ remainder 2
$\qquad = 3\,\text{r}\,2$ ——— Write this as 3 r 2.

Key point

When you can't divide by a number exactly, there is a **remainder**.

9 Reasoning Joanna has 48 badges.
   a How many rows of 8 can she make?
   b How many rows of 10 can she make? Are there any left over?

10 Work out
   a $26 \div 5$ **b** $39 \div 4$
   c $47 \div 7$ **d** $69 \div 9$

11 a How many boxes of 6 can you fill with 22 eggs?
    b Are any eggs left over?

Q10a hint

	26	
5	5	5	

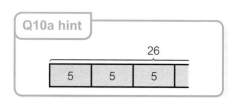

12 Problem-solving Cookies come in bags of 5.
Maria eats 2 cookies. She has 28 left.
How many bags of cookies did she buy?

13 Reasoning Javier needs 26 party invitations.
They come in packets of 6.
He says he will need 10 packets.
Is he right? How do you know?

Q13 hint

Write a calculation and one sentence
to explain.

14 Match each calculation to an answer in the box.
- **a** 36 ÷ 6
- **b** Half of 80
- **c** 30 ÷ 10
- **d** Double 26
- **e** Double 49
- **f** Half of 210

6	40		105
		52	
3			98

15 a To estimate 25 ÷ 6
- **i** round 25 to the nearest number in the 6 times table.
- **ii** work out 24 ÷ 6

25 ÷ 6 ≈ ☐

b Use the method from part **a** to estimate
- **i** 71 ÷ 7
- **ii** 56 ÷ 9

Q15ai hint

6, 12, 18, ⟨24⟩, 30, ...

Investigation   Reasoning / Problem-solving
1 Think of a number less than 100.
2 Halve it.
3 If the result is a whole number, halve it again.
4 Repeat step 3 until there is a remainder.
5 Try different starting numbers.
6 Which number can you halve the most often before you get a remainder?

---

16 Explore How many ways can you share £1 equally using coins?
Look back at the maths you have learned in this lesson.
How can you use it to answer this question?

17 Reflect Look back at Q14.
Toby says, 'I started with 36 ÷ 6, because that was the first question.'
Isy says, 'I looked at all the questions. Then I started with 30 ÷ 10,
because I knew the answer without having to do any working out.'
Edward says, 'I started with the first number in the box, 6.
Then I looked at the calculations to see which one it belonged to.'
How did you start?
Discuss Toby's, Isy's, Edward's and your ways of starting with a
classmate. Which is best? Why?

Explore

Reflect

2.5 Multiplying and dividing by 10, 100 and 1000

You will learn to:

- Multiply and divide by 10, 100 and 1000.

Why learn this?
We use a decimal system. That means that our numbers are based on multiplying and dividing by 10.

Fluency
Work out
- 3 × 4
- 2 × 6
- 5 × 3
- 10 ÷ 2
- 18 ÷ 3

Explore
What is a googol?

CONFIDENCE

Exercise 2.5

Warm up

1 Work out

  a 3^2 **b** 2^2 **c** 9^2

2 What happens to a number when you

  a multiply it by 1

  b divide it by 1?

Investigation   **Reasoning**

1 a Copy this place-value table.

	Ten thousands	Thousands	Hundreds	Tens	Units
3 × 10				3	0
22 × 10					
7 × 100					
15 × 100					
8 × 1000					
38 × 1000					

b Use your calculator to do the multiplications. Write your answers in the table, putting the digits in the correct columns.

c Work out the answer to 35 × 100 without using a calculator.

2 a Copy this place-value table.

	Ten thousands	Thousands	Hundreds	Tens	Units
80 000 ÷ 10		8	0	0	0
6000 ÷ 10					
52 000 ÷ 100					
3000 ÷ 100					
40 000 ÷ 1000					
7000 ÷ 1000					

b Use your calculator to do the divisions. Write your answers in the table, putting the digits in the correct columns.

c Work out the answer to 2400 ÷ 100 without using a calculator.

Discussion What is the rule for ×100? ÷1000?

Topic links: Mean, Square numbers, Measurements

3 Multiply each number by 10.
  a 8   **b** 74
  c 116   **d** 125

4 Multiply each number by 100.
  a 9   **b** 27
  c 49   **d** 203

5 Multiply each number by 1000.
  a 7   **b** 53
  c 87   **d** 132

6 Divide each number by 10.
  a 70   **b** 80
  c 120   **d** 400

7 Divide each number by 100.
  a 600   **b** 900
  c 1400   **d** 2000

8 Divide each number by 1000.
  a 5000   **b** 45 000
  c 91 000   **d** 6000

9 Work out these calculations.

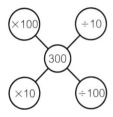

10 There are 1000 mm in 1 metre. How many millimetres are there in
  a 5 metres
  b 9 metres
  c 10 metres?

11 STEM / Real A microscope makes objects look 10 times bigger than in real life. Part of an object is 2 mm wide.
How wide does it look under the microscope?

12 Reasoning Work out
  a 10^2 **b** 100^2 **c** 1000^2

13 Work out the mean of these numbers.
5, 1, 12, 4, 8, 6, 3, 7, 2, 12

14 Explore What is a googol?
Is it easier to explore this question now you have completed the lesson?
What further information do you need to be able to answer this?

15 Reflect Write down two ways that multiplying or dividing by 10, 100 or 1000 is helpful in everyday life.

Key point

Multiplying by 10 moves the digits 1 place to the left.
Multiplying by 100 moves the digits 2 places to the left.
Multiplying by 1000 moves the digits 3 places to the left.

Key point

Dividing by 10 moves the digits 1 place to the right.
Dividing by 100 moves the digits 2 places to the right.
Dividing by 1000 moves the digits 3 places to the right.

Q10a hint

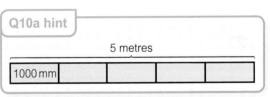

Q15 hint

Think about measures and money.

Explore

Reflect

2.6 Using the four operations

You will learn to:
- Use addition, subtraction, multiplication and division
- Solve simple ratio and proportion problems.

CONFIDENCE

Why learn this?
Knowing which operation to use is important when solving problems.

Fluency
Work out
- $8 + 4$
- $8 - 4$
- 8×4
- $8 \div 4$

Explore
How many tables do you need in a classroom?

Warm up

Exercise 2.6

1 Work out
  a $88 + 14$
  c 7×6
  b $113 - 45$
  d $32 \div 4$

2 Work out
  a 2×50
  c 5×30
  e 40×5
  b 3×20
  d 60×3
  f 20×7

3 Reasoning Work out the missing numbers in these calculations.
  a $23 + \square = 53$
  c $9 \times \square = 72$
  b $\square - 37 = 26$
  d $\square \div 7 = 9$

4 James and Karen run a cake stall to raise money for charity.
  a One cake costs 20p. What is the total cost of 4 cakes?
  b On Monday, 3 students buy 6 cakes between them and share them equally.
  How many cakes does each student have?
  c On Tuesday, they start with 20 cakes. They sell 10 cakes.
  How many cakes do they have left?
  d On Wednesday, Ahmed buys 2 cakes and Kai buys 4 cakes.
  How many cakes do they buy altogether?

5 How many days are there in
  a 3 weeks
  b 5 weeks
  c 8 weeks?

6 In a radio factory, 1 in every 8 radios is checked for quality.
  How many radios are checked when they make
  a 32 radios
  b 48 radios
  c 72 radios?

Q2a hint
$2 \times 50 = 2 \times 5 \times 10$
$= 10 \times 10 = \square$

Key point
The **four operations** are add (+), subtract (−), multiply (×) and divide (÷).

Q3a hint
What number do you need to add to 23 to make 53?
Can you do the inverse calculation to find the number?

Key point
In a word problem, you need to work out which operation to use. Look for key words in the question.
'Each' often means divide.
'Total' or 'altogether' often mean you add or multiply.
'Left' often means subtract.

Q6a hint
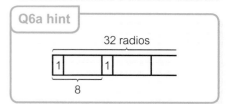

7 Jamal is making lucky dip bags.
For every sticker he puts in a bag, he adds 2 balloons and 3 sweets.
Copy and complete the table to show how many stickers, balloons and sweets he puts in each bag.

Stickers	1	4	6		
Balloons				18	
Sweets					30

Worked example

Two brothers share some money. Oscar gets £3 for every £2 that Ryan gets. They share £50. How much do they get each?

£3 + £2 = £5 ——— Add the two amounts together.

£50 ÷ £5 = 10 —— Work out the number of £5 in £50.

£3 × 10 = £30

£2 × 10 = £20

Oscar gets £30,
Ryan gets £20.

£50

£2	£3	£2	£3	£2	£3	

£5   £5   £5

Multiply Oscar's share by the number of £5. Do the same for Ryan.

8 Manjinder makes a tile pattern with 1 grey tile for every 3 red tiles.
How many of each colour are there in
a 12 tiles   **b** 20 tiles   **c** 24 tiles?
Discussion What do you notice about your answers to Q8 parts **b**
and **c**? How many of each colour would there be in 240 tiles? 48 tiles?

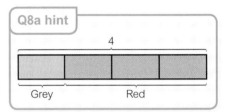

Q8a hint

4

Grey   Red

9 a It costs £20 for a group of 4 to visit a museum.
How much will it cost 5 groups of 4?
b A bag contains 6 apples. Each apple costs 30p.
How much does the bag of apples cost?
c At a sports club there are 3 boys for every 4 girls.
There are 28 members. Work out the numbers of boys and girls.
d There are 8 boxes. There are 4 books in a box.
Someone takes out 1 book from each box.
How many books are left in the boxes altogether?

10 Explore How many tables do you need in a classroom?
Is it easier to explore this question now you have completed the lesson?
What further information do you need to be able to answer this?

11 Reflect Patty explains how she uses bar models to help her
answer Q9a. She says, 'I look at the first bit of information only:
"It costs £20 for a group of 4." Then I draw a picture of this.
I look at the next bit of information: "How much will it
cost 5 groups of 4?" Then I draw a picture of this too.
Now I look at my picture and can see that I need to
find 5 lots of £20, which is 5 × £20 = £100.'
Try drawing your own bar models for Q9b.
Compare what you did with a classmate.
Discuss with your classmate how bar models help you to solve maths
problems.

£20

group of 4

£20	£20	£20	£20	£20
group of 4	group of 4	group of 4	group of 4	group of 4

Reflect

2.7 Positive and negative numbers

You will learn to:
* Use simple negative numbers
* Continue a sequence.

Why learn this?
Scientists use negative numbers to record changes in temperature in the Arctic and Antarctic.

Fluency
* Which is greater, 26 or 37?
* Which is hotter, 21 °C or 28 °C?

Explore
How much does the temperature difference between night and day vary through the year?

Exercise 2.7

1 Write the next three numbers in each sequence.
   a 0, 3, 6, 9, □, □, □   **b** 0, 4, 8, 12, □, □, □   **c** 36, 32, 28, □, □, □

2 Write each set of numbers in order, smallest first.
   a 26, 15, 32, 18, 31, 42, 7   **b** 38, 67, 86, 56, 2, 42, 98
   c 101, 90, 112, 121, 111, 109

3 This temperature scale shows positive and negative temperatures in degrees Celsius (°C).
   a What was the temperature on
      i Monday   **ii** Tuesday
      iii Wednesday   **iv** Thursday?
   b Is the temperature getting warmer or colder from Monday to Thursday?

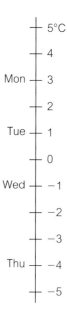

Worked example

The temperature is −2 °C. It gets 5 °C warmer.
What is the new temperature?

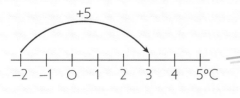

Use a number line.
Start at −2°C.
Count up 5°C.

3 °C

4 Find the new temperatures.
   a The temperature is 3 °C. It increases by 4 °C.
   b The temperature is −3 °C. It goes up by 4 °C.
   c The temperature is −5 °C. It rises by 9 °C.

Q4 Literacy hint

'Rise', 'increase' and 'go up' all mean the same thing.

45

5 Find the new temperatures.

   a The temperature is 3°C.
     It decreases by 8°C.

   b The temperature is 5°C.
     It goes down by 9°C.

   c The temperature is 2°C.
     It falls by 9°C.

Q5a hint

Use a number line. Start at 3°C and count back 8.

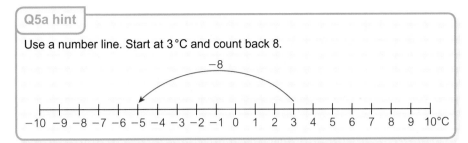

6 a Copy this temperature scale.

   Mark these temperatures on it.
   A 5°C **B** −4°C **C** 2°C **D** 10°C **E** −6°C **F** −9°C **G** 8°C
   The first one has been done for you.

   b Which is the lowest temperature? **c** Which is the largest number?

Q5 Literacy hint

'Decrease', 'go down' and 'fall' all mean the same thing.

7 Write the correct symbol, < or >, between each pair of temperatures.

   a 3°C ... 9°C   **b** 8°C ... 2°C   **c** −3°C ... 5°C

   d 6°C ... −2°C   **e** −4°C ... −3°C   **f** −2°C ... −7°C

Q7 hint

Use the temperature scale in Q6 to help you.

8 Write the correct symbol, < or >, between each pair of numbers.

   a 4 ... 7   **b** 5 ... 2   **c** 9 ... −1

   d −6 ... 3   **e** −3 ... −8   **f** −7 ... −2

Key point

The symbol > means greater than.
'5 > 2' means '5 is greater than 2'.
The symbol < means less than.
'−6 < −4' means '−6 is less than −4'.

Worked example

Find the next three numbers in this sequence.

8, 5, 2, ☐, ☐, ☐

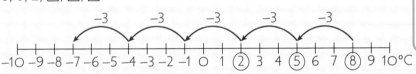

The next three numbers are: −1, −4, −7.

Circle the numbers on a number line.
Count down to find the size of each step.
Count down in the same size steps to find the next three numbers in the sequence.

9 Find the next three numbers in each sequence.

   a 13, 10, 7, ☐, ☐, ☐   **b** 23, 13, 3, ☐, ☐, ☐   **c** 13, 8, 3, ☐, ☐, ☐

   d 19, 13, 7, ☐, ☐, ☐   **e** 34, 22, 10, ☐, ☐, ☐ **f** 4, 1, −2, ☐, ☐, ☐

10 Real Here are the goal differences of some football teams.
   Arrange each set of numbers in order of size, smallest first.

   a 7, 8, 19, −2, −5, −14, −9   **b** −4, −6, −2, −11, −6, 7, −13

   c −21, −30, 24, 63, −12, −41, 23, −15

Q10 Strategy hint

Use a number line to help.

11 Explore How much does the temperature difference between night and day vary through the year?
   What have you learned in this lesson to help you answer this question?
   What other information do you need?

Q10 Literacy hint

Goal difference
= goals scored by team
   − goals scored against team.

12 Reflect

   a Is 1 less than or greater than 2?

   b Is −1 less than or greater than −2?

   c Draw a number line from 2 to −2. Check your answers to parts **a** and **b** on your number line. Are they correct?

   d Compare your answers and number line with others in your class.

Explore

Reflect

Master
P29

CHECK

Strengthen
P49

Extend
P53

Test
P57

2 Check up

Log how you did on your
Student Progression Chart.

Adding and subtracting

1 Work out
  a 30 + 50 + 10   **b** 24 + 45   **c** 49 + 33
  d 128 + 48   **e** 425 + 277

2 Work out
  a 80 − 60   **b** 67 − 21   **c** 53 − 27
  d 124 − 56   **e** 335 − 107

3 Edmund has 73 counters. He thinks he needs 37 more to make 100.
Is he correct? Write a calculation to show why.

4 Write down the next three numbers in each sequence.
  a 3, 9, 15, 21, ☐, ☐, ☐   **b** 39, 35, 31, 27, ☐, ☐, ☐

Multiplying and dividing

5 Work out
  a 4 × 3   **b** 1 × 4   **c** 8 × 7

6 Which of the numbers in the box are multiples of 4?

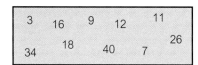

3   16   9   12   11
      26
34   18   40   7

7 Work out
  a double 16   **b** half of 46

8 Work out
  a 72 ÷ 9   **b** 36 ÷ 4

9 Work out
  a 5 × 100   **b** 18 × 10   **c** 34 × 1000

10 Work out
  a 230 ÷ 10   **b** 5600 ÷ 100   **c** 4000 ÷ 1000

11 Work out 21 ÷ 5.

12 Work out 8^2.

13 Copy and complete these calculations.
  6 × 8 = 48
  48 ÷ 6 = ☐
  48 ÷ 8 = ☐

14 One Easter egg costs £3. What is the total cost for 7 Easter eggs?

15 One table needs 6 chairs. How many tables will there be for 72 chairs?

Number skills

16 In a bag of marbles there are 3 red marbles for every 5 blue ones.

How many red marbles are in a bag of 24 marbles?
How many blue marbles?

17 Which is the warmest?

18 The temperature is 5 °C.
It falls by 8 °C.
What is the new temperature?

19 The temperature is −3 °C.
The temperature rises by 10 °C.
What is the new temperature?

20 Write the correct symbol, < or >, between each pair of numbers.
   a −3 ... 6
   b −2 ... −5
   c 6 ... −4
   d −7 ... −3

21 Write these numbers in order, starting with the smallest.
   7, −6, −2, −8, −4, 4

22 Work out the missing numbers.
   a 18 + □ = 26
   b 56 ÷ □ = 8

23 **How sure are you of your answers? Were you mostly**
   😟 **Just guessing**   😐 **Feeling doubtful**   🙂 **Confident**
   What next? Use your results to decide whether to strengthen or extend your learning.

Challenge

24 Use only the number 4 and the operations +, −, × and ÷.
   Make as many numbers as you can.
   You can use up to four 4s in each calculation.

25 a Choose two of these cards.

   b Make two different numbers from the two cards.
   c Subtract the smaller number from the larger number.
   d Repeat for other pairs of cards.
   e What do you notice about all your answers to part c?

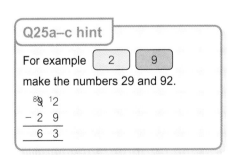

Q25a–c hint

For example [2] [9]
make the numbers 29 and 92.

  8̸ 12
− 2 9
  6 3

Q25e hint

Which times table do the answers come from?

2 Strengthen

You will:
• Strengthen your understanding with practice.

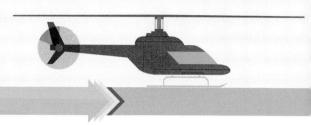

Adding and subtracting

1 Write the next three numbers in each sequence.
  a 14, 17, 20, 23, ☐, ☐, ☐
  b 20, 26, 32, 38, ☐, ☐, ☐
  c 7, 16, 25, 34, ☐, ☐, ☐
  d 39, 35, 31, 27, ☐, ☐, ☐

2 Work out
  a 32 + 45
  b 53 + 46
  c 46 + 31
  d 62 + 54

3 Work out
  a 64 + 28
  b 25 + 37
  c 46 + 8
  d 83 + 72
  e 26 + 91
  f 37 + 84

4 Work out
  a 348 + 491
  b 223 + 585
  c 438 + 195
  d 164 + 52
  e 75 + 139

5 Work out
  a 86 − 42
  b 47 − 23
  c 72 − 41
  d 89 − 33

6 Work out
  a 52 − 34
  b 63 − 17
  c 74 − 35
  d 81 − 66

Q1a hint
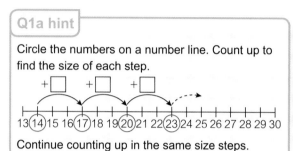

Q3a hint
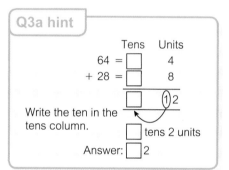

Q4a hint
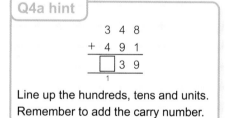

Q5a hint
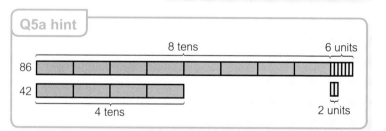

Q6a hint
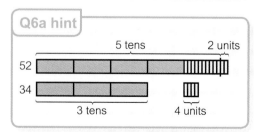

7 Work out
   a 346 − 182
   b 925 − 671
   c 518 − 236
   d 764 − 493

8 Work out
   a 375 − 188
   b 942 − 366
   c 638 − 479
   d 127 − 73
   e 164 − 47
   f 212 − 65

9 What do you add to
   a 91 to make 100
   b 97 to make 100
   c 93 to make 100
   d 94 to make 100?

10 Write the number you need to add to each number to make 100.
   a 74   **b** 36
   c 59   **d** 27

Multiplying and dividing

1 Draw a diagram to help you work out these multiplications.
   a 3 × 4
   b 8 × 9
   c 9 × 3
   d 5 × 7

2 Work out these square numbers.
   a 4^2 **b** 2^2
   c 3^2 **d** 6^2
   e 9^2 **f** 5^2

3 Which of the numbers in the box are square numbers?

14	25	8	18	10
6	4	9	81	36

4 Use the given multiplication facts to answer the division questions.
   a 6 × 4 = 24. What is 24 ÷ 6?
   b 5 × 8 = 40. What is 40 ÷ 8?
   c 6 × 9 = 54. What is 54 ÷ 9?
   d 9 × 10 = 90. What is 90 ÷ 9?

5 Work out
   a 20 ÷ 4   **b** 45 ÷ 5
   c 63 ÷ 9   **d** 24 ÷ 8

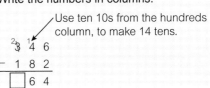

Q7a hint

Write the numbers in columns.
Use ten 10s from the hundreds column, to make 14 tens.

Q8a hint

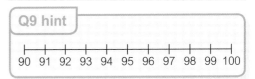

Make sure that you line up the columns. When you borrow from a column, remember to reduce the number by 1.

Q9 hint

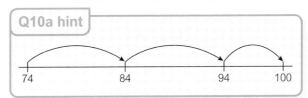
90 91 92 93 94 95 96 97 98 99 100

Q10a hint

74   84   94   100

Q1a hint

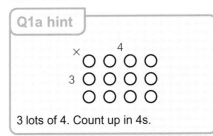

3 lots of 4. Count up in 4s.

Q2a hint

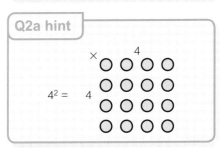

4^2 =

Q4a hint

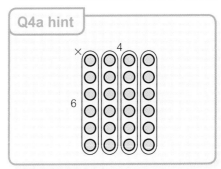

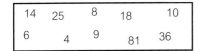

6 Work out these divisions. The first one has been done for you.

   a 32 ÷ 5 = 6 r 2

   b 29 ÷ 4

   c 67 ÷ 8

   d 25 ÷ 3

   e 19 ÷ 7

> **Q6a hint**
>
> Count in 5s until you get close to 32.
> ① ② ③ ④ ⑤ ⑥
> 5, 10, 15, 20, 25, 30
> How many 5s?
> What is the remainder?

7 Copy this place-value table.
Write the answer to each calculation in the table.

   a **i** 9 × 1   **ii** 9 × 10

     iii 9 × 100   **iv** 9 × 1000

   b **i** 12 × 1   **ii** 12 × 10

     iii 12 × 100 **iv** 12 × 1000

T Th	Th	H	T	U

8 Work out

   a 8 × 100

   b 17 × 10

   c 23 × 10

   d 96 × 100

   e 15 × 1000

   f 126 × 1000

> **Q8a hint**
>
> | Th | H | T | U |
> |----|----|----|----|
> | | | ← | 8 |
> | | | | |

9 Draw a place-value table like this.
Write in the answers to these calculations.

   a **i** 6000 ÷ 1   **ii** 6000 ÷ 10

     iii 6000 ÷ 100   **iv** 6000 ÷ 1000

   b **i** 11 000 ÷ 1   **ii** 11 000 ÷ 10

     iii 11 000 ÷ 100 **iv** 11 000 ÷ 1000

3000 ÷ 1
3000 ÷ 10
3000 ÷ 100
3000 ÷ 1000

T Th	Th	H	T	U
	3	0	0	0
		3	0	0
			3	0
				3

10 Work out

   a 80 ÷ 10

   b 21 000 ÷ 100

   c 15 300 ÷ 10

   d 9000 ÷ 1000

Number skills

1 In every box of chocolates, there are 2 strawberry creams.
How many strawberry creams are in

   a 5 boxes

   b 7 boxes

   c 9 boxes

   d 10 boxes?

> **Q1a hint**
>
>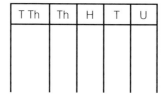

2 A pattern has 1 blue square for every 2 red squares.
How many blue squares in 12 squares?

B	R	R									

12

3 Hammond puts coloured blocks together.
He puts 3 blue blocks with every 2 orange blocks.

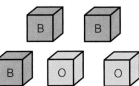

Q3 hint

Each set of blue and orange blocks has 5 blocks.

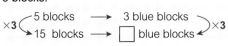

×3 ⤵ 5 blocks → 3 blue blocks ⤵ ×3
15 blocks → ☐ blue blocks ⤴

  a Hammond uses 15 blocks. How many blue blocks does he use?
  b How many blue and orange blocks will he use in
    i 25 blocks   **ii** 35 blocks   **iii** 50 blocks?

Q4a hint

Start at 3 °C. Count up 2.

4 Use the thermometer to find the new temperature after these changes.
  a 3 °C rises by 2 °C   **b** 0 °C rises by 5 °C
  c −3 °C rises by 4 °C   **d** −6 °C rises by 11 °C

5 Use the thermometer in Q4 to calculate the new temperature after these changes.
  a 7 °C falls by 2 °C   **b** 5 °C falls by 4 °C
  c 0 °C falls by 3 °C   **d** 7 °C falls by 9 °C

6 Write the correct symbol, < or >, between each pair of numbers.
  a 8 … 5   **b** −6 … −2   **c** −2 … −5   **d** 9 … −3

7 Write these numbers in order, smallest first.
  a 5, −3, 8, 9, −4, 7, 0
  b −4, −7, −8, 2, −3, 6
  c −5, 5, −3, 3, 2, −4, 1

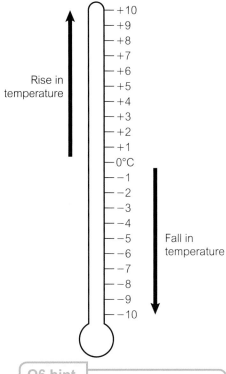

Rise in temperature

Fall in temperature

8 Copy and complete to find the missing numbers.
  a 12 + ☐ = 23   23 − 12 = ☐
  b 15 + ☐ = 32
  c 39 − ☐ = 18   39 − 18 = ☐
  d 28 − ☐ = 16
  e 5 × ☐ = 35   35 ÷ 5 = ☐
  f 4 × ☐ = 20
  g 36 ÷ ☐ = 9   36 ÷ 9 = ☐
  h 32 ÷ ☐ = 4

Q6 hint

Use the thermometer in Q4 to help.
Put the bigger end of the symbol next to the bigger number, e.g. 100 > 2 and 3 < 99.

Enrichment

1 Sally has £10. Geoff has some money too.
Use these facts to write and solve four problems.
Write one problem using each operation
  a add   **b** subtract   **c** multiply   **d** divide.
Compare your problems with others in the class.

2 Reflect Write these operations in order from easiest to hardest.
  A Adding   **B** Subtracting   **C** Multiplying   **D** Dividing
Discuss with a classmate the one you find hardest.
What makes it hard?
Ask your classmate for any tips on how to make this operation easier.

Q7 Strategy hint

Copy the list of numbers.
Which is smallest?
Write it down. Cross it off the list.
Repeat.

Reflect

2 Extend

You will:

• Extend your understanding with problem-solving.

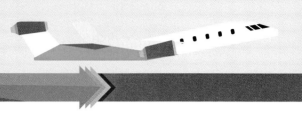

1 Seera has 40p, Brenda has 60p, Kieran has 20p, Liam has 70p and Chelsie has 30p.
How much do they have altogether?

Q1 hint

Give your answer in pence, then in £.

2 Milo is a milkman. The table shows the deliveries he makes during the week.

	Monday	Tuesday	Wednesday	Thursday	Friday	Saturday
Milk (bottles)	56	84	62	75	85	95
Bread (loaves)	36	24	26	31	54	67
Yoghurt (pots)	24	45	24	35	37	19

a How many more bottles of milk does he deliver on a Saturday than a Monday?
b What is the difference between the largest and smallest numbers of yoghurt pots he delivers?
c What is the difference between the largest and smallest numbers of loaves of bread he delivers?

Q2b hint

largest number of yoghurt pots −
smallest number of yoghurt pots = ☐

3 Raheem has £138. Gemma has £83.
How much more money has Raheem got?

4 Work out
a 8^2 b 14^2 c 21^2 d 51^2 e 73^2 f 99^2

Q4 hint

A small 2 means 'squared'.
Use the x^2 key.

5 Add each set of numbers in your head.
a 7, 8, 6   b 14, 27, 16, 22
c 11, 17, 9, 13   d 15, 24, 15, 31, 10

Q5 hint

Look for
• pairs of numbers that make useful totals
• repeated numbers.

6 Yoghurt is sold in 125 g pots and in 500 g pots.
Each 125 g pot of yogurt contains 50 g of carbohydrate.
How much carbohydrate is there in a 500 g pot of yoghurt?

7 A car travels 45 miles for each gallon of diesel.
How many gallons of diesel does it need for 360 miles?

8 **Problem-solving** Zunera delivers goods from the depot to Watford, to Reading, to Swindon and to Oxford, and then returns to the depot. The distances between places are shown in the table.

From	To	Miles
Depot	Watford	21
Watford	Reading	42
Reading	Swindon	44
Swindon	Oxford	30
Oxford	Depot	65

Q6 Strategy hint

How many 125 g pots make a 500 g pot?

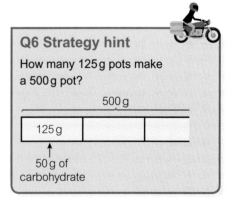

a Zunera says her total journey is about 200 miles. Is she correct?
b How can you tell without a precise calculation?

Q8b hint

Round the numbers before adding.

Topic links: Area, Measures, Converting units

9 The maximum safe weight in a lift is 800 kg.
The average weight of an adult man is 84 kg.
a Is it safe for 6 men to travel in the lift?
How can you tell without a precise calculation?
b How many 84 kg men could travel safely in the lift?

Q9a hint
Think about how much 6 men would weigh.

10 **Reasoning / Problem-solving** Gary bought 5 DVD box sets.
These cost him £19, £39, £69, £29 and £89.
a Round each price to the nearest £10.
b Add the rounded prices to estimate how much he spent.
c Is your answer to part **b** an overestimate or an underestimate?
d Work out exactly how much he spent.
Use your answer to check your answer to part **c**.

Q10c hint
Did you round each number up or down?

11 **Problem-solving** Penny rounds a number to the nearest 10 and gets 240.
What numbers might Penny have been rounding?

12 **Reasoning** In a school there are 7 Year 7 classes.
The table gives the number of students in each class.

Q12 hint
Approximate (round) the number in each class. Write your calculation.

Class	Number of students
7A	24
7B	25
7C	27
7D	26
7E	23
7F	24
7G	26

Without a precise calculation, are there more than 200 pupils in Year 7?

Discussion Is there of a quick way to calculate the exact number in your head?

13 There were 7947 home supporters and 3488 away supporters at a football match.
a How many supporters were there altogether?
b How many more home supporters were there than away supporters?

Q13a hint
Line up the digits in the columns Th H T U when adding and subtracting.

14 Write down the change from £1 when you spend
a 23p
b 67p
c 76p
d 89p
e 94p

Q14 hint
There are 100p in £1.

15 Majid has 267 shells.
89 of them are cockle shells, 65 are whelks and 79 are periwinkles.
The rest are conch shells.
How many conch shells does he have?

16 **Real** Five teams play in a rugby tournament. The numbers of points scored and conceded by each team are shown in the table.

Team	Points scored	Points conceded
Angleton Antelopes	67	52
Bickle Bisons	45	73
Chadham Cheetahs	50	51
Dipbury Drakes	99	45
Empingly Elks	41	81

Q16 Literacy hint

'Points conceded' means the points scored against a team.

a Work out the points difference for each team.
b Who had the greatest points difference?
c Write the teams in order of points difference, from highest to lowest.
d **Reasoning** Add all the points differences together. Explain your answer.

Q16a hint

Points difference
= Points scored – Points conceded
Points difference can be negative.

17 What do you need to add to each number to make 1000?
a 360　　　b 30　　　c 127　　　d 389　　　e 476

18 George had £100. He has £37 left.
How much has he spent?

19 A weather station in the Antarctic records these maximum temperatures during a week in September.

Day	Monday	Tuesday	Wednesday	Thursday	Friday	Saturday	Sunday
Temperature (°C)	−21	−15	−8	−6	−12	−10	−9

a Write the temperatures in order, coldest first.
b What is the difference in °C between the coldest and warmest days?
c On the following Monday the temperature warms up by 14 °C. What is the temperature on the following Monday?

Q19b hint

Start at the coldest and count up to the warmest.

20 Another weather station, in Greenland, also records the maximum temperature each day.

Day	Monday	Tuesday	Wednesday	Thursday	Friday	Saturday	Sunday
Temperature (°C)	−3	2	−2	−5	1	3	−4

a What is the temperature difference between the warmest and coldest days?
b Write the temperatures in order, coldest first.
c What is the rise in temperature between Thursday and Friday?
d What is the fall in temperature between Tuesday and Wednesday?

21 **Problem-solving** A DIY store sells sandpaper in packs of 8 sheets.
a How many sheets are there in
　　i 6 packs　　ii 9 packs?
b i Mel needs 58 sheets of sandpaper. How many packs must she buy?
　　ii How many spare sheets will she have?

22 **Reasoning**
a i Write down the squares of the odd numbers up to 9.
　　ii Are your answers odd or even?
b i Write down the squares of the even numbers up to 10.
　　ii Are your answers odd or even?

23 Work out the area of a square with side length
a 2 cm　　b 8 cm　　c 5 m　　d 10 cm　　e 20 mm　　f 30 m

Q23a hint

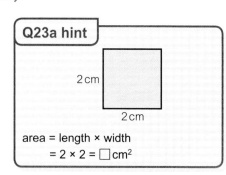

2 cm

2 cm

area = length × width
= 2 × 2 = ☐ cm²

24 The largest denomination bank note in Scotland is £100.
  a Ewan has six £100 notes. How much does he have?
  b Katrina takes £2000 out of the bank in £100 notes.
    How many notes is this?

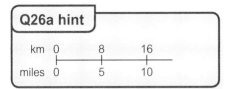

Q24 Literacy hint
The largest denomination bank note means the bank note with the highest face value.

25 The USA printed some $1000 notes in 1934.
  a How many of these notes make $20 000?
  b How much are 32 notes worth?

26 8 kilometres = 5 miles
  a Karen cycles 25 miles. How far is this in kilometres?
  b A car rally stage is 64 km. How far is this in miles?
  c Which is further, 15 miles or 25 km?

Q26a hint

km	0		8		16
miles	0		5		10

27 A fisherman caught 24 fish.
  He caught 1 salmon for every 5 trout.
  a How many trout did he catch?
  b How many salmon did he catch?

28 In a school 2 students wear glasses for every 5 who don't.
  There are 84 students in the school.
  a How many wear glasses?
  b How many don't wear glasses?

29 Sadie is making a bead necklace. For every 2 blue beads,
  she uses 2 red beads and 5 green beads.
  a How many red beads does she need for a necklace
    with 72 beads?
  She then reuses the beads to make 4 identical bracelets.
  b How many beads of each colour does she need for 1 bracelet?

30 Work out the side length of a square with area
  a 196 cm²   b 841 mm²   c 3136 m²
  d 361 cm²   e 8836 km²   f 1849 m²

Q30a hint

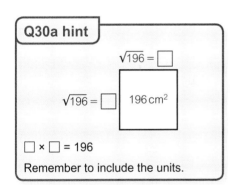

$\sqrt{196} = \square$

$\sqrt{196} = \square$ 196 cm²

$\square \times \square = 196$

Remember to include the units.

31 Use the multiplication facts to help you find the missing numbers.
  a 12 × 13 = 156, so 156 ÷ 13 = □
  b 26 × 48 = 1248, so 1248 ÷ 26 = □
  c 184 × 6 = 1104, so 1104 ÷ 184 = □
  d 51 × 49 = 2499, so 2499 ÷ 51 = □

Investigation   Problem-solving

Happy and unhappy numbers
1 Start with a two-digit number (e.g. 37).
2 Split the number into its separate digits (e.g. 3 and 7).
3 Square each digit (e.g. 3² and 7²).
4 Add the results together (e.g. 9 + 49 = 58).
5 Repeat steps 2 to 4 for the answer in step 4 (e.g. 58).
6 Repeat steps 2 to 5 to find the first 10 terms in a sequence. If you make a 3-digit number,
  split it into separate digits and continue to repeat the steps. What happens?
7 Write down the next five terms without working them out.
8 Try a different starting number. Does the same thing always happen?

32 **Reflect** Which question in these extend lessons was the hardest?
  Discuss with a classmate what made it hard. Ask your classmate for
  any tips on how to make this type of question easier.

Reflect

2 Unit test

Log how you did on your Student Progression Chart.

1 Add the numbers in each set.
   a 20, 30, 60
   b 3, 9, 7, 4, 1

2 Find the new temperatures.
   a The temperature is $-3\,°C$. It rises by $6\,°C$.
   b The temperature is $4\,°C$. It falls by $7\,°C$.

3 Write down the next three numbers in each sequence.
   a 5, 11, 17, 23, □, □, □
   b 52, 49, 46, 43, □, □, □
   c 12, 8, 4, 0, □, □, □

4 Which numbers in the box are multiples of 3?

14	20	11
16	6	12

5 Lily puts cupcakes into boxes.
   For every vanilla cake, she adds 3 chocolate cakes.
   In a box of 24 cakes
   a how many vanilla cakes are there
   b how many chocolate cakes are there?

6 Add these numbers together.
   a 46 + 32
   b 74 + 27
   c 339 + 562

7 Work out
   a 46 − 25
   b 63 − 27
   c 142 − 67
   d 847 − 558

8 Use approximation to estimate these calculations.
   a 43 + 88
   b 97 − 32
   c 134 − 76

9 a What do you need to add to 33 to make 100?
   b Subtract 84 from 100.

10 Write these temperatures in order, coldest first.
   $5\,°C$ $-5\,°C$ $-8\,°C$ $3\,°C$ $-7\,°C$ $-1\,°C$ $1\,°C$

11 Work out 7^2.

12 Work out
  a 560 ÷ 10
  b 108 × 10
  c 63 × 100
  d 800 ÷ 100
  e 29 000 ÷ 1000
  f 57 × 1000

13 Orange paint is made by mixing 7 litres of yellow paint with 2 litres of red paint.
  Mike has made 45 litres of orange paint.
  a How much yellow paint has he used?
  b How much red paint has he used?

Challenge

14 In this grid each number has been created using only 3s.
  a Work out how to make each number, using as many of +, −, × and ÷ as you like.

9	3	7
27	2	5
18	15	8

  b Choose another number under 5 and create a grid for a friend to solve.

15 Play this game with a partner.
  Take turns to roll two dice. Make a two-digit number from the numbers showing. For example, 1 and 2 could make 12 or 21.
  Score a point for each number that the two-digit number is a multiple of, not counting the number itself. For example, 12 is a multiple of 2, 3, 4 and 6, so 12 scores 4 points.
  Score 3 points for a square number.
  The winner is the first to reach 20 points.

16 Reflect
  a Which of these statements best describes your work on calculating in this unit?
   • I did the best I could
   • I could have tried harder.
  b Discuss with a classmate:
   i Why you chose that statement.
   ii Whether it was true for every lesson.
  c Write down one thing you will do to make sure you do the best you can in the next unit.

3.1 Using functions

You will learn to:
- Find outputs of simple functions.

CONFIDENCE

Why learn this?
A function is a way of writing rules or instructions. It can be used to work out how much fertiliser to use.

Fluency
Work out
- double 3
- 4 lots of 5
- half of 8.

Explore
How can a farm manager use a function to work out how much to pay his staff?

Exercise 3.1

Warm up

1 Work out
  a 9 + 7
  b 11 − 4
  c 6 × 8
  d 12 ÷ 6

2 Work out
  a 12 add 9
  b 13 subtract 3
  c 2 multiplied by 9
  d 24 divided by 4.

Worked example

Work out the **output** of this **function machine**.

Input   Output

3 ⟶ [Add 4] ⟶ ☐

3 + 4 = 7

Key point

A **function** is a relationship between two sets of numbers. The numbers that go into a **function machine** are called the **input**. The numbers that come out are called the **output**.

3 Work out the outputs of these function machines.

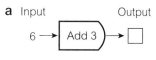

  a Input   Output

  6 ⟶ [Add 3] ⟶ ☐

  b Input   Output

  9 ⟶ [Subtract 5] ⟶ ☐

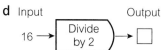

  c Input   Output

  4 ⟶ [Multiply by 5] ⟶ ☐

  d Input   Output

  16 ⟶ [Divide by 2] ⟶ ☐

Topic links: Multiplication facts

4 Work out the outputs of these function machines.

a Input 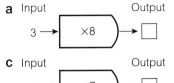 Output
3 → ×8 → □

b Input Output
12 → −9 → □

c Input Output
6 → +7 → □

d Input Output
35 → ÷5 → □

Key point

In a function machine, every input gives an output.

5 Work out the outputs of these function machines.

a Input 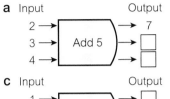 Output
2 → → 7
3 → Add 5 → □
4 → → □

b Input Output
9 → → □
12 → Subtract 4 → □
15 → → 11

Q5a hint

Write
2 + 5 = 7
3 + 5 =

c Input Output
1 → → □
3 → Multiply by 3 → □
6 → → □

d Input Output
8 → → □
10 → Divide by 2 → □
20 → → □

Discussion Will the outputs of a 'divide by 2' function machine always be whole numbers?

6 a Work out the missing outputs of this function machine.

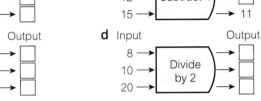

Input   Output
2 →   → 8
4 →   +6   → □
7 →   → □
9 →   → □

b Copy and complete the table to show the inputs and outputs of the function machine.

Input	2	4	7	9
Output	8			

7 Copy and complete the table to show the inputs and outputs of the function machine.

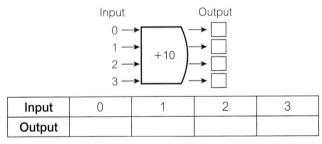

Input   Output
0 →   → □
1 →   → □
2 → +10   → □
3 →   → □

Input	0	1	2	3
Output				

8 Real A café owner pays her staff £7 per hour.

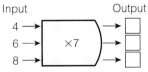

Input   Output
4 →   → □
6 →   ×7   → □
8 →   → □

a Use this function machine to work out how much she must pay them for shifts of

i 4 hours   **ii** 6 hours   **iii** 8 hours.

b Copy and complete the table to show all the inputs and outputs.

Input (hours)	4	6	8
Output (£)			

9 In 2014, the price of a first class stamp is 60p.

The price of a second class stamp is 50p.

They come in books of 6 or 12 stamps.

a Use the function machines to work out the price of a book of stamps.

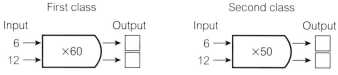

b Copy and complete the tables to show the price of a book of stamps in pence and in pounds.

Q9b hint

To change a price in pence to a price in pounds, divide by 100.

First class		
Input (number of stamps)	6	12
Output (price in pence)		
Price in pounds (£)		

Second class		
Input (number of stamps)	6	12
Output (price in pence)		
Price in pounds (£)		

Investigation

Reasoning

This function machine decodes the secret message 5 2 9 13.

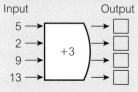

1 Work out the outputs of the function machine.

The table shows the letters of the alphabet with a code number.

1	2	3	4	5	6	7	8	9	10	11	12	13
a	b	c	d	e	f	g	h	i	J	k	l	m

14	15	16	17	18	19	20	21	22	23	24	25	26
n	o	p	q	r	s	t	u	v	w	x	y	z

2 Use the table to work out a letter for each output number.

3 What word does the secret message spell?

4 Work out a secret message for a partner to decode.

You must give them the input values and the function, and they have to work out the output values and the message.

Q2 hint

When the output is 20, the letter is t.

10 Explore How can a farm manager use a function to work out how much to pay his staff?

Is it easier to explore this question now you have completed the lesson? What further information do you need to be able to answer this?

11 Reflect

a Bella says, 'A function always has inputs and outputs.'

Is Bella correct?

b Kim says, 'Each input gives only one output.' Is Kim correct?

c What else can you say about functions? Discuss with a classmate.

Q11 hint

Look back at your work on functions to help you decide.

Explore

Reflect

Active Learn   Pi 1, Section 3.1

3.2 Function machines

You will learn to:
- Describe simple functions using words or symbols.

Why learn this?
Lots of maths is about finding the relationship between two numbers, like how much wool you need to knit four pairs of mittens.

Fluency
Which operation, +, −, × or ÷, is missing from each of these?
- 12 ☐ 8 = 4
- 6 ☐ 3 = 18
- 14 ☐ 2 = 7
- 14 ☐ 2 = 12

Explore
What shoe size would you wear in Australia?

Exercise 3.2

1 What two numbers can you multiply together to give an answer of
a 12
b 16
c 24
d 30?

2 Work out the missing outputs of these function machines.

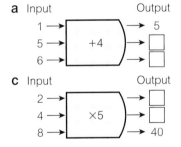

a Input → +4 → Output
1 → 5
5 → ☐
6 → ☐

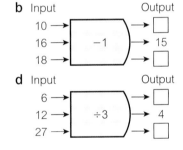

b Input → −1 → Output
10 → ☐
16 → 15
18 → ☐

c Input → ×5 → Output
2 → ☐
4 → ☐
8 → 40

d Input → ÷3 → Output
6 → ☐
12 → 4
27 → ☐

3 Write down the missing function for this function machine.

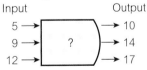

Input → ? → Output
5 → 10
9 → 14
12 → 17

4 Write down the function for each machine.

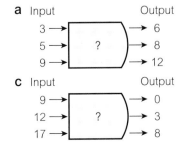

a Input → ? → Output
3 → 6
5 → 8
9 → 12

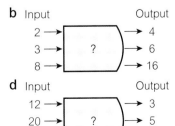

b Input → ? → Output
2 → 4
3 → 6
8 → 16

c Input → ? → Output
9 → 0
12 → 3
17 → 8

d Input → ? → Output
12 → 3
20 → 5
28 → 7

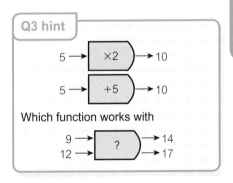

Q3 hint

5 → ×2 → 10

5 → +5 → 10

Which function works with

9 → ? → 14
12 → → 17

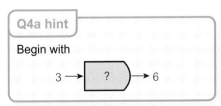

Q4a hint

Begin with

3 → ? → 6

Warm up

5 A chef looks at some recipes to see how much rice is used for the number of people.
The table shows the values he finds.

Number of people	2	4	8
Amount of rice (g)	100	200	400

He writes these values on this function machine.

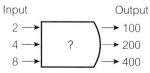

a Write down the function.

b Discussion How much rice should the chef cook per person? How can you work this out from the function machine?

c How much rice should the chef cook for 5 people?

Q5b Literacy hint

'per person' means 'for each person'.

6 Problem-solving Work out the missing output in this function machine.

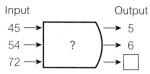

Q6 hint

Work out the function first.

Investigation | **Problem-solving**

Here are 5 input, 5 output and 5 function cards.

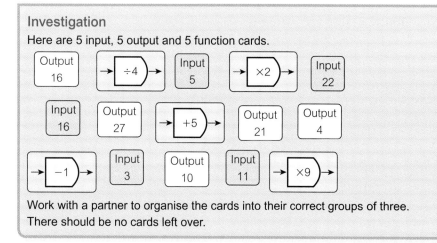

Work with a partner to organise the cards into their correct groups of three.
There should be no cards left over.

---

7 Explore What shoe size would you wear in Australia?
Is it easier to explore this question now you have completed the lesson?
What further information do you need to be able to answer this?

8 Reflect Sophie describes what she did for the investigation.

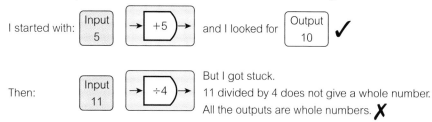

a What do you think Sophie did next?

b Discuss with a classmate the steps you took for working on the investigation.
Were your steps the same as Sophie's or different to hers?
What about to each other?
Did it matter?

3.3 Simplifying expressions

You will learn to:
- Simplify expressions.

Why learn this?
Simplifying the results of a survey can tell companies important information about their products and services.

Fluency
What are the missing numbers?
$2 + 2 + 2 + 2 = \square \times 2 = \square$

Explore
Abbie does a health and fitness quiz in a magazine. Her answers are N, Y, Y, N, Y, Y, Y, N, Y, Y. What do the test results tell us about Abbie?

Exercise 3.3

1 Work out

   a $5 \times £3$ **b** $£4 + £12$ **c** $45p - 30p$ **d** $50p \div 5$

2 Match each yellow card with a blue card that gives the same answer.

$3 + 3$	$4 + 4 + 4$	$10 - 5$	2×5	$8 \div 2$

$10 \div 2$	$5 + 5$	2×3	$8 - 4$	3×4

Worked example

Simplify

a $p + p$

$p + p = 2p$

b $2p + 3p$

$2p + 3p = 5p$

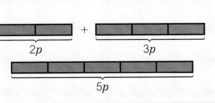

3 Sam has three different length rods.
Simplify

x y z

   a $x + x$

   b $y + y + y$

   c $3x + 3x$

   d $4y + y$

   e $3z + 2z$

Discussion Why is $x + x + x$ the same as $3x$?

Key point
In maths, if you do not know a value, you can use a letter to represent it.

Key point
$1x$ is written as x.

Warm up

4 Simplify

    a $4m + 3m$ **b** $7n + 2n$ **c** $9q + 3q$ **d** $8x + 2x + x$

    Discussion Is $3x + 2x$ the same as $2x + 3x$? How do you know?

5 Problem-solving Write three additions that give an answer of $8x$.

6 Simplify

    a $5y - 3y$ **b** $7y - 3y$ **c** $12b - 4b$ **d** $4r - 2r$

    Discussion What is $3y - y$?

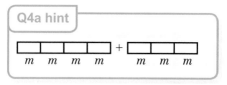

Worked example

Simplify $4b + 2b - b$

$4b + 2b - b = 6b - b$
$\qquad\qquad\quad = 5b$

> Work from left to right:
> First work out $4b + 2b$, then subtract b.

7 Simplify

    a $6m + 4m - 3m$

    b $8x - 3x + 3x$

    c $2x + 2x - x$

    d $9p + p - 2p$

8 Reasoning The diagram shows four cards. a is a positive number.

| $5a$ | $3a - a$ | $6a - 2a$ | $10a$ |

Tom chooses these two cards

| $6a - 2a$ | $10a$ |

and adds the **expressions**.

$6a - 2a + 10a = 4a + 10a$
$\qquad\qquad\qquad\quad = 14a$

    a Choose two other cards and add the expressions.

    b Choose two different cards and add the expressions.

    c What is the greatest total you can get by adding the expressions
       from two cards? Show how you worked out your answer.

9 **Explore** Abbie does a health and fitness quiz in a magazine.
    Her answers are N, Y, Y, N, Y, Y, Y, N, Y, Y. What do the test results tell
    us about Abbie?
    Is it easier to explore this question now you have completed the lesson?
    What further information do you need to be able to answer this?

10 **Reflect**
    a Elwin says, '*Simplify* in maths means *write simpler*.'
       Do you agree with Elwin?
       Write down a question (and answer) from this lesson to show why
       you agree or disagree.
    b Annie says, 'Simplifying always involves adding.'
       Do you agree with Annie?
       Write down a question (and answer) from this lesson to show why
       you agree or disagree.

Q4a hint

Q5 hint

$\square x + \square x = 8x$

Q6a hint

$\underset{5y}{\text{OOOOO}} - \underset{3y}{\text{OOO}} = \underset{}{\text{OO}}$

$5y \quad - \quad 3y \quad = \quad \square$

Key point

An **expression** contains numbers
and letters.

3.4 Writing expressions

You will learn to:

- Write expressions given a description in words.

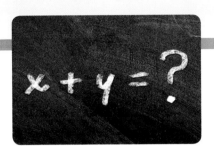

Why learn this?
To explain something in English you use words. In maths you can use algebra.

Fluency
Which of these does not give an answer of 8?
A 6 add 2
B double 4
C 6 less than 15
D 4 subtracted from 12

Explore
How can a 'mind reader' always work out the number you thought of when you tell them your answer to this calculation?
'Think of a number, add 1, multiply the result by 2 then subtract 2.'

Exercise 3.4

1 Work out
   a twice 5
   b three times 7
   c 4 more than 8
   d the total of 6, 3 and 4
   e 5 less than 9
   f 3 less than 14

2 Work out the missing outputs of these function machines.

   a Input 3 →, 6 → ×6 → Output
   b Input 7 →, 9 → +12 → Output
   c Input 50 →, 80 → ÷10 → Output
   d Input 11 →, 23 → −9 → Output

3 Sue knows the green stick is 3 cm longer than the red stick.

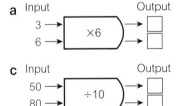
3 cm

   Write down how to work out the length of the green stick.

Key point
You write an expression by using letters to stand for numbers.

4 Ava has y books. Write an expression for the number of books each of these people have.
   a Tim has 2 more books than Ava.
   b Erin has 6 more books than Ava.
   c Danel has 3 fewer books than Ava.
   d Gilen has 9 fewer books than Ava.

Q4a hint
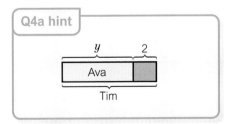
y | 2
Ava
Tim

5 Abi has a bag containing n tennis balls.
   Write an expression for the number of tennis balls these people have.
   a Kylie has 1 more than Abi.
   b Julia has 5 more than Abi.
   c Stefan has 2 fewer than Abi.
   d Katrina has 7 fewer than Abi.

Warm up

Worked example

a Draw a function machine to write an expression for 7 more than x.

Input   Output

$x \rightarrow \boxed{+7} \rightarrow x + 7$

> '7 more than x' means '$x + 7$'.

b Use the function machine to work out the output when $x = 3$.

Input   Output

$3 \rightarrow \boxed{+7} \rightarrow 3 + 7 = 10$

> **Substitute** 3 for x, then work out $3 + 7$.

Literacy hint

Substitute means 'replace'.

6 a i Copy and complete this function machine to write an expression for 5 more than y.

Input   Output

$y \rightarrow \boxed{+5} \rightarrow$

  ii Use the function machine to work out the output when $y = 11$.

 b i Copy and complete this function machine to write an expression for 6 less than m.

Input   Output

$m \rightarrow \boxed{-6} \rightarrow$

  ii Use the function machine to work out the output when $m = 15$.

7 a Draw a function machine to write an expression for
   i 12 more than n **ii** n with 3 taken away.
 b Work out the output of each function machine in part **a** when $n = 15$.

Worked example

Katy earns £x. Sam earns twice as much as Katy.

a Write an expression for the amount Sam earns.

Sam $= x \times 2$
    $= 2x$

> Visualise or draw a function machine.
>
> Input   Output
>
> $x \rightarrow \boxed{\times 2} \rightarrow 2x$

b Katy earns £40.
How much does Sam earn?

Sam $= 2 \times 40$
    $= £80$

> Input   Output
>
> $40 \rightarrow \boxed{\times 2} \rightarrow 80$

Key point

You write numbers before letters.
$x \times 2 = 2$ lots of x
    $= 2x$

8 George earns £y. Kabir earns 3 times as much as George.
 a Write an expression for the amount Kabir earns.
 b George earns £30. How much does Kabir earn?

Q8 hint

Write the numbers before the letters: $\square y$.

9 Madhu owns n DVDs.
Gill owns twice as many DVDs as Madhu.
 a Write an expression for the number of DVDs Gill owns.
Fatima owns 5 times as many DVDs as Madhu.
 b Write an expression for the number of DVDs Fatima owns.

Topic links: Multiplication facts to 10 × 10

10 Problem-solving In a Year 7 class, there are twice as many Chelsea supporters as Spurs supporters. There are 3 times as many Arsenal supporters as Chelsea supporters.
There are x Spurs supporters.
Write an expression for the number of Arsenal supporters in terms of x.

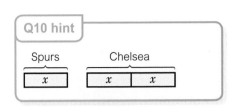

Q10 hint

Spurs   Chelsea

x x x

11 Modelling Zoe charges £9 per student to attend a dance class.
There are y students in the class.
  a Write an expression for the total amount she charges for a class.
  b How much does she charge for 5 students?
  c How many students must she have in the class to make £72?

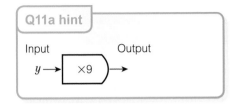

Q11a hint

Input   Output

$y \rightarrow$ [×9] $\rightarrow$

12 Tyrone writes this story to describe the expression $g + 5$.
The first week Dave swims g lengths.
The second week he swims 5 more lengths than the first week.
Write a different story to describe each of these expressions.
  a $m + 12$ **b** $p - 30$ **c** $9n$

Discussion What stories have other students in your class written?

13 Match each yellow description card to its correct blue expression card.

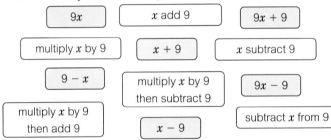

9x | x add 9 | 9x + 9

multiply x by 9 | x + 9 | x subtract 9

9 − x | multiply x by 9 then subtract 9 | 9x − 9

multiply x by 9 then add 9 | x − 9 | subtract x from 9

14 Explore How can a 'mind reader' always work out the number you thought of when you tell them your answer to this calculation, 'Think of a number, add 1, multiply the result by 2 then subtract 2.'?
Is it easier to explore this question now you have completed the lesson?
What further information do you need to be able to answer this?

15 Reflect This lesson used bar models (like in the hint for Q4).
It also used function machines (like in the Worked example).
Paul prefers bar models. Lucinda prefers function machines.
They both draw pictures for these three descriptions in Q13.
x add 9
x subtract 9
multiply x by 9

Paul's bar models

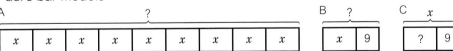

A   ?
| x | x | x | x | x | x | x | x | x |

B   ?
| x | 9 |

C   x
| ? | 9 |

Lucinda's function machines

D   E   F
$x \rightarrow$ [−9] $\rightarrow$? $x \rightarrow$ [×9] $\rightarrow$? $x \rightarrow$ [+9] $\rightarrow$?

  a Which bar model matches each description?
  b Which function machine matches each description?
  c Discuss with a partner if you prefer bar models or function machines. Explain why.

Explore

Reflect

3.5 STEM: Using formulae

You will learn to:
- Substitute positive integers into simple formulae written in words
- Substitute integers into simple formulae written in letter symbols.

CONFIDENCE

Why learn this?
Doctors use formulae to work out how much medicine a patient needs.

Fluency
Work out
- 25 − 5
- 14 + 12
- 6 × 3
- 36 ÷ 4

Explore
How can you work out the force acting on a moving object?

Warm up

Exercise 3.5: Science formulae

1 a Copy and complete this function machine to write an expression for 4 more than x.

Input   Output
$x \rightarrow \boxed{+4} \rightarrow$

  b Use the function machine to work out the output when $x = 7$.

2 This function machine works out the pressure when force is applied to a $2\,m^2$ area.

Force $\rightarrow \boxed{\div 2} \rightarrow$ Pressure

Use the function machine to work out the pressure when the force is
  a 6   **b** 10   **c** 24

> **Q2a hint**
>
> $6 \rightarrow \boxed{\div 2} \rightarrow \square$

> **Key point**
>
> A **formula** shows the relationship between different quantities.
> You can write a formula using letters to stand for quantities.
> A formula always has an equals sign '='.

Worked example

The **formula** to work out the pressure when a force is applied to an area of $5\,cm^2$ is
pressure = force ÷ 5
Work out the pressure when the force is 30.

pressure = force ÷ 5
       = 30 ÷ 5   ⟵ Write the formula first.
       = 6   ⟵ Substitute the value for the force into the formula.

3 STEM The formula to work out the pressure when a force is applied to an area of $8\,cm^2$ is pressure = force ÷ 8
Work out the pressure when the force is
  a 16   **b** 24   **c** 40

> **Q4 Literacy hint**
>
> Resistance slows down the current passing through a lamp.

4 STEM The formula to work out the voltage (V) needed for a lamp is
$V = 2 \times$ resistance
Work out the voltage needed when the resistance is
  a 3   **b** 4   **c** 5

> **Q4a hint**
>
> $V = 2 \times$ resistance
>   = 2 × 3
>   = $\square$

Topic links: Multiplication facts to 10 × 10, Range   **Subject links:** Science (Q2–10)

5 STEM The formula to work out the amount of painkiller to give a child is amount of painkiller (mg) = mass of child (kg) ÷ 10
Work out the amount of painkiller to give a child of mass
a 30 kg   **b** 40 kg.

Q5 Strategy hint
Write down the formula.
Substitute the values.

6 STEM The table shows the boiling points of five liquids.

Name of liquid	Nitric acid	Nitrogen chloride	Lead chloride	Water	Sulfuric acid
Boiling point (°C)	83	71	954	100	330

a Write down the boiling point of water.
b Write down the boiling points in order of size starting with the smallest.
c Work out the range of the boiling points.

Q6 Literacy hint
The boiling point is the temperature at which a liquid boils.

Q6c hint
The formula to work out the range of a set of data is
range = highest value − lowest value

7 STEM The formula to work out the distance a car travels when you know the speed of the car and the time taken is
$d = s \times t$
a What do you think the letters d, s and t stand for?
b Copy and complete the workings to find the distance when
   i $s = 50$ and $t = 2$ **ii** $s = 60$ and $t = 3$
    $d = s \times t$ $d = s \times t$
      $= 50 \times 2$ $= \square \times \square$
      $= \square$ $= \square$

Discussion What units is the distance measured in? For example, when $s = 30$ miles per hour and $t = 4$ hours, $d = 30 \times 4 = 120$ ...?

8 STEM The formula to convert a weight to a mass is
$M = W \div 10$
a What do you think the letters M and W stand for?
b Use the formula to work out the mass when
   i $W = 40$ **ii** $W = 120$ **iii** $W = 600$

9 STEM / Modelling In a science experiment, four students measured their hand span and their height. The table shows the results.

Hand span (cm)	15	13	16	14
Height (cm)	145	128	155	138

Sadie thinks that the best formula you could use to work out the height (H) of a person when you know their hand span (S) is $H = 9S$.
Zosha thinks that the best formula is $H = 10S$.
Who is correct? Explain how you worked out your answer.

Q9 hint
$9S$ means $9 \times S$.

Q9 Strategy hint
Try the hand span values in both of the formulae. Which formula gives answers closest to the real heights of the students?

10 Explore How can you work out the force acting on a moving object?
Is it easier to explore this question now you have completed the lesson?
What further information do you need to be able to answer this?

11 Reflect Look back at the formula in Q7.
Would it matter if this formula used the letters a, b and c instead of d, s and t?
Write two sentences to explain:
Sentence 1: No, because ...
Sentence 2: Yes, because ...

Q11 hint
For sentence 1, if different letters were used, would your answers to questions **7bi** and **7bii** be the same?
For sentence 2, do the letters help you to understand a formula?

Explore

Reflect

3.6 Writing formulae

You will learn to:

* Write simple formulae using words and letter symbols.

CONFIDENCE

A	B	C	D	E
	The Cupcake Shop - First Quarter Sales			
	January	February	March	Total
Red velvet	£1,292	£1,156	£1,208	£3,656
Lemon drizzle	£2,047	£1,987	£1,999	£6,033
Vanilla	£1,795	£1,896	£1,689	£5,380
Fudge	£1,250	£1,346	£1,287	£3,883
Total revenues	£6,384	£6,385	£6,183	£18,952

Why learn this?

You can write a formula in a spreadsheet so that every time you change the data the spreadsheet does the calculation for you.

Fluency

Simplify
* $3 \times k$
* $4 \times m$
* $n \times 2$
* $y \times 5$

Explore

How do you write a formula in a spreadsheet?

Exercise 3.6

Warm up

1 Lin is y years old. Write an expression for the age of each of these people.
   a Alice is 5 years older than Lin.
   b Joe is 2 years younger than Lin.
   c Kai is twice as old as Lin.

Q1 hint

Draw a function machine.

$y \rightarrow \boxed{} \rightarrow$

2 a $x = y + 2$ Work out x when $y = 6$.
   b $m = 2n$ Work out m when n is 5.
   c $F = 5p$ Work out F when $p = 4$.

Q2b hint

$2n$ means $2 \times n$.

Worked example

Every day a butcher makes 24 sausages more than have been ordered.
a Write a formula in words for the number of sausages he makes each day.

number of sausages made = number of sausages ordered + 24

b Write a formula that connects the number of sausages made, m, to the number of sausages ordered, s.

$m = s + 24$

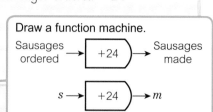

Draw a function machine.

Sausages ordered $\rightarrow \boxed{+24} \rightarrow$ Sausages made

$s \rightarrow \boxed{+24} \rightarrow m$

Key point

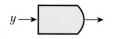

You can write a formula to work out an amount in words, then use letters to represent the quantities.

3 A swimming coach always brings two more floats than the number of students in the class.
   a How many floats does she bring when the number of students is
      i 1   ii 2   iii 3?
   b What do you do to the number of students to find the number of floats?

Topic links: Multiplication facts to 10 × 10, Division of whole numbers

Subject links: PE (Q3, Q6), Cookery (Q7), IT (Investigation)

c Copy and complete this word formula for the number of floats.

number of floats = _____ + _____

d Copy and complete this formula that connects the number of students, s, and the number of floats she brings, f.

$f = \Box + \Box$

Discussion Does it matter what letters you use in a formula?

Q3c hint

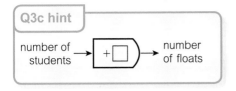

4 All items in a sale are reduced by £10.

a Work out the sale price of items when the original price is

   i £15   **ii** £20   **iii** £25

b Copy and complete this word formula for the sale price of an item.

sale price = _____ − _____

c Copy and complete this formula that connects the sale price of an item, x, and the original price of an item, y.

$x = \Box - \Box$

Q4a hint

What do you do to the original price to find the sale price?

5 Modelling A horse trekking centre always brings in 5 more horses than are booked.

a Write a word formula for the number of horses they bring in.

b Write a formula for the number of horses they bring in, h, and the number that are booked, b.

Worked example

Sally earns £9 per hour. Write a formula that connects the money she earns, m, to the hours she works, h.

number of hours × 9 = money she earns | Write the formula in words or as a function machine. |

$h \times 9 = m$

$m = 9h$ | Rearrange and simplify the formula. |

6 There are 7 players in a netball team.

a Copy and complete.

1 team = 7 players

2 teams = 2 × 7 = $\Box$ players

3 teams = 3 × 7 = $\Box$ players

n teams = n × 7 = $\Box$ players

b Write down the missing function for this machine.

c Write a formula to work out the total number of players, t, when you know the number of teams, n.

Q7 Literacy hint

'Per' means 'for each'.

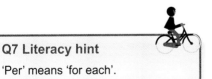

7 To make cheese scones you need 4 grams of cheese per scone.

a Copy and complete this function machine.

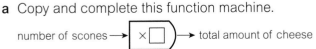

b Write a formula to work out the amount of cheese, C, you use when you know the number of scones, s.

Q7a hint

1 scone = 4 g

2 scones = 2 × 4 = $\Box$ g

3 scones = 3 × 4 = $\Box$ g

s scones = $\Box$ × $\Box$ = $\Box$ g

8 Real To work out the amount of food a cow needs each day you divide the mass of the cow by 40.

a Copy and complete this table.

Q8b hint

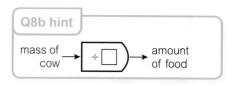

Mass of cow	Amount of food
400 kg	400 ÷ 40 = 10 kg
480 kg	480 ÷ 40 = ☐ kg
560 kg	560 ÷ ☐ = ☐ kg

b Write a formula to work out the amount of food, F, to give a cow of mass M kg.

Investigation   **Problem-solving**

Work with a partner to answer these questions.

Here is a section of a spreadsheet.

	A	B	C	D
1	5		15	
2	9		21	
3	7	4	11	
4	12		4	

cell A1 — (A1)   cell C1 — (C1)

1 The formula in cell C1 is =A1*3
   What will the new value in C1 be if you change the formula in C1 to =A1*7?
2 The formula in cell C2 is =A2+12
   What will the new value in C2 be if you change the formula to =A2+5?
3 The formula in cell C3 is =A3+B3
   What will the new value in C3 be if you change the formula to =A3-B3?
4 The formula in cell C4 is =A4/3
   What will the new value in C4 be if you change the formula to =A4/6?

---

9 Explore How do you write a formula in a spreadsheet?
Is it easier to explore this question now you have completed the lesson? What further information do you need to be able to answer this?

10 Reflect In this lesson you wrote your own formulae.
In lesson 3.5 you were given formulae to work with.
   a Which did you find more difficult – lesson 3.5 or this lesson?
   b Write down the question(s) you found most difficult.
   c Discuss the question(s) you wrote down with a partner.
      Explain what made them difficult.

Q10b hint

Write down the question number(s) only.

Explore

Reflect

Master
P59

CHECK

Strengthen
P76

Extend
P80

Test
P84

3 Check up

Log how you did on your
Student Progression Chart.

Functions

1 Work out the outputs of these function machines.

a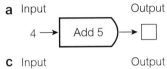

b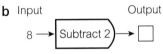

c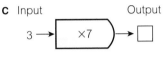

d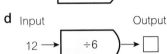

2 Here is a function machine.
Copy and complete the table to show all the inputs
and outputs of this machine.

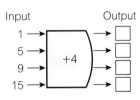

Input	1	5	9	15
Output				

3 Write down the function of each machine.

a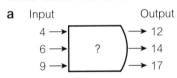

b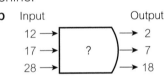

4 This function machine shows the number
of bananas a zoo keeper puts in a
monkey enclosure.
a What is the function?
b How many bananas does the zoo keeper
put in a monkey enclosure with 6 monkeys?

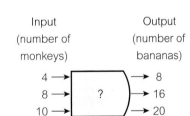

Expressions

5 Simplify
a $m + m$ **b** $n + n + n$ **c** $4p + 3p$
d $5q + q$ **e** $8x + 5x + 4x$

6 Simplify
a $7y - 4y$ **b** $10p - p$ **c** $9m + 2m - 3m$ **d** $6t - 4t - t$

7 Nia has x coins.
Write an expression for the number of coins these people have.
a Ben has 3 more than Nia.
b Jayden has 5 fewer than Nia.

8 Fin scores p points in a game of Scrabble®.
Niall scores 3 times as many points as Fin.
Write an expression for the number of points Niall scores.

9 a Copy and complete this function machine to write an expression for 15 less than h.

Input   Output

$h \rightarrow \boxed{-\square} \rightarrow \square$

b Use the function machine to work out the output when $h = 25$.

Formulae

10 The formula to work out the number of eggs needed for a recipe is
number of eggs = 2 × number of people
Work out the number of eggs needed for
a 3 people   **b** 8 people.

11 Use the formula $F = Q + R$ to work out the value of F when $Q = 12$ and $R = 5$.

12 Use the formula $P = mv$ to work out the value of P when $m = 5$ and $v = 2$.

13 There are 7 players in a netball team. The formula to work out the number of netball teams that can be made from the number of students is $t = s \div 7$
a What do you think the letters t and s stand for?
b Work out the value of t when $s = 28$.

14 A baker always makes 5 more cakes than the number ordered. Write a formula that connects the number of cakes made, m, and the number ordered, c.

15 It costs Nadine 4p to send one text message. Write a formula to work out the total cost, c, when you know the number of texts, t.

16 **How sure are you of your answers? Were you mostly**
😟 **Just guessing**   😐 **Feeling doubtful**   🙂 **Confident**
What next? Use your results to decide whether to strengthen or extend your learning.

Challenge

17 Write down two different functions for this function machine.

Input   Output

18 Lauren says that this function machine only gives outputs ending in 0 or 5.

Input   Output

Is she correct? Explain your answer.

19 Write four algebraic expressions that simplify to give $6x$.

3 Strengthen

You will learn to:
- Strengthen your understanding with practice.

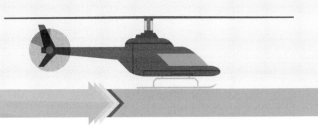

Functions

1 Work out the outputs of these function machines.

a Input → Output
£5 → Add £2 → ☐

b Input → Output
2 → +8 → ☐

c Input → Output
£5 → Subtract £1 → ☐

d Input → Output
7 → −3 → ☐

Q1a hint
5 + 2 = ☐
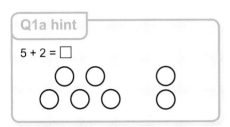

Q1c hint
5 − 1 = ☐
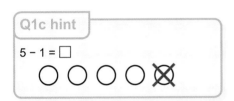

2 Work out the outputs of these function machines.

a Input → Output
1 →
5 → Add 4 → ☐☐

b Input → Output
7 →
10 → Subtract 6 → ☐☐☐
16 →

Q2a hint
1 + 4 = ☐
5 + 4 = ☐

3 Work out the outputs of these function machines.

a Input → Output
5 → Multiply by 3 → ☐

b Input → Output
3 → ×4 → ☐

c Input → Output
8 → Divide by 2 → ☐

d Input → Output
9 → ÷3 → ☐

4 **a** Work out the missing outputs of this function machine.

b Copy and complete the table to show all the inputs and outputs.

Input → Output
2 → → 20
5 → Multiply by 10 → ☐
8 → → ☐

Input	2	5	8
Output	20		

5 Follow these steps to find the function of this machine.

Input → Output
5 → → 10
6 → ? → 12
8 → → 16

a What are the possible functions for the first input and output?

Q5a hint
5 + ☐ = 10
5 × ☐ = 10

b Try both possible functions for 6 → ? → 12
Which one works?

c Check the function works for 8 → ? → 16

d Write down the function that works for all the inputs and outputs.

6 Write the function of each machine.

a Input   Output
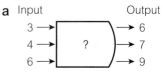

b Input   Output
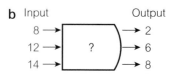

c Input   Output

Input		Output
14 →	?	→ 7
16 →		→ 8
18 →		→ 9

Expressions

1 Simplify

a $b + b$ ⬚ + ⬚

b $b + b + b$ ⬚ + ⬚ + ⬚

c $4b + 3b$ ⬚⬚⬚⬚ + ⬚⬚⬚

d $5b + b$ ⬚⬚⬚⬚⬚ + ⬚

e $3b + b + 2b$ ⬚⬚⬚ + ⬚ + ⬚⬚

> **Q1a hint**
>
> 1 block + 1 block = ☐ blocks
> b + b = ☐b

2 Simplify

a $b + b + b + b$ ⬚ + ⬚ + ⬚ + ⬚

b $3b + 2b$ ⬚⬚⬚ + ⬚⬚

c $5b - 2b$ ⬚⬚⬚☒☒

d $4b - 3b$ ⬚☒☒☒

e $7b - b$ ⬚⬚⬚⬚⬚⬚☒

f $6b - b - 4b$ ⬚☒☒☒☒☒

> **Q2c hint**
>
> 5 blocks − 2 blocks = ☐ blocks
> $5b$ − $2b$ = ☐b

> **Q2f hint**
>
> $1b$ is the same as b.

3 Simplify

a $2y + 4y$ **b** $7v + 2v$ **c** $8m + 2m + m$

d $7p - 6p$ **e** $11n - 5n$

> **Q3a hint**
>
> ⬚⬚ + ⬚⬚⬚⬚

4 Match the story to the calculation.

A Joe has 3 sweets. He gets 2 more.   **i** $x - 2$ **ii** $x + 3$

B Penny has 3 texts. She deletes 1.

C Suha has x sweets. She gets 3 more.   **iii** $3 - 1$ **iv** $3 + 2$

D Kunal has x texts. He deletes 2.

5 a Ella has a bag containing 5 apples. She puts in 4 more.
Write a calculation to show this.

b Will has a bag containing x apples. He puts in 4 more.
Write an expression to show this.

6 a Jamie has a box containing 9 pens. He takes out 5.
Write down a calculation to show this.

b Katya has a box containing y pens. She takes out 3.
Write down an expression to show this.

7 Match the story to the calculation.

A Joe has £8. Alice has twice as much.   **i** $x \times 2$ **ii** $x \times 5$

B Paula has 4 books. Hans has 5 times as many.

C Sham has £x sweets. Sita has twice as many.   **iii** 8×2 **iv** 4×5

D Erin has x books. Tao has 5 times as many.

8 It takes Emily 6 minutes to complete a puzzle.

It takes Aaron 4 times as long.

a How long does it take Aaron to complete the puzzle?

It takes Emily r minutes to complete a crossword.

It takes Aaron 4 times as long.

b Write an expression for the time it takes Aaron to complete the crossword.

9 Harsha earns £20.

Pavel earns twice as much.

a How much does Pavel earn?

Rhian earns £h.

Louis earns 3 times as much.

b Write an expression for the amount Louis earns.

Formulae

1 The formula to work out the number of nails you need to shoe a horse is

number of nails = 7 × number of horse shoes

Complete the workings to find the number of nails needed for

a 4 horse shoes

number of nails = 7 × 4 = ☐

b 8 horse shoes

number of nails = 7 × 8 = ☐

c 12 horse shoes

number of nails = 7 × ☐ = ☐

2 The formula to work out the number of shoes, s, you need for h horses is

$s = 4 \times h$

Complete the workings to find the number of shoes needed for

a 3 horses

$s = 4 \times h = 4 \times 3 =$ ☐

b 5 horses

$s = 4 \times h = 4 \times$ ☐ $=$ ☐

c 9 horses

$s = 4 \times h = 4 \times$ ☐ $=$ ☐

3 Copy and complete the workings using the formula $W = V + 7$ to work out the value of W when

a $V = 3$

$W = V + 7 = 3 + 7 =$ ☐

b $V = 9$

$W = V + 7 = 9 + 7 =$ ☐

c $V = 23$

$W = V + 7 = 23 +$ ☐ $=$ ☐

4 Copy and complete the workings using the formula $T = P + S$ to work out the value of T when

a $P = 8$ and $S = 4$

$T = P + S = 8 + 4 =$ ☐

b $P = 12$ and $S = 15$

$T = P + S = 12 +$ ☐ $=$ ☐

c $P = 9$ and $S = 0$

$T = P + S =$ ☐ $+$ ☐ $=$ ☐

5 Copy and complete the workings using the formula $X = 6Y$ to work out the value of X when

a $Y = 3$

$X = 6Y = 6 \times 3 =$ ☐

b $Y = 5$

$X = 6Y = 6 \times$ ☐ $=$ ☐

c $Y = 10$

$X = 6Y = 6 \times$ ☐ $=$ ☐

> **Q5 hint**
>
> $6Y$ means $6 \times Y$

6 Copy and complete the workings using the formula $R = ak$ to work out the value of R when

   a $a = 3$ and $k = 2$
       $R = a \times k = 3 \times 2 = \square$

   b $a = 7$ and $k = 5$
       $R = a \times k = 7 \times \square = \square$

   c $a = 8$ and $k = 6$
       $R = a \times k = \square \times \square = \square$

Q6 hint

$R = ak$ means $R = a \times k$.

7 Match the words to the function.

   i 5 more   **ii** 5 less   **iii** 5 times

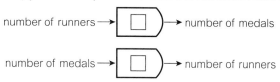

A   B   C

$\rightarrow \boxed{\times 5} \rightarrow$ $\rightarrow \boxed{-5} \rightarrow$ $\rightarrow \boxed{+5} \rightarrow$

8 In a fun run there are 5 more medals than the number of runners.

   a What is the function?

   b How many medals will there be for 20 runners?

   c Copy and complete the correct function machine.

      number of runners $\rightarrow \boxed{} \rightarrow$ number of medals

      number of medals $\rightarrow \boxed{} \rightarrow$ number of runners

Q8c hint

Try your answer to part **b** in each machine.

   d Complete the formula.

      Number of _____ = number of _____ + $\square$

9 In musical chairs, the number of chairs is 1 less than the number of players.

   a What is the function?

   b How many chairs for 3 players?

   c Copy and complete the function machine.

      number of .... $\rightarrow \boxed{} \rightarrow$ number of ....

   d Complete the formula.

      number of _____ = number of _____ − $\square$

Enrichment

1 Tyrone has spilt tomato ketchup on his homework. Work out the missing values.

      Input   Output

      $12 \rightarrow$ $\rightarrow 9$
      $18 \rightarrow$ $\rightarrow 15$
      $23 \rightarrow$
                 $\rightarrow 25$

2 Kim writes this happiness formula.

   happiness value = age + number of pets − number of siblings

   a Work out your happiness value.

   b Write a happiness formula of your own.

3 Reflect

   Look back at these Strengthen lessons.

   Find a question that you struggled to understand.

   Write down one word that describes how you feel when you struggle to answer a maths question.

   Write down two things you could do to help, when you are struggling.

Reflect

3 Extend

You will learn to:
• Extend your understanding with problem-solving.

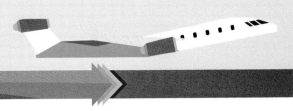

1 Work out the missing inputs and outputs of these function machines.

a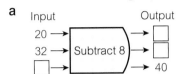

b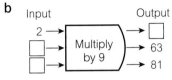

2 **Problem-solving** Use the numbers from the cloud to complete this function machine.

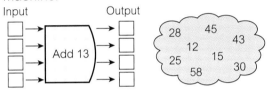

 3 **Problem-solving** The table shows the ages of the members of three 7-a-side rugby teams.

Team	Ages of members (years)						
A	18	14	16	16	17	20	18
B	25	22	23	22	20	18	24
C	17	26	32	28	19	25	28

The mean age of a team of 7 rugby players can be worked out using this function machine.

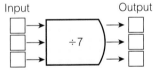

The input values are the total age of the members of the team.
The output values are the mean age.

a Copy and complete the function machine to work out the mean age of teams A, B and C.

b Which team has the oldest mean age?

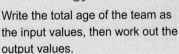

Q3a Strategy hint

Write the total age of the team as the input values, then work out the output values.

4 Here are three input cards and four function cards.

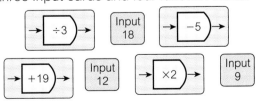

a Which input number and function will give the greatest possible output number?

b Which input number and function will give the smallest possible output number?

Unit 3 Expressions, functions and formulae 80

5 Problem-solving This is part of Heidi's homework.

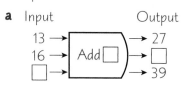

Complete these function machines.

a Input → Output

13 → Add ☐ → 27
16 → → ☐
☐ → → 39

b Input → Output

18 → Divide by ☐ → 3
☐ → → 5
54 → → ☐

Work out the missing numbers.

Q5 Strategy hint

Use the first input and output to work out the function.

6 Write down two possible functions for each of these function machines.

a Input → Output

8 → ? → 24

b Input → Output

25 → ? → 5

7 Work out the outputs of these two-step function machines.

a
1 →
3 → Add 2 → Multiply by 3 → 9
4 → → ☐
→ ☐

Q7a hint

1 + 2 = 3, then 3 × 3 = 9
3 + 2 = 5, then 5 × 3 = ☐
4 + 2 = ☐, then ☐ × 3 = ☐

b
9 →
13 → Subtract 1 → Divide by 2 → ☐
19 → → ☐
→ ☐

c
2 →
3 → Multiply by 5 → Subtract 4 → ☐
5 → → ☐
→ ☐

d
10 →
15 → Divide by 5 → Add 7 → ☐
25 → → ☐
→ ☐

8 Modelling This two-step function machine can be used to estimate the height of a child when you know their age.

Age (years) → Multiply by 6 → Add 80 → Height (cm)

Copy and complete the table to show an estimate of the height of children of different ages.

Age (years)	4	6	8	10
Height (cm)				

Discussion Do you think this function machine will work for children older than 11?

9 Modelling This function machine can be used to work out an estimate of the shoe size of a man.

Foot length (inches) → Multiply by 3 → Subtract 22 → Shoe size

Copy and complete the table to show the shoe sizes for different foot lengths for men.

Foot length (inches)	9	10	11	12
Shoe size				

Topic links: Mean, Ratio   **Subject links:** Science (Q16, Q17)

10 **Real** You can use this formula to work out how much food a horse needs each day.
amount of food (kg) = mass of horse (kg) ÷ 40
A horse has a mass of 480 kg.

   a How much food does the horse need each day?
   Horse food is a mixture of hay and oats. It has 3 kg hay for every 1 kg of oats.

   b i How many kilograms of hay does the horse need each day?
   ii How many kilograms of oats does the horse need each day?

   c Another horse has a mass of 640 kg.
   How many kilograms of hay does this horse need each day?

11 In this algebra wheel the **terms** in opposite circles add up to give the expression at the centre.
   Write down the terms missing from these algebra wheels.

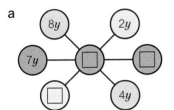

a

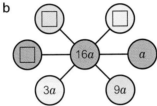

b

$x + 5x = 6x$
$2x + 4x = 6x$
$3x + 3x = 6x$

Q11 Literacy hint

A **term** is a number, a letter, or a number and letter multiplied together.

expression

$\overbrace{3x + 1}$
↑ ↗
terms

12 **Modelling** The function machine shows the height of 4 men and the width of their shoulders.

   a Write down the function.

   b Copy and complete this formula in words to work out the width of a man's shoulders when you know his height.

   width of shoulders = _____

   c Write a formula using letters to work out the width of a man's shoulders when you know his height. Use w for width and h for height.

   d Work out the width of the shoulders of a man who is 168 cm tall.

Input Height (cm)	Output Width of shoulders (cm)
180 →	→ 45
188 →	→ 47
160 →	? → 40
176 →	→ 44

Q12a hint

What do you need to divide the height by to get the width of the shoulders?

13 Sahid uses the formula $M = h - b$.
   This is what he writes.

   $M = h - b$
   $M = 24 - 8$
   $\quad = 16$

   a Write down the value of h.
   b Write down the value of b.

14 Here are two formulae. $P = 4r$ $T = P + Q$

   a Work out the value of P when $r = 7$.
   b Work out the value of T when $P = 28$ and $Q = 12$.
   c Work out the value of T when $r = 3$ and $Q = 25$.

Q14c hint

Work out the value of P first.

15 **Problem-solving** Here are three formulae.

   $A = 12 + g$ $M = d \times p$ $K = A - M$

   Work out the value of K when $g = 58$, $d = 6$ and $p = 8$.

Q15 Strategy hint

Decide which letters you need to find the values of before you can find K.

16 STEM / Modelling The maximum heart rate (in beats per minute) you should reach during exercise is found by subtracting your age from 220.

  a Work out the maximum heart rate for a person who is

    i 20 years old   **ii** 50 years old   **iii** 32 years old.

  b Write a formula to work out the maximum heart rate, M, when you know a person's age, A.

Q16b hint

$M = 220 - \Box$

  c Use your formula to check your answers to part **a**.

  d Use your formula to work out your maximum heart rate.

  e Harry is 65 years old. He goes for a run, and then measures his heart rate to be 148.

    Is this higher or lower than his maximum heart rate?

17 STEM / Modelling You work out your heart rate reserve by subtracting your resting heart rate from your maximum heart rate.

  a Simon has a maximum heart rate of 180 and a resting heart rate of 60.

    Work out his heart rate reserve.

  b Write a formula to work out the heart rate reserve, R, when you know the maximum heart rate, M, and the resting heart rate, H.

Q17b hint

$R = M - \Box$

  c Lin has a maximum heart rate of 200 and a resting heart rate of 70.

    Use your formula to work out her heart rate reserve.

 18 STEM / Modelling Aiden works out his fitness value by working out 15 multiplied by his heart rate reserve.

  a Aiden's heart rate reserve is 100. Work out his fitness value.

  b Write a formula to work out the fitness value, F, when you know a person's heart rate reserve R.

Q18b hint

$F =$

  c Aisha has a heart rate reserve of 80. Work out her fitness value.

  d Sandeep is 30 years old. His resting heart rate is 55.

    Use your formulae from Q16 and Q17 to work out his fitness factor.

19 Karen has two bags of counters.

The blue bag contains x counters and the yellow bag contains y counters.

  a Write an expression for the total number of counters in both bags.

Karen takes 2 counters out of the blue bag and puts them in the yellow bag.

  b Write an expression for the number of counters in

    i the blue bag   **ii** the yellow bag.

20 Reflect Miguel says, 'These Extend questions are like solving puzzles.'
Do you agree with Miguel?   Topic links: Mean, Ratio

Q20 hint

Look back at some of the Extend questions to help you decide. Begin your explanation with, 'I agree, because ...' or 'I disagree, because ...'. Give some examples from the questions you answered.

Reflect

3 Unit test

Log how you did on your Student Progression Chart.

1 Work out the outputs of these function machines.

a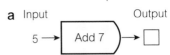

b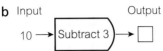

c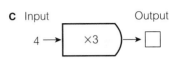

d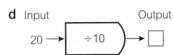

2 Copy and complete the table to show all the inputs and outputs of the function machine.

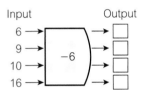

Input	6	9	10	16
Output				

3 Write down the function for each machine.

a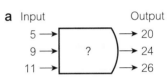

b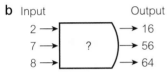

c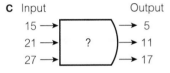

4 Simplify
   a $x + x + x + x$ b $2y + 6y$ c $4p + p$
   d $2m + 3m + 5m$ e $8g + 4g + g$

5 Simplify
   a $9x - 5x$ b $5v - v$
   c $8m - 3m - 4m$ d $7t - t - 3t$

6 Here are some algebra cards.

   a Choose two cards to make these statements correct.

   i ⬚ + ⬚ = 10y

   ii ⬚ − ⬚ = 10y

   b Choose three cards to make this statement correct.

   ⬚ + ⬚ − ⬚ = 10y

7 The formula to work out the number of prawns needed for a recipe is
   number of prawns = 8 × number of people
   Work out the number of prawns needed for
   a 4 people
   b 10 people.

8 Work out the outputs of this two-step function machine.

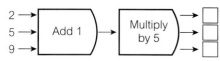

9 Ben earns £d per week.
  a Amy earns twice as much as Ben.
     Write an expression for the amount Amy earns per week.
  b Mia earns £12 per week less than Ben.
     Write an expression for the amount Mia earns per week.

10 $P = T + R$. Work out the value of P when $T = 18$ and $R = 6$.

11 $V = WR$. Work out the value of V when $W = 10$ and $R = 9$.

12 A tennis coach always brings 4 more racquets to the lesson than the number of students.
  a Write a formula to work out the number of racquets, r, the coach brings when there are s students.
  b Use your formula to work out the number of racquets the coach brings to the lesson when there are 12 students.

13 Cezar earns £9 per hour.
   Write a formula to work out Cezar's total pay, T, when you know the number of hours he works, k.

Challenge

14 Here are some formula cards.

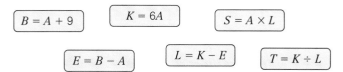

  a Use the formula cards to work out the value of each letter.

A	B	E	K	L	S	T
2						

  b Myles uses the table in part **a** to write a code.
     This is what he writes.

...	A	...	...	...	...	...	A	...	...
11	2	6	12	9	4	11	2	3	3

     Use the table in part **a** to decode the word.

15 **Reflect** Functions, expressions and formulae are all part of the topic of algebra.
   In algebra letters represent values we do not know.
   Copy and complete each of these statements with one of these words:

   easy   ok   difficult

   Functions are ...
   Expressions are ...
   Formulae are ...
   So far, I think algebra is ...
   If you answered mostly 'easy' and 'ok' does this surprise you? Why?
   If you answered mostly 'difficult', then look back at the questions you found most tricky. Ask a friend or your teacher to explain them to you.
   Then write the statements above again.

Reflect

4 Graphs

MASTER · Check P98 · Strengthen P100 · Extend P104 · Test P108

4.1 Real-life graphs

You will learn to:
- Read information from real-life graphs
- Draw graphs to show change over time.

Why learn this?
Midwives use graphs to check a baby's weight is increasing healthily over the first few months.

Fluency
What is the number halfway between
- 0 and 10
- 10 and 20
- 0 and 1
- 0 and 500?

Explore
When is the best time to go on holiday to Malaga?

Exercise 4.1

1 Write down the values shown with letters.

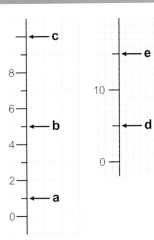

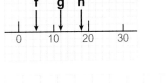

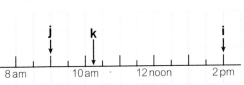

Warm up

Q2 hint

Write °C with your answers.

2 Daisy recorded the temperature each day last week.
5 °C, 8 °C, 2 °C, 5 °C, 11 °C, 4 °C, 5 °C
   a Work out the mode.
   b What is the range?

3 **Real** The graph shows the average daily temperature in Leeds.
   a Copy this sentence and fill in the gaps.
     The graph shows the average temperature every _____ for a _____ in December.
   b Which was the average temperature on
      i Saturday   ii Sunday   iii Tuesday?
   c On what days was the average temperature 5 °C?
   d What was the **minimum** average temperature?
   e What was the **maximum** average temperature?

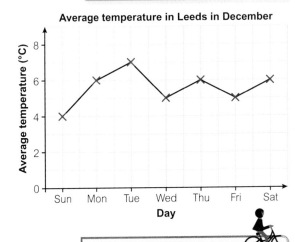

Average temperature in Leeds in December

Q3d and e Literacy hint

Minimum means 'lowest'.
Maximum means 'highest'.

Worked example

The table shows average temperatures in Truro for a week in December.

Day	Sun	Mon	Tue	Wed	Thu	Fri	Sat
Average temperature (°C)	7	6	8	9	11	10	12

Draw a graph to show these temperatures.

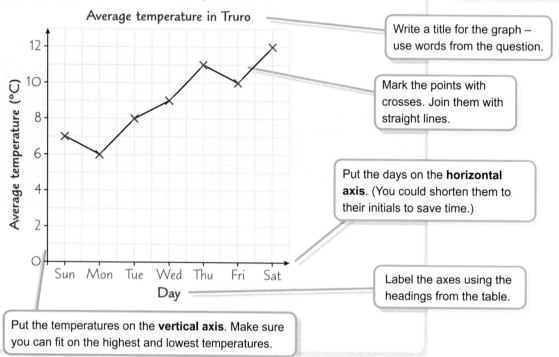

Write a title for the graph – use words from the question.

Mark the points with crosses. Join them with straight lines.

Put the days on the **horizontal axis**. (You could shorten them to their initials to save time.)

Label the axes using the headings from the table.

Put the temperatures on the **vertical axis**. Make sure you can fit on the highest and lowest temperatures.

4 Real The table shows average temperatures in Cardiff for a week in December.

Day	Sun	Mon	Tue	Wed	Thu	Fri	Sat
Average temperature (°C)	6	8	9	9	7	5	2

a Copy the axes from the graph in the worked example.
b On your axes, draw a graph to show the temperatures in the table.
c Fill in the missing words.
   From Sunday to _____ the temperature was increasing.
   From Wednesday _____ the temperature was _____.
d Work out the modal temperature that week.
e Work out the range of the temperatures.

5 Real / Problem-solving The graph shows the temperature in an office over one day.
a Look at the vertical axis. What values have been replaced by ⌇?
b How often was the temperature measured?
c What was the maximum temperature?
d When was the temperature 18 °C?
The Health and Safety Officer says that the temperature in the office should be at least 16 °C.
e Do you think the office manager should turn up the heating?
Discussion Why do we use ⌇ in a graph?
What would the graph look like if it started at 0 °C?

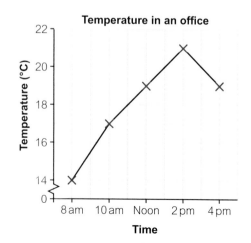

Topic links: Mode and range, Sequences   **Subject links:** Geography (Q3, Q4, Q7)

6 Real The table shows the temperatures in a warehouse.

Time	0700	0900	1100	1300	1500	1700
Temperature (°C)	10	11	13	15	14	13

a Draw a graph to show these temperatures. Use axes like the ones in Q5 choosing the right values for the vertical axis.

b What was the temperature at 3 pm?

c The Health and Safety Officer says the temperature in the warehouse should be at least 13 °C.
Estimate how long the temperature was below this between 7 am and 5 pm.

Q6a hint
What is the lowest temperature you need to show on the Temperature axis?

7 Real / Problem-solving Jack sees this graph in a holiday brochure.

a Look at the horizontal axis. What does F stand for?

b Which is the wettest month?

c Which are the driest months?

d Work out the range of monthly rainfall.

e How many months have less than 30 mm of rain?

f What is the mode of monthly rainfall?

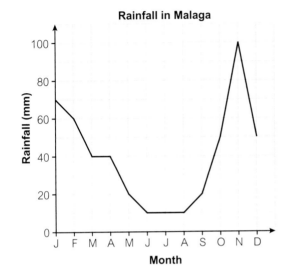

8 Real The graph shows the weight of a baby.

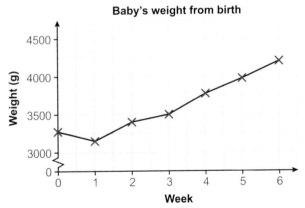

a How much did the baby weigh
  i at birth   **ii** at 4 weeks?

b How much weight did the baby gain in
  i weeks 0–3   **ii** weeks 3–6?

Discussion When was the baby gaining weight the fastest? How can you tell from the graph?

9 Explore When is the best time to go on holiday to Malaga? Is it easier to explore this question now you have completed the lesson? What further information do you need to be able to answer this?

10 Reflect Which do you find easier:
  • drawing graphs (like in Q4)
  • reading from graphs (like in Q5, Q7 and Q8)?
  Copy and complete this sentence to explain why.
  I find _____ graphs easier, because _____

4.2 Coordinates

You will learn to:
- Write the coordinates of points on a grid
- Plot points from their coordinates.

CONFIDENCE

Why learn this?
City maps use coordinates to show where the famous sights are.

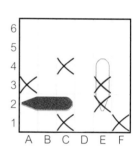

Fluency

Which line is
- horizontal
- vertical?

What are the missing numbers?

e   d   0   1   a   3   b   c

Explore
Which places have x-coordinate zero on a world map?

Exercise 4.2

Warm up

1 Trudi and Mel are playing battleships.
   a Trudi chooses D2. Will this hit a ship?
   b Write all the **coordinates** that will hit the red ship.
   c Mel has scored two hits on the blue ship. What coordinates does she need to sink the blue ship?

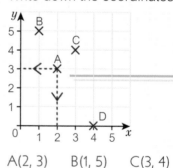

Worked example

Write down the coordinates of the points A, B, C and D.

Start with point A. Move down to the x-axis to find the x-coordinate. Move across to the y-axis to find the y-coordinate.

Key point
The x-axis is the horizontal axis.
The x-**coordinate** is the value on the x-axis.
The y-axis is the vertical axis.
The y-coordinate is the value on the y-axis.
The x-coordinate and y-coordinate together tell you where a point is.

A(2, 3)   B(1, 5)   C(3, 4)   D(4, O)

Do this for all the points.
Write the coordinates in brackets like this:
(x-coordinate, y-coordinate).

2 Copy and complete the coordinates of the points E, F, G and H.
   E(2, ☐)   F(☐, 1)   G(3, ☐)   H(☐, 5)

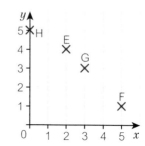

Topic links: Negative numbers, 2D shapes   **Subject links:** Geography (Q9)

3 Write down the coordinates of points J, K, L, M, and N.

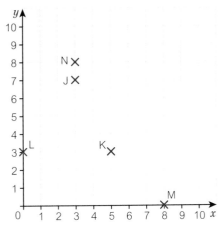

4 Problem-solving In a game, if you guess where the treasure is buried you win a prize.

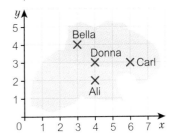

Players write their guesses on the map.
The treasure is at (4, 3). Who wins the prize?

5 a Copy the **axes** from Q4.
b Plot these points on your grid.
  A(1, 1)   B(1, 5)   C(5, 5)   D(5, 1)
c Join the points in order. Use a ruler.
d What shape have you drawn?
e Draw in the diagonals on your shape.
f Write the coordinates of the point where they cross.

Q5a Literacy hint

Axes is the plural of 'axis'.

Q5b hint

Use a sharp pencil. Mark each point carefully with a cross. Label it with its letter.

Key point

You can count back along the x-axis and the y-axis into negative values.

Worked example

Write down the coordinates of the points P, Q and R.

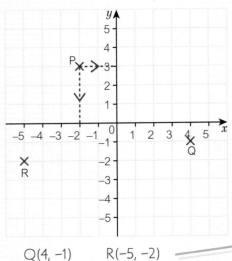

Move up or down to the x-axis to find the x-coordinate. Move across to the y-axis to find the y-coordinate.

P(–2, 3)   Q(4, –1)   R(–5, –2)

6 Write down the coordinates of these points.

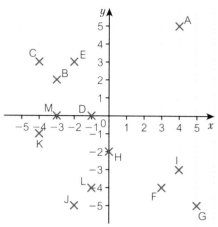

7 Reasoning
a Copy the axes from Q6. Do not copy the points.
b Plot these points.
P(3, 3)   Q(−1, 3)   R(−1, 1)
c Join P and Q, and Q and R.
You have drawn two sides of a rectangle.
d Draw the other two sides.
e Write down the coordinates of the 4th **vertex**.

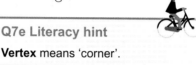

Q7e Literacy hint

Vertex means 'corner'.

8 Problem-solving Guy plots these points on a coordinate grid.
H(1, −2)   I(4, −2)   J(4, −5)
He says, 'To make a square, I need to plot K(−5, 1).'
Is he correct? If not, write down the coordinates to make a square.

Q8 Strategy hint

Plot the coordinates on a copy of the grid from Q6.

Investigation   Problem-solving / Reasoning

1 Draw a pair of x- and y-axes from −6 to +6.
2 Plot these points.
A(1, 2)   B(3, 6)   C(5, 2)
3 Join them in order. What shape have you made?
4 Draw a rectangle on your grid.
Write down the coordinates of its **vertices**.
Give the coordinates to a partner to plot.
Have they drawn the same rectangle?
5 Write down the coordinates for other quadrilaterals and triangles.
Give the coordinates to a partner to plot.
6 Write down the coordinates for a triangle where all the x- and y-values are negative.

Part 1 hint

You could copy the axes from Q6.

Q4 Literacy hint

Vertices is the plural of 'vertex'.

Part 5 hint

Draw them on your grid first.

---

9 **Explore** Which places have x-coordinate zero on the world map?
What have you learned in this lesson to help you answer this question?
What other information do you need?

10 **Reflect** Work in pairs. Decide who is person A and who is person B.
Person A: Your friend (person B) is asked to mark on a grid a point at this coordinate: (1, −3).
Your friend doesn't know what to do.
What would you say to explain to your friend?
Now swap roles.
Person B: Your friend (person A) is asked to read the coordinates of this point from a grid. Your friend doesn't know what to do. What would you say to explain to your friend?

Q10 hint

Listen carefully as the other person explains. Do you understand? If not, ask them to explain again with more detail.

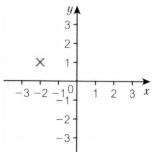

Active Learn Pi 1, Section 4.2

Explore

Reflect

4.3 Graphs of functions

You will learn to:
- Plot graphs of simple functions
- Read values from graphs.

Why learn this?
You can draw a graph for values you know, and then read more values from it.

Fluency
Work out
- 3 × 4
- 6 × 5
- 4 × 7
- 2 × 3
- 3 × 6
- 0 × 2

Explore
How can a graph help you learn the 7 times table?

Exercise 4.3

1 Write the outputs for these function machines.

a Input → +1 → Output
0, 1, 2, 3

b Input → ×5 → Output
0, 1, 2, 3

c Input → −3 → Output
7, 8, 9, 10

d Input → ×7 → Output
0, 1, 2, 3

2 Write down the coordinates of points A, B, C, D and E.

3 a Write the missing outputs for this **function** machine.

x → +5 → y
0 → 5
1 → 6
2 → □
3 → □

b Copy and complete this table to show all the x- and y-values for the function $y = x + 5$.

x	0	1	2	3
y	5	6		

c Write the pairs of x- and y-values as coordinates.

> **Key point**
> A **function** shows how x relates to y.
> A function always gives one output value for every input value.

> **Q3c hint**
> The first pair is (0, 5).
> The second pair is (1, □).

Warm up

4 a Copy and complete the table of values for the function $y = 2x$.

x	0	1	2	3
y				

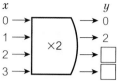

b Write the pairs of x- and y-values as coordinates.

5 Here is a table of values for the function $y = x + 7$.

x	0	1	2	3
y	7	8	9	10

a Write the pairs of x- and y-values as coordinates.
b Draw a coordinate grid with x- and y-axes from 0 to 10.
c Plot the coordinates you wrote in part **a**.
   Join the points with a straight line.
   Extend your line to the edge of the grid.

Q5b hint

You could copy the axes in Q2 but draw the axes to 10.

Worked example

a Complete the table of values for $y = x + 4$.

x	0	1	2	3
y				

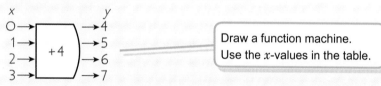

Draw a function machine.
Use the x-values in the table.

x	0	1	2	3
y	4	5	6	7

Work out the y-values in the function machine. Write them in the table.

(0, 4), (1, 5), (2, 6), (3, 7)

Write down the coordinates.

b Draw the graph of $y = x + 4$.

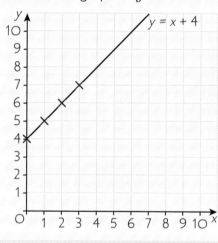

Draw a coordinate grid. Plot the points. Join them with a straight line to the edge of the grid.
Label the line $y = x + 4$.

6 a Copy and complete the table of values for $y = 3x$.

x	0	1	2	3
y				

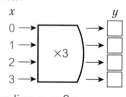

b Write down the coordinates from the table.
c Copy the axes from the worked example.
d Plot your points and draw the graph. Label your line $y = 3x$.

Topic links: Function machines, Times tables

7 a Copy and complete the table of values for $y = 5x$.

x	0	1	2	3
y				

b Draw the graph of $y = 5x$.
Label your line $y = 5x$.
Discussion How can you find the answer to 4×5 from your graph?

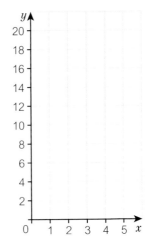

Q7b hint

Draw a pair of axes like this.

8 Reasoning Copy and complete this table of values from the graph.

x	0	1	2	3	4
y					

9 Reasoning Use the graph to find the value of

a y when $x = 2$

b x when $y = 5$

c y when $x = 2\frac{1}{2}$

d x when $y = 3\frac{1}{2}$

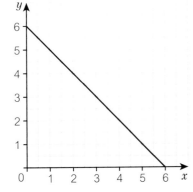

10 Reasoning a Copy and complete this table of values for $y = 6x$.

x	0	1	2	3
y				

b Copy the axes from Q9, but draw the y-axis up to 40, counting up in 5s.

c Draw the graph of $y = 6x$.

d Use your graph to work out

  i 4×6 **ii** 5×6 **iii** 6×6 **iv** $2\frac{1}{2} \times 6$

Key point

You could use a graph plotting package to draw this graph.

Q10c hint

Remember to label the graph with its equation.

11 Explore How can a graph help you learn the 7 times table?
Look back at the maths you have learned in this lesson.
How can you use it to answer this question?

12 Reflect Look back at Q10.

a Write down what you did to find 4×6 from your graph.

b Did you do the same process, or something different, to find 5×6?

c Imagine you were asked to draw the graph of $y = 8x$. Write down what you would you do to find 7×8 on this new graph.

Explore

Reflect

4.4 STEM: Scientific graphs

You will learn to:
- Draw line graphs to show relationships between quantities
- Read values from science graphs.

Why learn this?
Scientists draw graphs to show the results of experiments.

Fluency
What are the missing values?

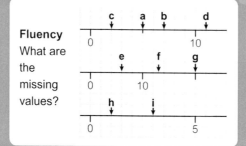

Explore
How do radiographers compare measurements from an ultrasound scan with a graph to predict when a baby will be born?

Exercise 4.4: Graphs for experiments

1 **STEM** Jay heated a beaker of water and then left it to cool. He recorded the temperature every 2 minutes. The graph shows his results.
   a How long did he heat the water for?
   b What temperature did he heat it to?
   c At the start of the experiment, the water was at room temperature. What was the room temperature?
   d How long did it take for the water to cool back down to room temperature?
   e Which was faster, the heating or the cooling?

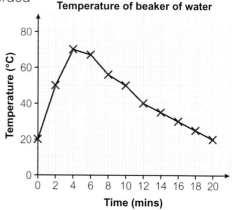

Temperature of beaker of water

2 **STEM** The table shows the amount of oxygen dissolved in fresh water at different temperatures.

Temperature (°C)	Oxygen dissolved (mg per litre)
0	15
10	11
20	9
30	7
40	6
50	5

Key point

Read the title to find out what the graph shows.
Read the axis labels to see what has been measured.

   a Copy these axes.
   b The horizontal axis shows the temperature.
     Label both axes, using the headings from the table.
   c Plot the points from the table on to your graph. Join them with straight lines.
   d Write a title for your graph.
   Discussion How can you use words in the question to help you to write a title and labels for the axes for your graph?
   e Use your graph to estimate the amount of oxygen dissolved in the water at 15°C.
   Discussion Why is your answer to part **e** an estimate, not an accurate value?

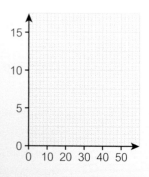

Subject links: STEM (all)

Worked example

Rory did an experiment with a spring. He hung different masses on the end of the spring, and measured how much it extended.

a Draw a graph to show his results.

Mass (g)	0	50	100	150	200
Extension (mm)	0	28	62	92	110

Literacy hint

'Extended' means 'stretched'. The extension is how much the spring stretched.

Extension of spring for different masses

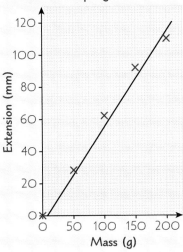

Plot the points. They are nearly on a straight line.
Draw a straight line through the points, with the same number of points on each side.

b Do you think there is a relationship between the amount of mass on the spring and the extension?

The graph is close to a straight line, so there is a relationship between the mass and the extension.

Key point

When the points on a graph are on a straight line, or close to a straight line, it shows there is a relationship between the two values.

3 STEM Kayden did an experiment with a length of fishing line. He hung different masses on the end of the line and measured how much it extended. Here are his results.

Mass (g)	0	50	100	150	200
Extension (mm)	0	18	42	64	78

a Copy the axes from the worked example.
b Draw a graph for Kayden's results. Is it close to a straight line?
c Do you think there is a relationship between the amount of mass on the spring and the extension?

Discussion What do you think the relationship is between the mass and the extension?

Q3b hint

If the points are close to a straight line, draw a line with the same number of points on each side.

4 STEM / Reasoning Jack, Amy and Emma did an experiment to see how much salt they could dissolve in 100 cm³ of water at different temperatures. Here are their graphs of the results.

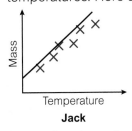
Jack

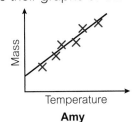
Amy

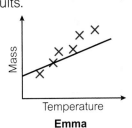
Emma

Whose line best shows the relationship between the temperature and the mass of salt dissolved?

5 STEM / Reasoning Alix did an experiment to see if syrup flows at different speeds at different temperatures.
She heated the syrup to different temperatures and timed how long it took to drip through a funnel. Here are her results.

Temperature (°C)	Time to drip through (seconds)
24	110
30	40
40	22
50	15
60	10
70	8

a Copy these axes. Extend them across to 70°C and up to 120 seconds. Temperature is on the horizontal axis. Label the axes and give the graph a title.

b Plot the points from the table. Join them with a smooth curve.

c Use your graph to estimate the time taken for syrup to drip through the funnel at 45°C.

d Copy the sentence. Fill in the missing word.
As the temperature _____ the syrup gets runnier.

Key point

Some sets of data give a curved graph.

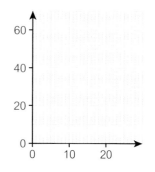

Q5b hint

You might find it easier to draw the curve if you turn the paper around.

Investigation

Problem-solving

1 Sunita and Polly did an experiment to test reaction times.
Sunita held a ruler at the same height each time. Polly held her hand ready underneath.
Sunita dropped the ruler and Polly caught it.
They recorded the measurement where Polly caught the ruler each time.
The first time, Polly caught the ruler at 26 cm. The second time she caught it at 15 cm.
Was she getting faster or slower at catching it? Explain.

2 Work with a partner and try this experiment yourself. Have five tries each at catching the ruler.

3 Write your results in a table like this.

Try	1	2	3	4	5
Catching distance (cm)					

4 Draw a graph to show your results.
Use axes like this.

5 Did your reaction time get better with more tries?

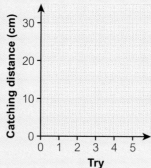

---

6 Explore How do radiographers compare measurements from an ultrasound scan with a graph to predict when a baby will be born?
Is it easier to explore this question now you have completed the lesson?
What further information do you need to be able to answer this?

7 Reflect In Q1, the graph showed the results of an experiment on how water temperature changes with time.
a Write down one other experiment shown on a graph in this lesson.
b Write down one experiment you have shown on a graph in a science lesson.
c Why do you think it helps to show the results of an experiment on a graph?

Q7c hint

Look back at Q3c and Q5c.

 Active Learn   Pi 1, Section 4.4

Explore

Reflect

4 Check up

Log how you did on your Student Progression Chart.

Coordinates

1 Write down the coordinates of the points marked with letters.

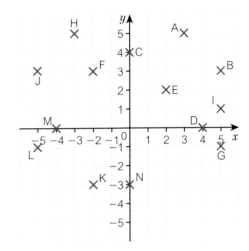

Graphs of functions

2 a Copy and complete the table of values for the function $y = x + 2$.

x	0	1	2	3
y				

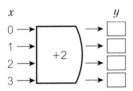

b Write the coordinates for the graph of $y = x + 2$ from the table of values.

3 Match each set of coordinates to a table of values.

A
x	0	1	2	3
y	6	7	8	9

i (0, 0) (1, 4) (2, 8) (3, 12)

ii (0, 0) (1, 1) (2, 2) (3, 3)

iii (0, 6) (1, 7) (2, 8) (3, 9)

B
x	0	1	2	3
y	0	4	8	12

C
x	0	1	2	3
y	0	1	2	3

4 a Copy and complete the table of values for $y = x + 3$.

x	0	1	2	3
y				

b Draw a pair of axes like this.

c Draw the graph of $y = x + 3$.

d Use the graph to find the value of

   i y when $x = 1\frac{1}{2}$

   ii x when $y = 5\frac{1}{2}$.

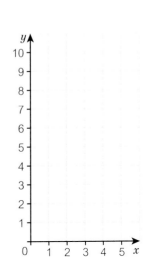

Real-life and science graphs

5 The table shows Lucy's gas bills for one year.
She gets a bill every 3 months.

Month	Mar	Jun	Sep	Dec
Bill (£)	120	90	85	140

  a Copy the axes and label them.
  b Plot the points from the table. Join them with straight lines.
  c Give your graph a title.

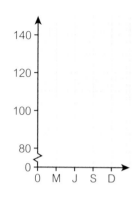

6 Sushma did an experiment.
She added lemon juice to water and measured the pH of the solution.
She drew this graph to show her results.

  a What was the pH after she had added 4 ml of lemon juice?
  b When the pH was 4, how much lemon juice had she added?
Acids have pH less than 7.
  c Does adding the lemon juice make the solution more acidic? Explain.

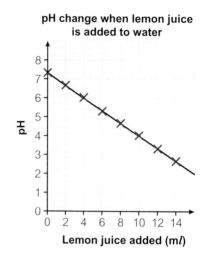

pH change when lemon juice is added to water

7 How sure are you of your answers? Were you mostly

  😞 Just guessing   😐 Feeling doubtful   🙂 Confident

What next? Use your results to decide whether to strengthen or extend your learning.

Challenge

8 a Plot these points on a coordinate grid.
     A(2, 2) B(5, 0) C(2, −2) D(−2, −2) E(−5, 0) F(−2, 2)
  b Join them in order. What shape have you drawn?
  c Copy the sentences. Fill in the missing letters.
    i The line from ___ to ___ crosses the y-axis at $y = 2$.
    ii The line from ___ to ___ crosses the x-axis at $x = -2$.

9 Write down the coordinates of five points on this graph line.
What do you notice?

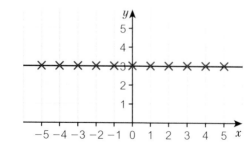

4 Strengthen

You will:

- Strengthen your understanding with practice.

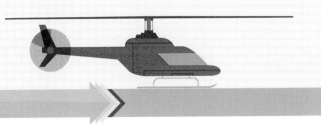

Coordinates

1 a Put your finger on point A on the grid. Move your finger down to the x-axis.
Write down the x-coordinate for A.

b Start at A again. Move your finger across to the y-axis.
Write down the y-coordinate for A.

c Copy and complete.   A(_____, _____)

x-coordinate y-coordinate

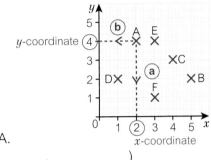

d Write down the coordinates of points B, C, D and E.

e Jenny says, 'The coordinates of F are (1, 3).'
Is she correct? Explain.

Q1c hint
x comes before y in the alphabet.

Q1d hint
Follow the steps in parts **a–c**.

Q1e hint
Write down the coordinates of F.
Compare them with Jenny's.

2 a Copy the axes from Q1. Do not copy the points A to F.

b Follow these steps to plot the point G(4, 2).

1 Write the coordinates, labelling them x and y.
2 Find the x-coordinate on the x-axis.
3 Find the y-coordinate on the y-axis.
4 Move up from the x and across from the y.
Put a cross at the meeting point.
5 Label the cross with its letter.

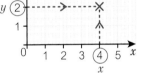

c Plot these points on your axes.
H(3, 2)   I(1, 5)   J(4, 0)   K(5, 4)   L(0, 1)

Q2c hint
Follow the steps in part **b**.

3 Write down the coordinates of the points M, N, P, Q, R, S and T.

Q3 hint
Follow the steps in Q1.

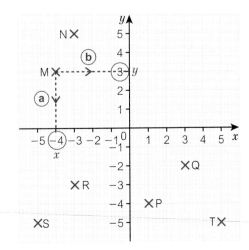

Graphs of functions

1 Copy and complete these function machines.

a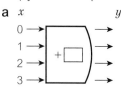

$y = x + 5$

b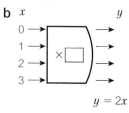

$y = 2x$

Q1 hint

What do you do to x to get y?

2 Draw function machines for
  a $y = x + 6$
  b $y = 4x$
  c $y = x + 3$
  d $y = 5x$

Q2 hint

Copy the machines and x-values from Q1.

3 Copy and complete the table of values for $y = x + 2$.

x	0	1	2	3
y	2			

When x is 0, y is 2.   When x is 1, y is ...

Q3 hint

Draw a function machine like the one in Q1a.

4 Use a new copy of this table for each part of the question.

x	0	1	2	3
y				

Copy and complete the table of values for
  a $y = x + 6$
  b $y = 4x$
  c $y = x + 3$
  d $y = 5x$
  e $y = x + 7$
  f $y = 10x$

Q4 hint

You could use your function machines from Q2 to help.

5 a Write down the coordinates to plot from this table of values.

x	0	1	2	3
y	5	6	7	8

Coordinates   (0, __)   (__, __)   (__, __)   (__, __)

b Copy this grid and plot the coordinates.
c Join the points with a straight line right to the edge of the grid.

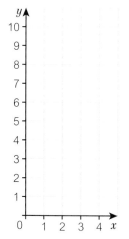

Q5a hint

(x-coordinate, y-coordinate)

6 Draw a graph for each table of values you made in Q4.

Q6 hint

Follow the steps from Q5. Make sure you can fit the highest y-value on the y-axis.

Topic links: Negative numbers, Function machines   **Subject links:** Geography (Real-life and science graphs Q2)

Real-life and science graphs

1 Real The graph shows Patti's temperature one morning.

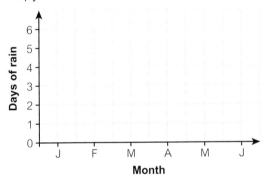

Patti's temperature

a Which axis shows
   i the temperature
   ii the time?

b What time was the first temperature reading?

c i What was Patti's temperature at 9 am?
   ii What was Patti's temperature at 10 am? Remember to write the units (°C).

d When was her temperature 39 °C?

e What was her
   i maximum (highest) temperature
   ii minimum (lowest) temperature?

Q1 Strategy hint

Before you start a graph question, read the title and the labels on the axes to see what they show.

Q1ci hint

Find 9 am on the Time axis. Move your finger up to the graph line. Now move your finger straight across to the Temperature axis.

Q1d hint

Start at 39 on the Temperature axis. Go across to the graph line and down to the Time axis.

2 Real The table shows the number of days of rain in Dubai for 6 months.

Month	Days of rain
January	6
February	5
March	5
April	3
May	1
June	0

a Copy these axes.

b What does the first J stand for on the horizontal axis?

c What does the second M stand for?

The table tells you that in January it rained on 6 days.

d Follow these steps to plot the number of days of rain for January.
   1 Find January on the Month axis.
   2 Find 6 on the Days of rain axis.
   3 Move up from January and across from 6.
   4 Put a cross at the meeting point.

e i How many days did it rain in February?
   ii Plot the point for this.

f Plot the points for the rest of the months.

g Read the first part of this question again, where it explains what the table shows.
   Use these words to help you complete the title for your graph.

   Days of _____

Q2e hint

Follow the steps in part **d**.

3 Real The cost of Carol's mobile phone calls are shown in the table.

Number of minutes	10	20	30	100
Cost of call (£)	2	4	6	20

a Copy these axes.
Plot the points in the table and join them up with a straight line.
Label your axes and give your graph a title.

b Use your graph to find how much Carol will pay if she uses the phone for

  i 70 minutes

  ii 25 minutes

  iii $1\frac{1}{2}$ hours.

c Last month, Carol's bill was £16. How many minutes did she spend on the phone?

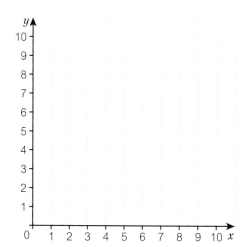

Q3a hint

Copy and complete this graph title:
Carol's _____

Enrichment

1 Draw a coordinate grid like this.

a Plot the points (2, 1) and (2, 5).
Join them with a straight line.
Plot the points (4, 5) and (2, 3).
Join them with a straight line.
Plot the point (4, 1). Join it with a straight line to the point (2, 3).
What letter have you drawn?

b Draw another letter on the grid.
Write instructions to draw the letter.
Give them to a partner to plot.

2 **Reflect** Look at these four ways to show the same coordinates.

brackets

(0, 2)
(1, 3)

table

x	0	1
y	2	3

function machine

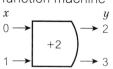

graph

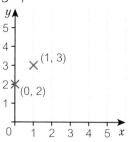

a Copy and complete these sentences.
I find _____ easiest for showing coordinates.
I find _____ hardest for showing coordinates.

b Discuss with a classmate the way you find the hardest.
What makes it hard?

Reflect

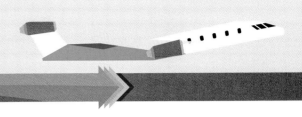

4 Extend

You will:

- Extend your understanding with problem-solving.

1 **Problem-solving** Mia's mother pays her pocket money directly into her bank account.

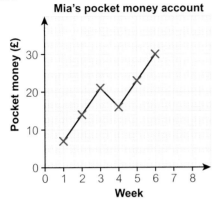

Mia's pocket money account

a In the first 3 weeks Mia saves all her pocket money.
   How much pocket money does she get each week?
b During which week does Mia **withdraw** some money?
c How much money does she withdraw?
d Mia is saving for a handbag that costs £40. When will she have enough money (if she doesn't spend any first)?

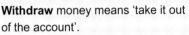

Q1b Literacy hint

Withdraw money means 'take it out of the account'.

Q1c hint

She still gets the same amount of pocket money that week.

2 **Reasoning** a Copy the coordinate grid.
   b Plot these points on your grid.
      A(1, 4) B(5, 4) C(5, 2) D(1, 2)
   c Join the points in order, with straight lines.
      What shape have you drawn?
   d Point E is the **midpoint** of the line joining A and B.
      Write down the coordinates of E.
   e Draw in the diagonals of the shape by joining A to C, and B to D.
      Write down the coordinates of the point where the diagonals cross.

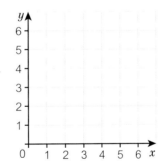

Q2d Literacy hint

The **midpoint** is in the middle of the line, which is halfway along.

3 **Reasoning** a Copy and complete this table of values for $y = 9x$.

x	0	1	2	3
y				

b Copy the axes from Q2.
   Make the x-axis go from 0 to 10 and the y-axis go from 0 to 100.
c Draw the graph of $y = 9x$. Label the graph line $y = 9x$.
d Use your graph to work out
   i 4×9 ii 7×9 iii 9 squared
   iv $72 \div 9$ v $45 \div 9$ vi $54 \div 9$

4 **Reasoning / Problem-solving** a Copy and complete this table of values for the graph.

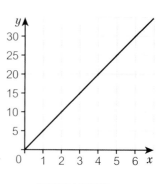

x	0	1	2	3	4	5	6
y							

  b Copy the sentence. Fill in the missing number.
    The y-values go up by ___ each time.
  c Which times table does the graph show? Explain.
  d Write four multiplication and division questions you could answer using this graph.

Q4c hint
Look at the y-values.

5 Here is a table of values for $y = 2$.

x	−5	0	3	5
y	2	2	2	2

For every x-value, the y-value is 2.

  a Draw a grid with x- and y-axes from −5 to +5.
  b Plot the points from your table on your grid.
    Join them with a straight line. Label your line $y = 2$.
  c Draw a table of values for $y = 5$.
  d Plot your points and join them with a straight line.
    Label your line $y = 5$.
  e **Reasoning** Where do you think the line $y = -3$ would be on the grid?
    Make a table of values for $y = -3$. Plot the points to check.

Q5c hint
Make a table like the one used for part b. For every x-value, the y-value must be 5.

6 Here is a table of values for $x = 1$.
  For every y-value, the x-value is 1.

x	1	1	1	1
y	−2	0	2	4

  a Draw a grid with x- and y-axes from −5 to +5.
  b Plot the points from your table on your grid.
    Join them with a straight line. Label your line $x = 1$.

7 **Reasoning / Real** To create a CGI movie, programmers have to explain to the computer what to draw, and where.
  Write down the lines the computer needs to draw to make
  a this square   b this rectangle.

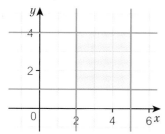
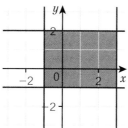

8 **Real / Problem-solving** A computer game is designed on a coordinate grid from 0 to 10 on both axes.
  There are aliens at (2, 5), (4, 6), (0, 3), (5, 2), (2, 8) and (9, 5).
  a A hedgehog travels on the line $y = 2x$.
    Will it get eaten by an alien? If yes, where?
  b A rabbit travels on the line $y = 4x$.
    Will it get eaten by an alien? If yes, where?
  c Write down the coordinates of a point where you could put another alien to eat the hedgehog.

Q8a hint
Plot the aliens. Draw on the line for the hedgehog.

Topic links: Square numbers, Times tables and related division facts, Shape, Mean and range

Subject links: Computing (Q7, Q8), Science (Q10, Q11), Geography (Q13)

9 Reasoning / Problem-solving
  a Draw a grid with x- and y-axes from −5 to +5.
  b Plot these coordinates: (−3, 4)   (3, 4)   (3, −2)
  c These points are 3 corners of a square. Write down the coordinates of the 4th corner.
  d Reasoning Write a similar question with coordinates for a different square. Give it to a partner to answer.

Q9c hint

Draw in the sides of the square to help you see where the 4th corner will be.

Q9d hint

Draw a square on a coordinate grid. Give your partner the coordinates of 3 corners.

10 STEM / Reasoning Petra does an experiment to see if honey flows faster when it is warm.
   She heats the honey to different temperatures and times how long it takes to run through a funnel.
   She takes two readings at each temperature.
   Here are her results.

Temperature (°C)	Time 1 (s)	Time 2 (s)	Mean time (s)
20	120	124	
30	72	68	
40	47	53	
50	35	39	
60	29	23	
70	23	17	

  a Work out the mean times and write them in a copy of the table.
  b Draw a pair of axes like this.
  c Extend the axes so that you can include the longest time from your table.
  d Plot a graph to show the mean times for the different temperatures.
    Join your points with a smooth curve.
  e Does the honey flow faster when it is warm? Explain.

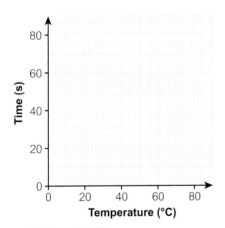

Q10e hint

You could compare the mean times taken at two different temperatures.

11 STEM Jess hung different masses on the end of a spring, and measured how much it extended. Dan then did the same.
   They plotted graphs of their results.

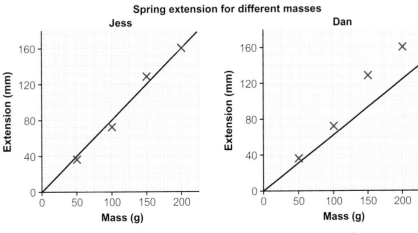

Spring extension for different masses

  a Which graph should you use to estimate the extension for a mass of 75 g? Explain.
  b Estimate the extension for a mass of 75 g.

12 **Real / Problem-solving** The graph shows the costs for a pay-as-you-go phone and a contract phone.

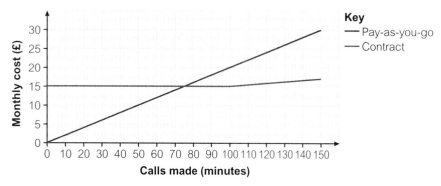

Key
— Pay-as-you-go
— Contract

a Surjeet makes less than 60 minutes of calls each month. Which type of phone should he get? Explain.

b Tyrone makes more than 2 hours of calls each month. Which type of phone should he get? Explain.

c What is the missing number in this sentence? The contract phone is better value if you make more than ____ minutes of calls each month.

Q12 Strategy hint
Use the key to see which line is for contract and which line is for pay-as-you-go.

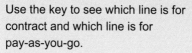

13 **Real / Problem-solving** The graph shows the average rainfall and temperature each month in Mumbai.

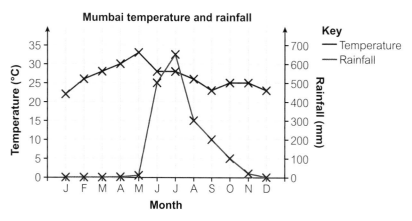

Key
— Temperature
— Rainfall

a Which is the wettest month in Mumbai?

b Which is the hottest month in Mumbai?

c Work out the range of the temperatures in Mumbai.

d Dinesh is travelling to Mumbai for business in October. Write a sentence to tell him what the weather should be like.

Q13 Strategy hint
Use the key to see which line is for rainfall and which line is for temperature. Read the vertical axes to see which is for temperature and which is for rainfall.

14 **Reflect**

a Sally says, 'A coordinate shows the exact point.' David says, 'Coordinates are always pairs of numbers.' Do you agree with Sally or David?

b Look back at the work you have done in these extend lessons. Write down two other facts about coordinates.

c Compare your facts with others in your class.

Q14a hint
Look at the questions you have answered in these lessons to help you decide.

Reflect

Master
P86

Check
P98

Strengthen
P100

Extend
P104

TEST

4 Unit test

Log how you did on your
Student Progression Chart.

1 The graph shows the temperature in a car parked in
a car park.
  a At what time was the maximum temperature?
  b What was the minimum temperature?
  c How often was the temperature recorded?
  d Between which two times was the temperature
    decreasing?
  e For how long was the temperature 20 °C or lower?

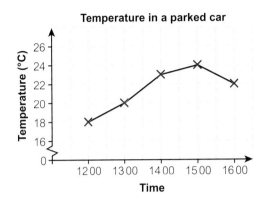

Temperature in a parked car

2 Write down the coordinates of the points marked with letters.

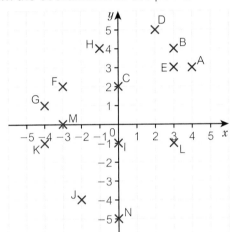

3 a Copy and complete the table of values for $y = x + 8$.

x	0	1	2	3
y				

  b Draw a pair of axes like this.
  c Draw the graph of $y = x + 8$. Label your line $y = x + 8$.
  d Use the graph to find the value of y when
    i $x = 2\frac{1}{2}$
    ii $y = 12\frac{1}{2}$.

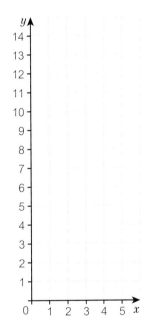

4 The graph shows Olive and Sian's savings.
  a When does Olive have £48?
  b How much does Sian have in July?
  c How much does Sian save from January
    to February?
  d Who has more money in June?
  e How much less does Olive have in July
    than in June?

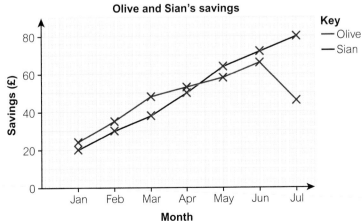

Olive and Sian's savings

Key
— Olive
— Sian

Challenge

5 The graph shows the average temperature and rainfall at
Stansted Airport last year.

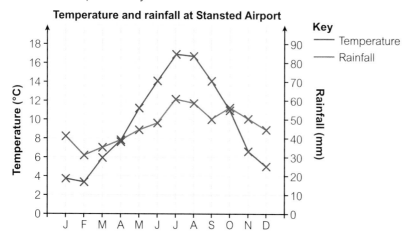

a Which was the hottest month?
b Which was the driest month?
c What was the minimum average temperature over the year?
d What was the range of the rainfall?
e How many months had over 50 mm of rain?
f What were the average temperature and rainfall in April?

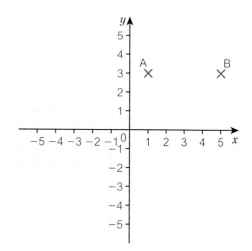

6 a Write down the coordinates of the midpoint of the line from
A to B on this coordinate grid.
b Write down the coordinates of two points that will make a
rectangle with A and B as the other corners.
c i Plot two more points at D(−1, −1) and C(3, −1).
ii A, B, C and D are four corners of a shape. Name the shape.
d Write down the coordinates of the midpoint of the line from
A to C.

7 **Reflect** Think back to answering the questions in this unit test.
a Write down a question you were sure you got correct.
What made you think you got this question correct?
b Write down a question you thought you may have got incorrect.
What made you think you got this question incorrect?
c Discuss with a classmate what you might do if you think you are
getting a question incorrect in a test.

5.1 Number rules and relationships

You will learn to:

* Use the priority of operations
* Understand the rules of multiplication
* Use the operation keys on a calculator.

Why learn this?
The order in which you do things is important. On a bicycle you look over your shoulder … signal … manoeuvre.

Fluency
* What is
  5×5, 6×6, 7×7,
  8×8, 9×9?
* Give 3 more multiplication or division facts for each of these calculations
  $5 \times 6 = 30$, $32 \div 8 = 4$

Explore
When would it matter if we chose to do calculations in the wrong order?

Exercise 5.1

1 Find the missing number.
   a $4 \times \square = 12$
   b $\square \times 9 = 36$
   c $3 \times \square = 27$
   d $\square \times 7 = 35$
   e $5 \times \square = 40$
   f $8 \times \square = 80$

2 Find the missing number.
   a $21 \div \square = 7$
   b $15 \div \square = 3$
   c $28 \div \square = 4$
   d $24 \div \square = 3$
   e $42 \div \square = 21$
   f $40 \div \square = 5$

3 Work out
   a 30×2
   b 2×50
   c 5×60
   d 50×4
   e $16 \div 4$
   f $36 \div 6$
   g $49 \div 7$
   h $81 \div 9$
   i $100 \div 10$

 4 Work out the value of each letter using a calculator.

   $15 \times H = 105$ $J \times 24 = 144$ $240 \div K = 30$ $L \div 8 = 12$

Worked example

Work out $6 + 3 \times 10$
$6 + 3 \times 10 = 6 + 30$ —— Work out the multiplication first.
$\qquad = 36$

5 Work out
   a $6 + 4 \times 2$
   b $6 \div 2 - 1$
   c $3 + 9 \div 3$
   d $21 \div 3 + 7$
   e $20 - 3 \times 4$
   f $12 - 4 \div 2$
   g $3 \times 5 - 10$
   h $20 \div 5 + 10$

Q1a hint
How many 4s make 12?
Use this related division fact to help.
$12 \div 4 = \square$

Q2 hint
Use a related division or multiplication fact to help.

Key point
The **operation** keys on a calculator are $+$, $-$, $\times$ and $\div$
To get the answer, press the '=' key.

Q4 hint
How many 15s make 105? Use the related division fact $105 \div 15 = \square$

Q5 hint
Multiplication and **D**ivision *before* **A**ddition and **S**ubtraction.

 Warm up

6 a Which pairs of calculations have the same answers?

   A $7 + 4 \times 2$ B $10 - 5 \times 2$ C $3 \times 2 + 2 \times 2$ D $6 \times 4 - 3 \times 3$

   E $12 \div 2 + 7 \times 2$ F $4 \times 5 - 2 \times 5$ G $25 \div 5 - 5 \times 1$

   b Which letter is the odd one out?

Investigation   Reasoning

1 Roll a dice to get three *different* numbers.

Multiply them together. Do this in as many different orders as you can. For example, like this:

$2 \times 3 \times 4$ $3 \times 4 \times 2$ $2 \times 4 \times 3$

Discussion Do you get the same or different answers?

2 Which multiplication in each set is easiest to work out?

   a $9 \times 3 \times 6$ $6 \times 9 \times 3$ $6 \times 3 \times 9$

   b $5 \times 40 \times 9$ $9 \times 50 \times 4$ $9 \times 40 \times 5$

Discussion How can you rearrange multiplications to make them easier to work out?

3 $11 \times 12 \times 13 = 1716$

Use this fact to work out

   a $12 \times 13 \times 11$

   b $13 \times 11 \times 12$

---

7 Work out

   a $4 \times 8 \times 5$
   b $7 \times 5 \times 8$
   c $5 \times 30 \times 6$
   d $4 \times 9 \times 5 \times 2$
   e $3 \times 6 \times 3 \times 5$

8 Real Max earns £3 a day for a paper round.
He does the paper round 5 days per week.
How much does he earn in 20 weeks?

 9 Reasoning

   a Work out each pair of calculations.

      i $5 + 7$
      ii $7 + 5$

   b **i** $82 + 47$
      ii $47 + 82$

   c **i** $6 - 2$
      ii $2 - 6$

   d **i** $45 - 19$
      ii $19 - 45$

   e **i** $72 - 63$
      ii $63 - 72$

   f **i** Which pairs of calculations have the same answer as each other?
      ii Which pairs of calculations don't have the same answer?
      iii Use the words *addition* or *subtraction* to complete these sentences:
         '_____ can be done in any order.'
         'The order is important in _____.'

> **Key point**
>
> Multiplication can be done in any order.

> **Q7 hint**
>
> Can you rearrange the multiplications to make them easier?

> **Q8 Literacy hint**
>
> 'Per week' means 'every week'.

> **Q9c ii hint**
>
> The '−' sign before an answer on the calculator means that the answer is a negative number.

Topic links: Related facts, Simple equations, Calculator skills

10 Reasoning

　a Work out each pair of calculations, using a calculator.

　　i 5 × 9

　　ii 9 × 5

　b i 90 ÷ 10

　　ii 10 ÷ 90

　c i Which pairs of calculations have the same answer?

　　ii Which pairs of calculations don't have the same answer?

　　iii Use the words *multiplication* or *division* to complete these
　　　sentences:

　　　'_____ can be done in any order.'

　　　'The order is important in _____.'

　Discussion Which calculations have the same answer if you swap
　the order round?

　　20 + 4　　　20 − 5　　　20 ÷ 4　　　20 × 4

11 Work these out, from left to right.

　a 3 × 4 ÷ 2

　b 18 ÷ 3 × 4

　c 20 ÷ 5 ÷ 4

> **Key point**
>
> When you have only × and ÷, or
> only + and −, then just work from left
> to right.

12 Work these out, from left to right.

　a i 12 + 54 + 18

　　ii 54 + 18 + 12

　b i 35 − 12 + 14

　　ii 12 + 14 − 35

　c i 42 − 11 − 15

　　ii 42 − 15 − 11

13 Problem-solving A competition prize is either a one-off payment
　of £200, or £2 on Monday, £4 on Tuesday and doubling the amount
　every day for a week.
　Which is the better offer?

> **Q13 hint**
>
> Every day the amount doubles in
> value.
> Add up all the amounts to find the
> total:
> 2 + 4 + …

14 Explore When would it matter if we chose to do calculations in the
　wrong order?
　Choose some sensible numbers to help you explore this idea.
　Then use what you've learned in this lesson to help you answer the
　question.

15 Reflect Antony says, 'I remember the priority of operations as
　My **D**ear **A**unt **S**ally.'
　What do you think the M, D, A and S stand for?
　Make up your own sentence with words beginning with M, D, A and
　S to help remember the priority of operations.
　Do you like this way of using initial letters to help you remember
　things?

Explore

Reflect

5.2 Multiples

You will learn to:

- Recognise multiples of 2, 5, 10 and 25
- Work out multiples.

CONFIDENCE

Why learn this?
Recognising multiples will help you do multiplication and division calculations.

Fluency
- Write the next 3 terms
  5, 10, 15, 20, …
  7, 14, 21, 28, …
- Which of these numbers are in the 2, 5 or 10 times tables?
  10, 12, 15, 20, 22, 24

Explore
What is the most popular size of multipack in the supermarket?

Exercise 5.2

Warm up

1 Work out
 a 4 × 5   **b** 3 × 6   **c** 7 × 2
 d 8 × 10   **e** 7 × 5

2 a Write the first 10 **multiples** of
   i 10   **ii** 5
 b What do you notice?
 c Copy and complete these sentences.
   i Multiples of 10 end in ☐.
   ii Multiples of 5 end in ☐ or ☐.

> **Key point**
> A **multiple** of a number is in that number's multiplication table.

3 a Write the first 10 multiples of 2.
 b What do you notice?
   Copy and complete this sentence.
   'Multiples of 2 are all _____ numbers.'

4 Are these numbers **odd** or **even**?

| 245 | 476 | 381 | 340 | 2000 |
| 246 | 1356 | 2003 | 40008 | 9999 |

Write them under separate headings.

Odd	Even

> **Key point**
> The last digit of an **odd number** is 1, 3, 5, 7 or 9
> The last digit of an **even number** is 2, 4, 6, 8 or 0

5 True or false?
 a 32 is a multiple of 2   **b** 22 is a multiple of 5
 c 21 is a multiple of 10   **d** 35 is a multiple of 5
 e 30 is a multiple of 10   **f** 31 is a multiple of 2

> **Q5 hint**
> Look back at the multiples you wrote in Q2 and Q3.

6 a Write the first 10 multiples of 3.
 b Which of these numbers are in the 3 times table?

   12   13   15   21   25   27

7 Reasoning Copy these numbers.

18   25   27   30   32   37   45

   a Ring the multiples of 10, using a coloured pencil.
   b Ring the multiples of 5, in a second colour.
   c Ring the multiples of 2, in a third colour.
   d Ring the multiples of 9, in a fourth colour.
   e Copy and complete these sentences.
      i 45 is a multiple of ☐ and ☐.   ii 18 is a multiple of ☐ and ☐.   iii 30 is a multiple of ☐, ☐ and ☐.

   Discussion Which number has no ring round it? Why?

Q7d hint

Write the first few multiples of 9 (the first few numbers in the 9 times table).

Investigation   Reasoning

1 Copy the headings. Write the answers.
2 Are the answers in each column odd or even?
3 Try at least three more examples of your own for each type, to see if you get the same result.

odd × odd	even × even	odd × even	even × odd
3 × 5	4 × 2	3 × 6	4 × 5
7 × 5	2 × 6	5 × 4	2 × 7

4 Copy and complete these statements.
   odd × odd = _____   even × even = _____   odd × even = _____   even × odd = _____

Discussion How can you use this to help you remember multiplication facts?

---

8 Reasoning
   a Start at 0. Keep adding 25 to make the first eight multiples of 25
   b What pattern do you notice in your list of multiples?
   c Which of these numbers are multiples of 25?   425   555   620   875
   d A fairground ride costs 25p a turn.
      Which of these people could spend all the money they have left on this ride?
      Matt £3.75   Andrew £4.20   Rosie £2.50   Lou £2.45

9 Reasoning Match a blue number with a red multiple so that no numbers are left over.

   2   3   5   9   10   25   125   63   21   60   44   15

Q9 hint

Look back at the multiples of 3 and 9 that you wrote in Q6 and Q7.

10 Reasoning Choose a number to make these statements true.
   a 12 is a multiple of ☐   b 30 is a multiple of ☐   c 16 is a multiple of ☐
   d ☐ is a multiple of 5   e ☐ is a multiple of 9   f ☐ is a multiple of 25

11 Reasoning Which is the odd one out in each of these lists?
   Explain your reason using the word 'multiple'.
   a 14, 25, 32, 48, 58   b 4, 8, 12, 15, 20, 24
   c 10, 25, 50, 75, 125   d 18, 36, 42, 45, 81
   e 15, 21, 30, 35, 50

Q11 Strategy hint

Are they multiples of 2? Or 3?

12 Explore What is the most popular size of multipack in the supermarket?
   Look back at the maths you have learned in this lesson.
   How can you use it to answer this question?

13 Reflect Cleo and David look again at Q9.
   Cleo says, 'I started by looking for multiples of 2 in the red list.'
   David says, 'I started by looking for numbers with 125 in their times table in the blue list.'
   Discuss with a classmate: Whose method do you like better, Cleo's or David's?
   Explain why you like that method best.
   How did you start Q9? What did you do next?
   If you did this question again, would you do it in the same way? Why?

Explore

Reflect

5.3 Multiplication

You will learn to:
- Multiply 3-digit numbers by a single digit
- Round numbers to the nearest 100 and 1000.

CONFIDENCE

Why learn this?
Multiplication helps you work out the cost of buying more than one of anything:
2 T-shirts, 5 MP3 downloads, 4 chocolate bars.

Fluency
Round to the nearest 10
- 36
- 42
- 234
- 768
- 393
- 713

Explore
How much pocket money will you get this year?

Exercise 5.3

Warm up

1 Work out

   a   39
     × 2

   b   57
     × 4

2 Multiply these numbers by 10 and by 100.
   a 9   **b** 45   **c** 67

3 Work out
   a 20×3 **b** 5×20 **c** 70×3
   d 4×800 **e** 3×500 **f** 7×300

4 **Estimate** the answer using **rounding** to the nearest 10.
   a $39 \times 2 \approx 40 \times 2 =$ **b** 57×4 **c** 62×5
   d 71×2 **e** 45×4

5 Match each number to its nearest 100.

| 599 | 482 | 425 | 539 | 379 | 610 |

| 400 | 500 | 600 |

6 Round each number to the nearest 1000.
   a 4900   **b** 3260   **c** 6095
   d 1458   **e** 16 326

Key point

Estimation means making a good guess.
Using **rounding** is a good way to estimate because it helps to check that your answer is sensible.

Q4 Literacy hint

'≈' means 'approximately equal to'

Key point

For rounding to the nearest 100
- 50 and above rounds up
- 49 and below rounds down.

rounds down   rounds up
200   250   300

Key point

For rounding to the nearest 1000
- 500 and above rounds up
- 499 and below rounds down.

rounds down   rounds up
7000   7500   8000

Topic links: Rounding, Partitioning   **Subject links:** Geography (Q14)

Worked example

a Estimate the answer to 249 × 6 by rounding to the nearest 100.
Estimate: 249 × 6 ≈ 200 × 6 = 1200

b Work out the exact answer.

×	200	40	9
6	1200	240	54

> Split the larger number into hundreds, tens and units.
> Write them along the top of a grid.
> Write 6 at the side of the grid.
> Multiply each part separately and write the answer in each space.

```
  1 2 0 0
    2 4 0
+     5 4
─────────
  1 4 9 4
```

> Add the three parts together.

Check: 1494 is reasonably close to 1200

> Check your answer against the estimate.

7 Estimate these multiplications by rounding to the nearest 100.
  a 299 × 2   **b** 4 × 195
  c 304 × 3   **d** 5 × 802

8 Work out the exact answer to each part in Q7.
  Use your estimate from Q7 to check that your answer looks sensible.

9 Reasoning
  a Work out
    i 305 × 4
    ii 6 × 324
    iii 3 × 324

  Discussion What do you notice about the answers to parts **a ii** and **iii**?
  Why has that happened?
  b Use your answers to part **a** to work out
    i 305 × 8
    ii 3 × 648

> **Q9b hint**
>
> When you multiply by double the number, the answer doubles too.

Worked example

Work out 254 × 7 using the column method.

```
  2 5 4
×     7
───────
      8
  2
```

> Multiply each digit in the top row by the digit in the bottom row.
> Start in the units column.
> 7 × 4 = 28
> That's **2** tens and 8 units.

```
  2 5 4
×     7
───────
    7 8
  3 2
```

> In the tens column:
> 7 × 5 = 35
> 35 + **2** = 37
> That's **37** tens altogether.

```
    2 5 4
×       7
─────────
  1 7 7 8
    3 2
```

> In the hundreds column:
> 7 × 2 = 14
> 14 + **3** = 17

10 Work out

    a 321 × 3

    b 216 × 4

    c 624 × 5

    d 751 × 6

Q10a hint

$$\begin{array}{r} 321 \\ \times\ \ \ 3 \\ \hline \end{array}$$

11 Match one of these estimated answers to each word problem below. Then work out the exact answer for each one.

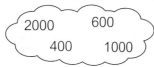

    2000   600   400   1000

    a In a school for Y7–Y11 there are 210 students in each of the 5 year groups.
How many students is that in total?

    b A smartphone costs £195.
How much will 3 smartphones cost?

    c A jet plane flies at 505 mph.
How far would it fly in 4 hours?

    d Ceris earns £138 a week in her part-time job.
How much does she earn in 4 weeks?

Q11a hint

5 year groups

| 210 | 210 | 210 | 210 | 210 |

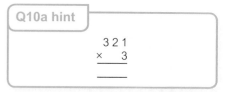

Q11c Literacy hint

505 'mph' means 505 'miles per hour'.

12 A flight costs £512.
How much do 8 flights cost?

13 A book has 210 pages.
How many pages are there in 9 books?

14 A library shelf holds 196 books.
How many books will 4 shelves hold?

15 A wind turbine turns 217 revolutions in 1 minute.
How many revolutions does it turn in 5 minutes?

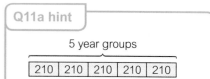

Q12 Strategy hint

Write the calculation.
Estimate the answer by rounding the cost to the nearest 100. Then work out the exact answer.
You could draw a bar model to help.

16 Explore How much pocket money will you get this year?
Look back at the maths you have learned in this lesson.
How can you use it to answer this question?

17 Reflect In this maths lesson, you were asked to estimate.
List other subjects where estimating is sometimes helpful.
List situations from real life where estimating is sometimes helpful.
Look at your lists and think about how you used estimating in this lesson. Discuss with a classmate if estimating is used in the same way every time.

Explore

Reflect

5.4 Division

You will learn to:
- Divide 3-digit numbers by a single digit
- Decide whether you can divide a number by 2, 5, 9 or 10
- Begin to identify factors of numbers.

Why learn this?
Division helps solve practical problems. Dividing your phone credit by the cost of a text message tells you how many messages you can send.

Fluency
Which of these numbers are odd and which are even?
4, 7, 10, 11, 13, 16, 20, 21, 30, 35

Explore
What is the link between multiples and division?

Exercise 5.4

1 Work out

  a $24 \div 6$ **b** $45 \div 9$ **c** $30 \div 6$

  d $81 \div 9$ **e** $72 \div 8$

2 Write the first six multiples of

  a 5   **b** 2   **c** 10   **d** 9

3 Copy and complete.

  a $3 \times 10 = 30$ $30 \div 10 = \square$

  b $5 \times 10 = 50$ $50 \div 10 = \square$

  c $8 \times 10 = 80$ $80 \div 10 = \square$

  d A number in the 10 times table divides by $\square$.

  e A number that divides by $\square$ is a multiple of 10.

4 Which of these numbers divide by 10?

  30   45   72   80   95   100

  Discussion What do you notice about the last digit of numbers that divide by 10?

> **Q4 hint**
>
> Are they in the 10 times table?

5 Copy and complete.

  a $4 \times 5 = 20$ $20 \div 5 = \square$

  b $7 \times 5 = 35$ $35 \div 5 = \square$

  c $9 \times 5 = 45$ $45 \div 5 = \square$

  d $6 \times 5 = 30$ $30 \div 5 = \square$

  e A number in the 5 times table divides by $\square$.

  f A number that divides by $\square$ is a multiple of 5.

Warm up

6 Which of the numbers in the box

   a divide by 5

   b divide by 10?

   12   15   20   22
      30   35   43

   Discussion Do numbers that divide by 10 always divide by 5?
Do numbers that divide by 5 always divide by 10?

7 Copy and complete these sentences.

   a A number in the 2 times table can be divided by □.

   b A number that divides by □ is a multiple of 2.

Q7 hint

Look at the multiples of 2 that you wrote in Q2 part **b**.

8 Look at the multiples of 5 that you wrote in Q2 part **a**.

   a Copy and complete this sentence.
'The last digit of a number that divides by 5 is either □ or □.

   b Which of the numbers in the box

      i divide by 5

      ii divide by 10

      iii divide by 2?

      230   554   225   500   605   552
        850   3000   3010   3011   4065

Investigation   **Problem-solving / Reasoning**

   1 Write the first 12 numbers in the 9 times table.

   2 Add together the digits of each 2-digit or 3-digit number:

      1 + 8 = □   2 + 7 = □   3 + □ = □   ...

      You may need to add them a second time to get to a single-digit answer.

      Discussion What is the **sum** of the digits for every number in
the 9 times table?

   3 Which of these numbers do you think divide by 9?

      216   273   414   621   387   429

   4 Use a calculator to check your answers to Q3.

Literacy hint

The **sum** means the total when you add numbers together.

---

9 Look at the numbers in the grid.

125	126	127	128	129	130
135	136	137	138	139	140
145	146	147	148	149	150

Q9 Strategy hint

Look at one number at a time.
Work along the rows.

Copy and complete this table.

Multiples of 2	Multiples of 5	Multiples of 9	Multiples of 10
	125		

Discussion Are any numbers in the grid multiples of 2, 5 *and* 9?

10 Which of these divisions will have a remainder?

   a 225 ÷ 10

   b 225 ÷ 2

   c 225 ÷ 5

   d 225 ÷ 9

Q10a hint

Is 225 a multiple of 10? If not, then
225 ÷ 10 has a remainder.

Topic links: Related facts, Time

11 Use the bar models to work out

a 135 ÷ 5

135 ÷ 5 = (100 ÷ 5) + (30 ÷ 5) + (5 ÷ 5)

| 20 | 20 | 20 | 20 | 20 |

20 + ☐ + ☐

135 ÷ 5 = 20 + ☐ + ☐ = ☐

b 252 ÷ 6

252 ÷ 6 = (240 ÷ 6) + (12 ÷ 6)

☐ + ☐

252 ÷ 6 = ☐ + ☐ = ☐

Worked example

Work out 648 ÷ 4

$$\begin{array}{r} 1\ \ldots\ldots \\ 4\overline{)6^248} \end{array}$$

Look at the digits in 648, starting on the left.
4 goes into 6 once, so write a 1 in the hundreds column above.
The difference between 6 and 4 is **2**, so write these 2 hundreds in the tens column, to make **24** tens.

$$\begin{array}{r} 1\ 6\ldots \\ 4\overline{)6^248} \end{array}$$

4 goes into 24 exactly 6 times, so write a 6 in the tens column above.

$$\begin{array}{r} 1\ 6\ 2 \\ 4\overline{)6^248} \end{array}$$

4 goes into 8 exactly twice, so write a 2 in the units column above.

12 Use a written method to work out these divisions.

a 4)128 **b** 5)255 **c** 3)369 **d** 189 ÷ 3

e 378 ÷ 6 **f** 192 ÷ 3 **g** 532 ÷ 4 **h** 415 ÷ 5

13 Sara receives £135 for 9 hours' work. What is her hourly rate?

14 David travelled 324 miles in 6 hours.
How far did he travel in an hour?

15 5 friends win £265 to share between them.
How much does each person get?

16 How many teams of 4 can be made from 256 people?

17 **Explore** What is the link between multiples and division?
Choose some sensible numbers to help you explore this idea.
Then use what you've learned in this lesson to help you answer the question.

18 **Reflect** In the last lesson you did lots of multiplication. In this lesson you did lots of division.
Which do you think is easier, multiplication or division?
Copy and complete this sentence:
_____ is easier, because _____.

Q18 hint
Look back at some of the questions you answered in these lessons. What was easier to do? What was harder to do?

Explore

Reflect

5.5 Solving problems

You will learn to:

- Solve problems involving multiplication and division
- Use a calculator to solve multiplication and division problems.

CONFIDENCE

Why learn this?
Have you got enough money to buy what you need? Multiplication and division are skills everyone uses when shopping.

Fluency
- Which of these numbers is a multiple of 5?
  57   123   275
- Which of these numbers is a multiple of 9?
  29   45   70

Explore
Have you been alive for one million hours? Has your teacher?

Exercise 5.5

Warm up

1 Work out
   a 126 × 4   b 324 × 5   c 249 ÷ 3   d 712 ÷ 4

2 Work out
   a 3 × 4 + 6   b 10 − 2 × 3   c 4 + 12 ÷ 6   d 15 ÷ 5 + 7

3 Work out the remainder for each division.
   a 42 ÷ 8   b 23 ÷ 4   c 29 ÷ 7   d 35 ÷ 6
   e 28 ÷ 5   f 49 ÷ 8   g 29 ÷ 3

4 Real A car can take 4 people.
   How many cars would 208 people need?

> **Q4 hint**
>
> 208
>
> | 4 | 4 | ... |

5 Real A school is running a 5-a-side competition.
   How many teams could you make from 275 students?

6 Real Lynn earns £12 per hour.
   How much does she earn for 3 hours' work?

> **Q6 hint**
>
> 3 hours
>
> | £12 | £12 | £12 |

7 How many weeks is 364 days?
   Is this more or less than the number of days in a year?

 8 What is the total cost of 3 items that are £8.45 each?

> **Q8 hint**
>
> Convert the prices into pence to make a 3-digit number.

 9 Real Eggs are packed in trays of 18.
   How many trays would you need
   to pack 342 eggs?

10 Boxes of juice hold 24 cartons each.
   How many cartons are there in 32 boxes?

11 Finance How many 55p stamps can you buy for £9.90?

12 Real How many minibuses carrying 9 people each are needed to take 100 students to a tournament?

Q12 hint

There needs to be a space for everyone, so does the answer need to round up or down?

13 Real A bumper pack of spring bulbs contains 125 bulbs.
How many bulbs are in 5 packs?

14 Real A car on a busy road takes 5 hours to travel 125 miles.
How many miles per hour is this?

15 You need 25 screws to make up a chest of drawers.
How many chests of drawers can you make using a packet of 240 screws?

16 Finance Dave needs £499 for a school skiing trip. He can save £24 a week from his allowance.
How many weeks will it take him to pay for the trip?

17 Zoë uses 18 beads to make a necklace.
How many necklaces can she make from 310 beads?

18 Finance How many doughnuts costing 45p each can you buy for £5?

19 Pears are packed in bags of 6.
How many bags would you need to pack 125 pears?

Q19 hint

Do you need to round up or down?

20 Real / Problem-solving Choose the correct calculation for each problem. Then work it out.

Q20 hint

Multiplication and **D**ivision before **A**ddition and **S**ubtraction

  a Farmer Holland's 24 chickens each lay 8 eggs every week.
How many 12-egg trays per week will he need to pack them?

$$24 \times 8 \times 12 \qquad 24 + 8 \div 12 \qquad 24 \times 8 \div 12 \qquad 24 \div 12 \div 8$$

  b Bags of peanuts from the wholesaler are packed on cards of 8 bags per card and in boxes of 32 cards. Joe buys 4 boxes.
How many bags of peanuts is that?

$$32 \div 4 \times 8 \qquad 4 \times 32 \times 8 \qquad 32 \div 8 \times 4 \qquad 32 \div 8 \div 4$$

  c 4 art folders cost £12.
How much will 3 folders cost?

$$12 \div 3 \times 4 \qquad 12 \times 4 \times 3 \qquad 4 \div 3 \times 12 \qquad 12 \div 4 \times 3$$

21 Explore Have you been alive for one million hours? Has your teacher?
Look back at the maths you have learned in this lesson.
How can you use it to answer this question?

22 Reflect In this lesson, Q4 and Q6 had hints suggesting you use bar models. Look back at these questions.
Were the bar models useful to you?
Write a sentence that explains how they were useful, or why you didn't use them.
Did you use bar models to help you answer any other questions?
If yes, then show a classmate how a bar model helped you.

Explore

Reflect

5.6 Factors and primes

You will learn to:
- Find factors of numbers
- Identify prime numbers.

CONFIDENCE

Why learn this?
The retail industry uses factors and multiples to find the best way to package their goods.

Fluency
- What are the first six multiples of
  2 4 5 9?
- Which of these numbers divide by 2, 5 or 10?
  45 68 90 132 200

Explore
How many different ways could the chairs in your school hall be arranged to seat all of Y7?

Exercise 5.6

Warm up

1 Find the missing numbers.
  a ☐ × 4 = 24   **b** 4 × ☐ = 40   **c** 4 × 7 = ☐
  d 9 × 4 = ☐   **e** 4 × ☐ = 48

2 Write two numbers that divide into
  a 10   **b** 12   **c** 15   **d** 20   **e** 32

3 Follow these steps to find all the **factors** of 12.
  a Is 1 a factor?   1 × ☐ = 12
     So 1 and 12 are a **factor pair**.
  b Is 2 a factor?   2 × ☐ = 12
     So 2 and ☐ are a factor pair.
  c Is 3 a factor?   3 × ☐ = 12
     So 3 and ☐ are a factor pair.
  d Is 5 a factor?
  e Have you found all the factors of 12?

> **Key point**
> A **factor** is a whole number that will divide exactly into another number.
> A **factor pair** is two numbers that multiply together to make a number.

4 Find all the factors of these numbers.
  a 24   **b** 18   **c** 28   **d** 30

5 **a** Copy and complete these diagrams to show the factor pairs of the numbers in the middle. The first one has been done for you.

> **Q5a hint**
> The opposite numbers multiply together to make the middle number. So the opposite numbers are a factor pair of the middle number.

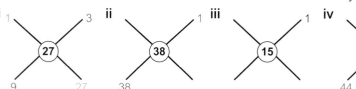

  b Write the factors in a list.
     i Factors of 27 are: 1, 3, ☐, ☐
     ii Factors of 38 are: ☐, ☐, ☐, ☐
     iii Factors of 15 are: ☐, ☐, ☐, ☐
     iv Factors of 44 are: ☐, ☐, ☐, ☐, ☐, ☐

  Discussion Is 1 a factor of every number? Is a number a factor of itself?

Topic links: Division with and without remainders, Sequences, Halving

6 Reasoning

a Work out the factors of these square numbers and list them in order.

i   ii   iii 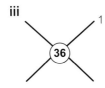 1   iv

Q6a hint

Where there is a repeated factor (for example, 3 × 3), just write it once in the list of factors.

b How many different factors does 9 have?

c How many different factors does 16 have?

d How many different factors does 36 have?

e How many different factors does 49 have?

f Copy and complete these sentences using 'odd' or 'even'.
'Square numbers have an _____ number of factors.'
'Non-square numbers have an _____ number of factors.'

Q6f hint

Look at your factor lists in Q5b.

7 Write all the factors of 10, 14 and 25.
Put them into factor pairs to check that you've got them all.
Discussion 25 has factor pairs 1 × 25 and 5 × 5, so what are its factors?

Key point

A **prime number** has exactly two different factors: 1 and itself.
1 is not a prime number because it only has one factor.

8 Write all the factors of
a 3   **b** 11   **c** 17   **d** 23
Discussion What do you notice about your answers?

9 Reasoning Which of these numbers are **prime numbers**?

3   10   11   14   17   23   25   27

Q9 hint

Does the number have exactly two factors, or more than two?

10 Copy and connect these numbers to the correct labels.

Factor of 8	Prime number	Multiple of 8

16   11   2   24   19   7   4   8

Q10 hint

Some numbers will connect to two labels.

11 Reasoning Write a number to fit each description.

a A multiple of 3 that is also a factor of 24

b A factor of both 12 and 15

c Two even numbers that are a factor pair of 20

d Two odd numbers that are a factor pair of 15

e An odd-and-even factor pair of 30

f A multiple of both 2 and 9

12 Explore How many different ways could the chairs in your school hall be arranged to seat all of Y7?
What have you learned in this lesson to help you answer this question?
What other information do you need?

13 Reflect Compare your answers to Q11 with a classmate.
Did you both get the same answers for parts **a–f**?
If no, are you still both correct? Check each others' answers.
If yes, discuss if these are the only answers. Can you find any more?

Explore

Reflect

5.7 Common factors and multiples

You will learn to:
- Recognise and use multiples, factors and primes
- Find common factors and multiples
- Work out the HCF and LCM of two numbers
- Work out if a number is divisible by 3, 4 or 6.

Why learn this?
Common factors and multiples are used to help organise people at events such as parties and weddings.

Fluency
- Divide these numbers by 10:
  420   560
- What are two multiples of 8?
- What are two factors of 10?

Explore
How many bags of rolls and packs of burgers will I need so that no rolls or burgers are left over?

Exercise 5.7

1 Pick out one number to fit each description.

   6   9   20   49   75

   a A multiple of 25   **b** A factor of 45   **c** A multiple of 2
   d A factor of 24   **e** A square number

2 Write a list of all the factors for each number.
   a 15   **b** 21   **c** 20   **d** 18

3 Which are the multiples of 4 in this list?
   12   66   134   144   82   70   76   900   748

4 Real Leap years are always multiples of 4.
   Which of these years were leap years?
   1956   1982   1984   2000   2006   2008   2014
   Discussion When are the next two leap years?
   Were you born in a leap year?
   Was anyone in your class or your family born in a leap year?
   How can you tell?

Key point
- Half of a multiple of 4 is an even number.
- If you halve a multiple of 4, then halve it again, you get a whole number.

Key point
- A multiple of 100 is also a multiple of 4.
- If the last two digits in a number make a multiple of 4, the whole number is a multiple of 4.

Investigation | Problem-solving / Reasoning

1 Write the first six multiples of 3 and 6.
2 Add together the digits of each 2-digit number:
   12: 1 + 2 = 3   24: 2 + 4 = 6
3 What kind of number do the digits add up to? Does this work for all the multiples?
Discussion How is this rule different to the rule for multiples of 9?
4 Check, by adding the digits, which of the following numbers are multiples of 3, 6, both or neither:
   264   123   415   312   621   100

Topic links: Number relationships, Sequences

5 Problem-solving Use these number cards to make a 2-digit and a 3-digit number to match each statement.

| 2 | 3 | 4 | 5 | 6 | 7 | 8 | 9 |

a 3 is a factor of ☐☐ and ☐☐☐
b 5 is a factor of ☐☐ and ☐☐☐
c ☐☐ and ☐☐☐ are multiples of 9
d ☐☐ and ☐☐☐ are multiples of 4

Worked example

a What are the **common factors** of 15 and 27?

Factors of 15: ①③ 5, 15
Factors of 27: ①③ 9, 27
Common factors: 1 and 3

> Write lists of factors of both numbers.
> Circle the factors that appear in both lists.

b What is the **highest common factor (HCF)** of 15 and 27?

HCF: 3

> Find the *largest* number in the list of common factors.

6 a Write a list of all the factors of
    i 12   **ii** 20   **iii** 18   **iv** 24   **v** 32
 b What is the highest common factor of
    i 12 and 20   **ii** 12 and 18   **iii** 20 and 32   **iv** 18 and 24?

7 Work out the HCF of these pairs of numbers.
  a 15 and 21   **b** 24 and 32   **c** 20 and 30   **d** 25 and 45

8 a List the first 8 multiples of these numbers.
    i 2   **ii** 3   **iii** 4   **iv** 5   **v** 10
 b What are the common multiples of
    i 2 and 3   **ii** 4 and 10   **iii** 4 and 5
    iv 5 and 10   **v** 2 and 5?
 c For each pair, what is the **lowest common multiple (LCM)**?

9 A tub of ice cream holds enough for 8 scoops. Ice cream cones come in packs of 12.
 a What is the LCM of 8 and 12?
 b How many tubs of ice cream and packs of cones do you need to make sure no ice cream and no cones are left over?

10 Explore How many bags of rolls and packs of burgers will I need so that no rolls or burgers are left over?
What have you learned in this lesson to help you answer this question?
What other information do you need?

11 Reflect In this lesson, Q6 and Q8 suggest you write lists.
Copy and complete this sentence:
Lists helped me to answer the questions because _____.
Where else have lists helped you in maths? Copy and complete:
Lists help me to find _____ because _____.

5 Check up

Log how you did on your Student Progression Chart.

Multiplication and number rules

1 Work out
  a $3 + 5 \times 2$
  b $6 + 10 \div 5$
  c $5 \times 7 \times 2$
  d $26 - 6 \times 4$
  e $30 \div 6 - 5$
  f $3 \times 6 \div 2$

2 a Work out 321×4
  b Use your answer to part **a** to work out 321×8

3 Round 7189 to the nearest
  a 10
  b 100
  c 1000

4 Estimate the answer to
  a 29×6
  b 213×8

Division

5 Copy and complete
  a $7 \times 10 = 70$ $70 \div 10 = \square$
  b $8 \times 5 = 40$ $40 \div 5 = \square$
  c $12 \times 2 = 24$ $24 \div 2 = \square$

6 Which of these numbers

   10   18   24   25   28   35   40

  a divide by 2
  b divide by 5
  c divide by 10?

7 Work out $621 \div 3$

8 Work out the remainder of
  a $39 \div 5$
  b $21 \div 6$

Solving problems

9 Joel can type 108 words a minute.
How many words can he type in 8 minutes?

10 a How many 9-seater minibuses are needed to transport 127 people?

    b Have you rounded up or down?

11 Christmas crackers come in boxes of 6 crackers.
How many boxes would 216 crackers fill?

12 Emily earns £480 a week.
How much does she earn in 4 weeks?

13 208 students go on a trip in 4 equal size coaches.
How many students are on each coach?

Multiples, factors and primes

14 Write the first three multiples of 9.

15 True or false?

    a 17 is a multiple of 2

    b 35 is a multiple of 5

    c 21 a multiple of 3

    d 34 is a multiple of 9

    e 410 is a multiple of 10

16 a Write down the factors of 8 and the factors of 20.

    b What are the common factors of 8 and 20?

    c What is the highest common factor (HCF) of 8 and 20?

17 True or false?

    a 36 is a multiple of 6.

    b 36 is a factor of 6.

    c 6 is a factor of 36.

    d 36 is a prime number.

18 What is the lowest common multiple (LCM) of 3 and 5?

19 **How sure are you of your answers? Were you mostly**

    😦 **Just guessing**   😐 **Feeling doubtful**   🙂 **Confident**

    What next? Use your results to decide whether to strengthen or extend your learning.

Reflect

Challenge

20 How many different ways can you split a group of 24 children into equal groups so that no-one is left out?

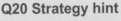

> **Q20 Strategy hint**
>
> Use all the factor pairs of 24.
> For example, 1 × 24 could mean
> 1 group of 24 children or 24 groups
> of 1 child in each.
> 2 × 12 ... 3 × 8 ....

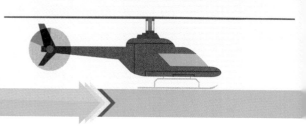

5 Strengthen

You will:
- Strengthen your understanding with practice.

Multiplication and number rules

1 Use the correct priority of operations to work out these calculations.
Put brackets round the part that needs to be worked out first.
Part **a** has been started for you.

a $3 \times 4 + 6 = (3 \times 4) + 6 = \square + 6 = \square$

b $7 + 2 \times 5$ **c** $30 \div 5 - 2$ **d** $30 - 5 \times 2$

e $27 + 3 - 8$ **f** $4 \times 6 \div 8$

Q1 hint

Multiplication and **D**ivision before **A**ddition and **S**ubtraction

2 Complete this table for the 8 times table.

×	8
1	8
2	
5	
10	
20	
50	
100	

Q2 hint

Use doubling, multiplying by 5 and multiplying by 10.

3 Use the table from Q2 to work out

a 55×8 **b** 52×8 **c** 151×8 **d** 175×8

e 235×8 **f** 164×8 **g** 237×8

Q3a hint

Work out these multiples of 8 separately, then add them together.

×	8
5	
50	
55	

4 Work out

a 315×6 **b** 4×438 **c** 364×5 **d** 3×721

e 524×8

Q4a hint

×	6
300	
10	
5	
315	

5 Use rounding to estimate the answer to

a 79×3 **b** 4×78 **c** 27×3 **d** 5×39

6 Round these numbers to the nearest 100. Use the number lines to help.

a 503   500   600   **b** 171   100   200

c 829   800   900

Q5a hint

79 is approximately $\square$
And $\square \times 3 = \square$

7 Use rounding to estimate the answer to

a 2×119 **b** 203×4 **c** 198×3

8 Round 3947 to the nearest

Q7a hint

Round 119 to the nearest 100.

a 10   3940   3950

b 100   3900   4000

c 1000   3000   4000

9 Work out these multiplications using the grid method.

a Work out each missing answer and add them together to find 18 × 32.

×	10	8
30	30 × ☐ =	☐ × ☐ =
2	☐ × ☐ =	☐ × ☐ =

b Copy and complete this grid to work out 34 × 16.

×		
30		

c Now work out 24 × 31.

Division

1 Match the divisions that have the same answer.

27 ÷ 3   32 ÷ 8   42 ÷ 6   27 ÷ 6

36 ÷ 4   35 ÷ 5   24 ÷ 6

2 Write each division answer with a remainder.

a 13 ÷ 5
b 6 ÷ 4 = ☐ remainder ☐
c 7 ÷ 3
d 11 ÷ 9
e 28 ÷ 5

3 Work out

a 4⟌8
b 4⟌84
c 4⟌848
d 2⟌468
e 369 ÷ 3
f 684 ÷ 2

4 Work out

a 5⟌10
b 5⟌105
c 5⟌125
d 3⟌159

5 Work out

a 5⟌5
b 5⟌525
c 4⟌816
d 6⟌624

6 Work out

a 3⟌35
b 11
   3⟌35⁷
c 4⟌185
d 856 ÷ 4
e 59 ÷ 5
f 596 ÷ 5

Solving problems

1 **Problem-solving** A school has 261 students and 9 equal size classes. How many are in each class?

2 **Problem-solving** A high-speed train travels 120 miles in one hour. How far does it travel in 6 hours?

3 **Problem-solving / Finance** A skiing trip costs £699 per person. What is the total cost for 3 people?

Q2a hint

13 ÷ 5 = 2 remainder 3

	13	
5	5	3

Q4a hint

5 doesn't go into 1, so work out how many 5s go into 10.

Q5b hint

5 doesn't go into 2, so first put a 0 in the answer line above the 2. Then work out how many 5s go into 25.

Q6a hint

How many 3s go into 5? What's the remainder?

  1☐ r☐
3⟌35

Q1 hint

Draw a bar model.

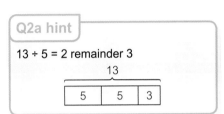

4 Reasoning Jannah answers the question, 'How many 5-seater cars do you need for 27 people?', like this:
27 ÷ 5 = 5 remainder 2
So you need 5 cars.
Is she right? Explain your answer.

Q4 hint

Will all 27 people fit in 5 cars?
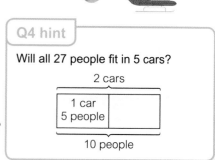

5 Problem-solving How many 5 ml doses of medicine are in a 375 ml bottle?

6 Problem-solving How many 4-person tents would 128 campers need?

Multiples, factors, and primes

1 These numbers are multiples of 10.
400   10   230   1760   50   610
a What is the same about them?
b Which of these numbers are multiples of 10?
403   60   6   730   500   7106

2 These numbers are multiples of 5.
15   80   10   35   20   100   265
a What is the same about them?
b Which of these numbers are multiples of 5?
13   75   32   105   98   50   300   85

3 These numbers are multiples of 2.
14   20   50   104   78   56   10   82
a What is the same about them?
b Which of these numbers are multiples of 2?
100   46   23   97   61   58   316   42

4 Copy and complete these statements and labels.
The first one has been done for you.

a   2 × 5 = 10
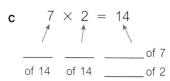
factor   factor   multiple of 2
of 10   of 10   multiple of 5

b   3 × 4 = 12
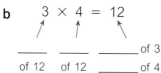
_____ _____ _____ of 3
of 12   of 12   _____ of 4

c   7 × 2 = 14

_____ _____ _____ of 7
of 14   of 14   _____ of 2

d Write down 2 factors of 6.

Q4d hint

Write a multiplication first.
☐ × ☐ = 6

e Write down 2 factors of 18.   **f** Write down 2 multiples of 10.

5 Write down all the multiplications you can, to fit this statement.
☐ × ☐ = 12

Q5 hint

You could use a multiplication square to help.

6 Find the factors of
a 25   **b** 16   **c** 28
d 32   **e** 40   **f** 24

7 Complete each sentence using the numbers in the box.

a 2 is a factor of ☐, ☐, ...   2   14   90   15   21   103   782

b 10 is a factor of ☐, ☐, ...   10   12   20   25   30   400   525

c 5 is a factor of ☐, ☐, ...   5   30   19   15   65   140   255

8 Use these sets of multiples to help you with part **a**.

First 10 multiples of 3

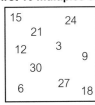

15   24
   21
12   3
      9
   30
6   27   18

First 10 multiples of 4

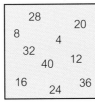

   28
8   20
      4
   32
      40   12
16   36
      24

First 10 multiples of 5

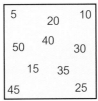

5   10
   20
      40
50   30
   15   35
45   25

This Venn diagram shows the common multiples of 3 and 4.
a Draw Venn diagrams to show the common multiples of
  i 3 and 5   **ii** 4 and 5.
b Write the lowest common multiple of
  i 3 and 4   **ii** 3 and 5   **iii** 4 and 5.

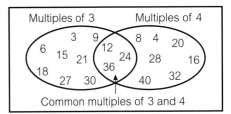

9 Complete this sentence about prime numbers, using either '1' or '2' in the spaces.
'A prime number has only ☐ factors: ☐ and itself.'

10 Explain why these numbers are not prime.
The first two have been started for you.
  a 6 is not prime because 2 × ☐ = 6, so 2 and ☐ are factors of 6
  b 9 is not prime because ☐ × ☐ = 9, so ☐ is a factor of 9
  c 10 is not prime because ....
  d 21 is not prime because ....

11 Which of these numbers are prime?
  2   5   12   13   15   18   19   22   29

> **Q8b hint**
> What is the smallest number in the overlap of your Venn diagram?

> **Q10 hint**
> If a number can be made by multiplying two numbers (other than 1 and itself) together, it is not prime.

> **Q11 hint**
> Does the number have any factors except 1 and itself?

Enrichment

1 Reasoning Which number is the odd one out?
For each one, explain why.
  a 5, 10, 16, 20   **b** 12, 16, 18, 21   **c** 7, 9, 12, 15
Discussion Compare your number and explanation with a classmate.
Are they the same?

2 **Reflect** Toby, Edward and Isy look at Solving problems Q1–6.
Toby says, 'I looked at the words. "Total" usually means add. "How many are in each" usually means divide.'
Edward says, 'I wrote down the key information. "261 students; 9 classes." "120 miles in one hour; 6 hours." '
Isy says, 'I drew bar models.'
Discuss each strategy with a classmate. Do you find the strategies helpful? Why? Do you have any other strategies for problem-solving? If yes, tell your classmate about them.

5 Extend

You will:
- Extend your understanding with problem-solving.

1 Work out

  a $2 \times 8 \times 5 \times 3$ **b** $6 \times 7 \times 5$ **c** $18 \div 6 + 24 \div 4$

  d $15 \div 3 + 2 \times 6$ **e** $10 + 15 \div 5 - 6$

> **Q1 hint**
>
> Use the priority of operations.

2 Which of these amounts could you pay exactly, using only

  a £10 notes   **b** £50 notes?

£32	£90	£75
£450	£11 500	

3 Write three 4-digit numbers that are each

  a multiples of 6   **b** multiples of 9   **c** multiples of 25

4 **Reasoning** Use the fact that $15 \times 32 = 480$ to work out

  a $480 \div 32$ **b** $480 \div 16$ **c** 30×32 **d** 15×64

  e 16×15 **f** $480 \div 64$ **g** 15×33 **h** 16×32

> **Q4 Strategy hint**
>
> Look for doubles and halves of the calculation you have been given.

5 Use a written method to multiply

  a 3124×5 **b** 2846×4 **c** 4092×6

> **Q5 hint**
>
> Use the same method for 4-digit numbers as you used for 3-digit numbers.

6 A building company is fitting 9 new kitchens.
Each kitchen costs £5125.
What is the total cost of all the kitchens?

7 Work out

  a $3865 \div 5$ **b** $3756 \div 3$ **c** $8364 \div 4$ **d** $7326 \div 9$

8 **Problem-solving / Reasoning**
Rearrange these digits to get   **4** **8** **2** **9**

  a the *largest* possible answer to $\square\square\square \times \square$

  b the *smallest* possible answer to $\square\square\square \times \square$

> **Q8 Strategy hint**
>
> Use what you know about place value.

9 **Real** The Winter Olympics are held every 4 years, when the year is a multiple of 2 but *not* a multiple of 4.
In which years between 1980 and this year were there Winter Olympics?

10 **Problem-solving** Cans are packed in trays of 24.
There are 5 trays in a box.
How many cans are packed in 10 boxes?

> **Q10 hint**
>
> Work out how many are packed in one box first.
>
> 1 box
>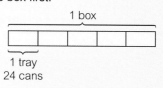
> 1 tray
> 24 cans

11 **Problem-solving** 101 gymnasts want to enter a gymnastics competition.

  a How many teams of 6 can they make?
How many gymnasts are left over?

  b There must be one teacher for every 20 gymnasts.
How many teachers do they need?

  c The teams will travel to the competition in minibuses.
Each minibus can carry 18 passengers.
How many minibuses will they need?

> **Q11c hint**
>
> Passengers include teachers and gymnasts.

Topic links: Time, Metric measures, Volume   **Subject links:** PE (Q9)

12 **Reasoning** All these divisions have a remainder.
For each one, explain how you can tell.

    a 645 ÷ 4   **b** 678 ÷ 9

    c 313 ÷ 3   **d** 345 ÷ 25

13 Abigail needs 128 stamps.
How many books of 6 stamps does she need?

14 **Problem-solving** What different size teams could a class of 30
students be arranged in, without anyone being left out?

    1 team of 30, 2 teams of ▢, …

Q14 hint

Use factor pairs.

15 **Reasoning** Harriet wants to plant 48 seedlings in equal rows.
How could she arrange them?

16 Work out

    a 2 × 3 + 5 × 6

    b 6 × 5 ÷ 3 × 4

    Discussion Does changing the order make a difference in part **b**?
Why is this?

Q16a hint

Use the priority of operations
to multiply the pairs of numbers
together *before* adding.

17 Choose the missing word for each sentence.

    prime   multiples   even   divisible   odd   square   factors

    a 21 is not prime because it has more than two _____.

    b No numbers greater than 10 and ending in 5 are prime because they
are _____ of 5.

    c All _____ numbers have an odd number of factors.

    d All _____ numbers have only two factors.

    e 27 is not prime because it is _____ by 3 and 9.

    f The only _____ prime number is 2.

18 **a** Copy the Venn diagram and write these numbers in the correct
places.

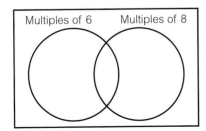

    1 6 8 12 14
    16 18 20 24
      30 40 48

    b What is the lowest common multiple of 6 and 8?

19 **Real** Teabags come in packs of 20. A cafe owner buys 8 packs of
Earl Grey and 244 packs of breakfast tea.
How many teabags is this altogether?

Q19 hint

Work out the total number of packs
first.

20 **Real** Light bulbs come in packs of 6.
How many light bulbs are there in 72 packs?

21 A card seller displays her cards in rows of 27.
One table has room for 9 rows.
How many cards will fit on 3 tables?

22 **Real** Nick can borrow a library book for 3 weeks. He reads 9 pages
a day before going to sleep. The book has 216 pages.
Will he be able to finish it in the 3 weeks?

 23 **Real / Finance**

    a Which is better value, £7.50 for 30 daffodil bulbs or £9.60 for 40
daffodil bulbs?

    b Which is better value, 4 batteries for £3.99 or 6 batteries for £6.01?

Q23 hint

Find the cost of one item in each deal.

24 **Finance** The US dollar ($) is made up of 100 cents. A 'quarter' is the
slang name for a coin worth 25 cents.
How many quarters make $5?

25 **Reasoning** True or false?
Write one or two calculations to explain each answer.

    a 48 is a square number.

    b 450 is a multiple of 9.

    c 32 is a factor of 8.

    d 49 is a square number.

    e 39 is a prime number.

    f There are no even prime numbers.

    g A number can be both a factor and a multiple of a number.

26 **Reasoning**

    a Write down all the prime numbers that are less than 20.

    b Multiply any two numbers from your list.
How many factors does your answer have?

    c Repeat this for another two numbers.

    d What is the missing number in this sentence?
'When you multiply two prime numbers, the answer has exactly
__ factors.'

27 **Real** Lilly takes two 5 ml spoonfuls of cough medicine 4 times a day
for 5 days.
How much of a 250 ml bottle of medicine is left over?

Q27 hint

Work out how much medicine she takes in
• 1 day
• 2 days.

28 **a** Copy the Venn diagram and write the numbers in the square in the
correct places.

Q28a hint

Where do you put a number that is a factor of both 20 and 30?
A number that is *not* a factor of either 20 or 30 goes *outside* the circles, but *inside* the rectangle.

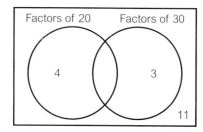

    b What are the common factors of 20 and 30?

    c What is the highest common factor of 20 and 30?

29 Draw Venn diagrams to find the common factors and the highest common factor of these pairs of numbers.

    a 16 and 20

    b 40 and 32

    c 18 and 24

    d 12 and 36

30 Draw Venn diagrams to find the lowest common multiple of

    a 5 and 9

    b 5 and 6

    c 6 and 9

    d 6 and 15

    e 15 and 25

> **Q30 hint**
>
> Keep writing multiples on your diagram until you find a common one. Where will you put it?

Investigation   Reasoning

1 Use divisibility tests or a calculator to check which numbers in each set are prime numbers.

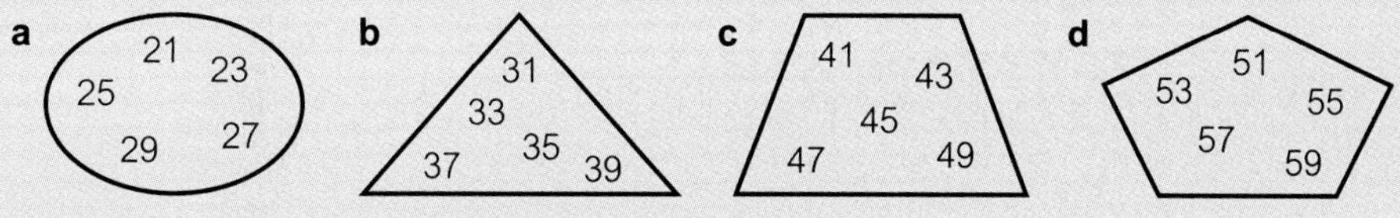

    a 21 23 25 29 27

    b 31 33 37 35 39

    c 41 43 45 47 49

    d 51 53 55 57 59

    Discussion Can a number ending in 5 be prime?

2 Write down all the prime numbers between 60 and 100.

---

31 Make lists of multiples to find the lowest common multiple of 2, 3 and 5.

32 What is the lowest common multiple of 4, 6 and 10?

33 Reasoning

    a Divide 27 by 2, then by 3, 4, 5, 6, 7, 8 and 9.

    b Which division in part **a** has the largest remainder?

    c Which calculation will have the largest remainder, $45 \div 10$ or $45 \div 4$?

34 **Reflect** Which do you find easiest, finding:

    • factors

    • multiples

    • primes?

> **Q34 hint**
>
> Think about what you have to do when finding them.

Reflect

5 Unit test

Log how you did on your Student Progression Chart.

1 Which of these numbers are multiples of 3?

18   20   27   100   99   53

2 Write down all the numbers from the cloud that are

a multiples of 9

b multiples of 4

c factors of 24

d factors of 20

e multiples of 25

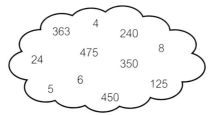

363   4   240   475   8   24   350   6   5   125   450   5

3 Work out

a 482 × 6

b 836 ÷ 4

4 Write these calculations in order from the smallest to the largest answer.

235 × 7   327 × 5   753 × 2   532 × 7   357 × 2

5 a Divide 21 by

i 4

ii 7

iii 9

b Which has the largest remainder?

6 Work out

a 3 + 4 × 5 − 2

b 20 ÷ 4 × 5

c 20 ÷ 5 − 4 + 7

7 124 people live in Moselle Drive. 3 times as many live in Beaumont Rd.
How many people live in Beaumont Road?

8 A model boat is made out of 145 matchsticks.
How many matchsticks are needed to make 5 model boats?

9 Write down all the factors of

a 8

b 20

c 27

10 What is the highest common factor of 18 and 30?

11 What is the lowest common multiple of 4 and 7?

12 Which of these numbers are prime numbers?

61　63　67　69

13 Decide whether each statement is true or false.
  a 81 is a square number.
  b 359 is a multiple of 9.
  c 6 is a factor of 24.
  d 24 is a factor of 6.
  e 51 is a prime number.

14 Work out
  a $108 \div 9$
  b $224 \div 4$

15 Flowers are sold in bunches of 6.
How many bunches can be made from 320 flowers?

16 Candles are packed in boxes of 8.
How many boxes are needed to pack 310 candles?

17 Write a number that is a factor of
  a 100, 175 and 350
  b 27, 45 and 72

18 Year 7 want to arrange the seats in the hall for a presentation.
There are 120 chairs.
How could they be arranged in equal size rows?
Find as many ways as you can.

Challenge

19 Show that each statement is *not* true, by giving two examples to prove it.
The first one has been started for you.
  a All numbers ending in 4 are divisible by 4.
      14 and ☐ end in 4 but are not multiples of 4.
  b All multiples of an odd number are odd.
  c All multiples of 5 are also multiples of 10.
  d 33 is a prime number.
  e All numbers have an even number of factors.
  f All numbers ending in 3 are divisible by 3.
  g $12\,345 \div 5$ will have a remainder.
  h $8371 \div 2$ will not have a remainder.
  i Factors of an even number are all even.

20 **Reflect** In this unit, did you work:
  • slowly
  • at average speed
  • quickly?
Is it always good to work quickly? Explain.
Is it always bad to work slowly? Explain.

6.1 Estimates and measures

You will learn to:
- Estimate, and choose suitable units, to measure length, mass and capacity
- Draw lines to the nearest mm and measure lines to the nearest cm
- Read a variety of scales
- Record estimates to a suitable degree of accuracy.

CONFIDENCE

Why learn this?
A poorly estimated length could have disastrous consequences.

Fluency
Match each object to its most suitable mass:

boy	horse	cat
500 kg	5 kg	50 kg

Explore
What measures do you need to work out the cost of sending a package?

Exercise 6.1

Warm up

1 Fill in the missing numbers on these number lines.

a 2 4 ☐ ☐ 10 ☐

b 25 50 ☐ 100 ☐ ☐

c 10 ☐ ☐ 40 ☐ 60

d 100 ☐ 200 ☐ ☐ 300

2 Reasoning What would you use to measure
a the height of a door   m   litres   g
b the mass of a bicycle   m   litres   kg
c the capacity of a mug of tea cm   ml   g?

3 STEM Write the measurements shown by each arrow.

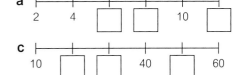

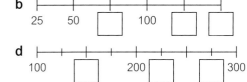

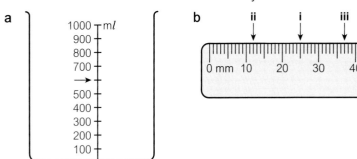

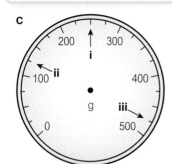

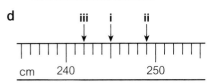

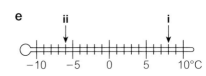

> **Key point**
>
> **Height** measures how tall an object is.
> **Mass** measures how much something weighs.
> **Capacity** is the amount or volume that a container can hold.

> **Q3b hint**
>
> What is each small space on the ruler? Write the units with your answer.

Topic links: Reading graph scales

4 Estimate the measurements shown on these scales.

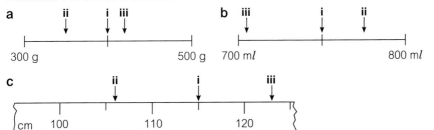

Key point

When you can't read a measurement exactly, you **estimate** the amount.

Q4 Strategy hint

Is the arrow halfway between two values? Is it closer to one value?

5 Draw a line with length
  a 8 cm   **b** 11 cm   **c** 7 cm
  Discussion Why is it important to be able to measure accurately?

6 For each line
  i estimate its length   **ii** measure it accurately.

  a ——————————————

  b ————————————————————

  c ————————————————

  Discussion Did your estimates get better?

Q6 hint

Carefully line up the zero marker on the ruler with the start of the line.

——————————

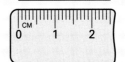

7 Reasoning Choose the most suitable unit of length: mm, cm, m or km to measure each item.
  a The height of a book
  b The length of the whiteboard
  c The distance between two towns
  d The width of the school hall
  e The width of a finger nail
  Discussion Which unit did you choose? Why?

8 The graph shows the results of a survey on people's pets.
  a How many people in the survey have a dog?
  b How many people have either a hamster or a parrot?
  c How many more people have a cat than a rabbit?
  d How many people took part in the survey?

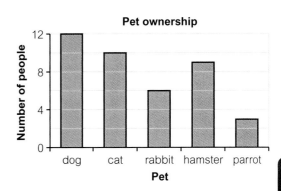

9 **Explore** What measures do you need to work out the cost of sending a package?
  Is it easier to explore this question now you have completed the lesson? What further information do you need to be able to answer this?

Explore

10 **Reflect** Look back at Q3.
  Which scale was easiest to read?
  Which scale was hardest to read?
  Discuss with a classmate what made some scales harder to read than others.

Q10 hint

a, b, c, d or **e**?

Reflect

6.2 Decimal numbers

You will learn to:

- Read and write numbers in figures and words
- Understand, compare, order and use decimals for tenths and hundredths, including in measures
- Read and interpret scales using decimals.

CONFIDENCE

Why learn this?
The judges at a long jump event order decimals to decide who has won the gold medal.

Fluency
Put < or > between each pair of numbers.

- 76 ☐ 32
- 121 ☐ 112
- 304 ☐ 340
- 615 ☐ 516

Explore
Where does the word 'decimal' come from?

Exercise 6.2

Warm up

1 Write these numbers in words.

  a 265

  b 2418

  c 8009

  d 7026

  e 24 638

2 Write these numbers in figures (numerals).

  a thirty-nine

  b four hundred and eighty-six

  c nine hundred and two

  d three thousand, one hundred and fifty-seven

  e eight thousand, five hundred and six

  f five thousand and forty

Q1 hint

Use a place-value table.

Ten Th	Th	H	T	U
			2	6	5
	8	0	0	9

Key point

H	T	U	.	tenths	hundredths
		0	.	1	
		0	.	0	1

0.1 = 1 tenth

0.01 = 1 hundredth

Worked example

Write the decimal shown by the diagram.

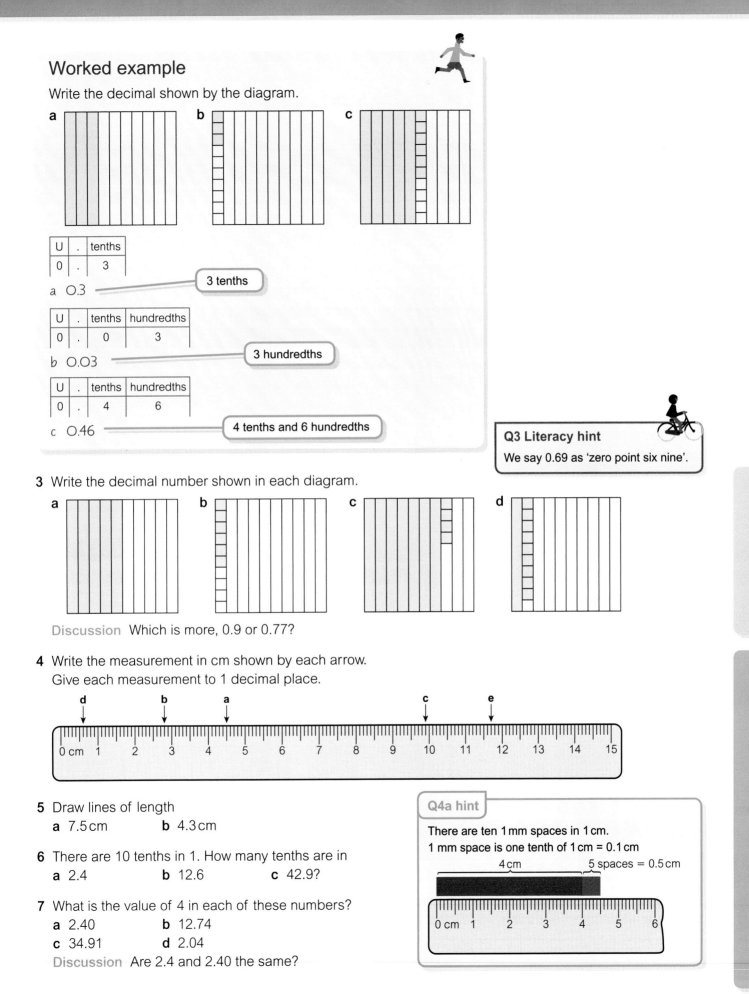

U	.	tenths
0	.	3

a 0.3 ——— 3 tenths

U	.	tenths	hundredths
0	.	0	3

b 0.03 ——— 3 hundredths

U	.	tenths	hundredths
0	.	4	6

c 0.46 ——— 4 tenths and 6 hundredths

Q3 Literacy hint

We say 0.69 as 'zero point six nine'.

3 Write the decimal number shown in each diagram.

a   b   c   d

Discussion Which is more, 0.9 or 0.77?

4 Write the measurement in cm shown by each arrow.
Give each measurement to 1 decimal place.

5 Draw lines of length
  a 7.5 cm   b 4.3 cm

6 There are 10 tenths in 1. How many tenths are in
  a 2.4   b 12.6   c 42.9?

7 What is the value of 4 in each of these numbers?
  a 2.40   b 12.74
  c 34.91   d 2.04
  Discussion Are 2.4 and 2.40 the same?

Q4a hint

There are ten 1 mm spaces in 1 cm.
1 mm space is one tenth of 1 cm = 0.1 cm

4 cm   5 spaces = 0.5 cm

8 Write the measurements shown by each arrow.

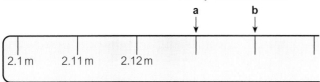

9 Copy and complete these heights.

   a 1 m 57 cm = 1.5 ☐ m   **b** 1 m 63 cm = 1.☐ ☐ m

   c 1 m 40 cm = ☐ . ☐ ☐ m   **d** 1 m 4 cm = ☐ . 0 ☐ m

   e 2 m 7 cm = ☐ . ☐ ☐ m

Q9a hint

1.6 —— 1 m 60 cm

1.57 —— 1 m 57 cm

1.5 —— 1 m 50 cm

10 Reasoning Write the measurement shown by each arrow.

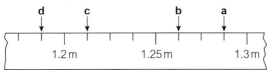

11 a What is the value of the 4 in each of these numbers?

    i 45.26   **ii** 12.54   **iii** 75.42   **iv** 24.68

   b What is the value of the 2 in each of the numbers in part **a**?

   c Which is larger, 3.4 or 3.24?

12 Write < or > between each pair of numbers.

   a 6.7 ☐ 6.9   **b** 6.6 ☐ 6.2   **c** 6.08 ☐ 6.03   **d** 6.01 ☐ 6.06

   e 2.29 ☐ 2.3   **f** 4.5 ☐ 4.48   **g** 7.09 ☐ 7.1   **h** 9.89 ☐ 9.98

Q12 hint

1 First compare the whole number parts.

2 If these are the same, compare the tenths.

3 If these are also the same, compare the hundredths.

13 Write these decimal numbers in order, from smallest to largest.

   a 4.5   6.7   2.9   5.8   1.6

   b 5.25   5.28   5.23   5.27   5.21

   c 4.52   4.3   4.67   4.7   4.19

   d 6.7   6.18   6.5   6.72   6.66

   e 9.09   9.42   9.1   9.39   9.4

14 Real Order these athletics scores to see who came first, second, third and fourth.

100 M SPRINT		TRIPLE JUMP	
NAME	TIME IN SECONDS	NAME	LENGTH IN METRES
C BLACK	16.4	C BLACK	14.1
R BROWN	16.39	R BROWN	14.08
B GREEN	16.28	B GREEN	14.23
D WHITE	16.3	D WHITE	14.2

Q14 hint

The fastest run and the longest jump win.

15 Explore Where does the word 'decimal' come from?
Is it easier to explore this question now you have completed the lesson?
What further information do you need to be able to answer this?

16 Reflect Discuss with a classmate:

   a the different values of 2 in the number 222.22

   b why 2.2 is different to 2.02

   c why 2.2 is the same as 2.20

   d why 2.22 is smaller than 2.3.

Active Learn   Pi 1, Section 6.2

Explore

Reflect

6.3 Metric units

You will learn to:
- Order metric measurements
- Convert between different units of measure
- Read and interpret scales
- Record measurements.

Why learn this?
When you buy furniture from the internet you need to understand measurements to make sure they'll fit in your home.

Fluency
What units would you use to measure the length of
- an ant
- a hand
- a corridor?

Explore
How many cars can you fit on a Eurotunnel train?

Exercise 6.3

1 Work out
  a 24 × 100   **b** 4 × 1000   **c** 30 × 100

2 Work out
  a 340 ÷ 10   **b** 5000 ÷ 1000   **c** 5800 ÷ 100

Investigation   Reasoning

1 Work out these calculations. Write the answers in the place-value table.

	Th	H	T	U	.	t	h
24.5 × 10					.		
3.67 × 10					.		
90.68 × 100					.		
4.03 × 1000					.		

	Th	H	T	U	.	t	h
30.8 ÷ 10					.		
870 ÷ 100					.		
32 ÷ 100					.		
2340 ÷ 1000					.		

2 Work out 38.75 × 100 without using a calculator.
3 Work out 9750 ÷ 1000 without using a calculator.

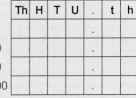

---

3 Work out
  a 5.6 × 10   **b** 4.55 × 100   **c** 12.02 × 1000   **d** 0.4 × 100

4 Work out
  a 543 ÷ 100   **b** 2750 ÷ 1000   **c** 20.4 ÷ 10   **d** 360 ÷ 1000

5 a Write the measurements shown by each
    arrow in cm and mm.
  b How many mm is 5 cm?
  c How many cm is 60 mm?
  Discussion How do you convert mm to cm?

Key point
1 kilometre (km) = 1000 metres (m)
1 metre (m) = 100 centimetres (cm)
1 centimetre (cm) = 10 millimetres (mm)

6 Write these units of length in order, smallest first.
    metre   centimetre   kilometre   millimetre

7 Write these lengths in order, smallest first.

    a 35 mm   3 cm   50 mm   3.6 cm

    b 125 mm   12.7 cm   120 cm   120 mm

Q7 hint

Convert them all to the same units.

8 Use the function machine to change metres into centimetres.

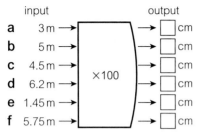

    a 3 m → ×100 → ☐ cm
    b 5 m → ☐ cm
    c 4.5 m → ☐ cm
    d 6.2 m → ☐ cm
    e 1.45 m → ☐ cm
    f 5.75 m → ☐ cm

Q8 hint

Write your answers like this:
3 m = ☐ cm

9 Use the function machine to change centimetres into metres.

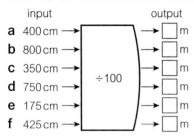

    a 400 cm → ÷100 → ☐ m
    b 800 cm → ☐ m
    c 350 cm → ☐ m
    d 750 cm → ☐ m
    e 175 cm → ☐ m
    f 425 cm → ☐ m

Q9 hint

Write your answers like this:
400 cm = ☐ m

10 Write these lengths in order, shortest first.

    a 400 cm   3.5 m   345 cm   4.2 m

    b 678 cm   6.7 m   6.87 cm   675 cm

    c 2.12 m   3 m   234 cm   303 cm

11 Real / Problem-solving A shed is 1200 mm wide.
Will a bike of length 135 cm fit across it?

12 Problem-solving

    a Two pieces of string are 235 cm and 1.24 m.
      What is the total length in centimetres?

    b A 250 cm length is cut off a 3 m roll of brown paper.
      How much of the roll is left?

13 Write the missing number. Choose from 10, 100 or 1000.

    a There are ☐ ml in a litre.
    b 1 centimetre = ☐ millimetres.
    c 1 kilometre is the same as ☐ metres.
    d 1 metre = ☐ centimetres.
    e There are ☐ grams in a kilogram.

Key point

1 kilogram (kg) = 1000 grams (g)
1 litre (*l*) = 1000 millilitres (m*l*)

14 Use the function machine to convert these units.

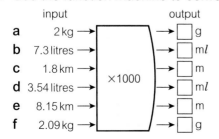

    a 2 kg → ×1000 → ☐ g
    b 7.3 litres → ☐ m*l*
    c 1.8 km → ☐ m
    d 3.54 litres → ☐ m*l*
    e 8.15 km → ☐ m
    f 2.09 kg → ☐ g

Topic links: Function machines

15 Use the function machine to convert these units.

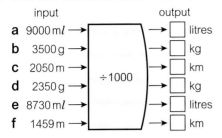

input
output

a 9000 m*l* → [÷1000] → ☐ litres
b 3500 g → → ☐ kg
c 2050 m → → ☐ km
d 2350 g → → ☐ kg
e 8730 m*l* → → ☐ litres
f 1459 m → → ☐ km

16 Write these measurements in order, smallest first.

a	3750 m	3.7 km	3570 m	3.65 km
b	2500 m*l*	2.6 litres	2450 m*l*	2.49 litres
c	4.5 kg	4390 g	4.45 kg	4510 g

17 Problem-solving A roll of cabling is 5 m long. Amy buys 250 cm and Matt buys 1.2 m. How much cabling is left on the roll?

18 Real Write the measurements shown on these scales.

a

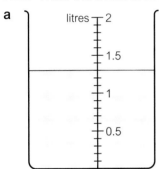

b

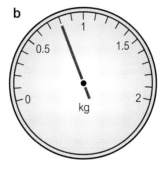

Q18 hint

Write the numbers and the units.

19 Problem-solving A £1 coin weighs 9.5 grams.
   a How many grams do 100 £1 coins weigh?
   b Is this more or less than a kilogram?

20 Problem-solving How many 120 g bags of peanuts can be filled from a 2.5 kg jar?

21 **Explore** How many cars can you fit on a Eurotunnel train?
   Is it easier to explore this question now you have completed the lesson?
   What further information do you need to be able to answer this?

22 **Reflect** Discuss with a classmate what you do when converting:
   a a smaller unit to a bigger unit, for example:
      130 cm to m
      1800 g to kg
   b a bigger unit to a smaller unit, for example:
      1.3 m to cm
      1.8 kg to g

Q22 hint

How do you decide:
 • whether to multiply or divide
 • what number to multiply or divide by?

Explore

Reflect

6.4 Adding and subtracting decimals

You will learn to:

- Recognise and extend number sequences by counting in decimals
- Add and subtract decimal numbers
- Extend mental methods of calculation, to include decimals.

CONFIDENCE

Why learn this?
Most real-life measurements are decimals. You need to be able to add them to work out accurate measurements.

Fluency
What is
- 15 + 27
- 38 − 16?
Which of these are the same value?

3.1   3.01   3.10   3.0

Explore
What is the total distance around a sports field?

Exercise 6.4

Warm up

1 Write the next three numbers in these sequences.
  a 34, 45, 56, 67, ..., ..., ...
  b 2, 4, 8, 16, ..., ..., ...
  c 100, 91, 82, 73, ..., ..., ...

2 Use the column method to work out
  a 275 + 65   **b** 837 − 34   **c** 805 − 492

3 Write the next three terms in these decimal number sequences.
  a 0.1, 0.3, 0.5, ..., ..., ...
  b 0.8 m, 1.2 m, 1.6 m, ..., ..., ...
  c 2.3, 2.2, 2.1, ..., ..., ...
  d 1.9 kg, 1.6 kg, 1.3 kg, ..., ..., ...

4 Write the next three terms in these decimal number sequences.
  a 0.25 m, 0.5 m, 0.75 m, ..., ..., ...
  b 1.25 cm, 1.45 cm, 1.65 cm, ..., ..., ...
  c 1.45, 1.35, 1.25, ..., ..., ...
  d 2.5, 2.25, 2.0, ..., ..., ...

5 Work out the missing numbers in these sequences.
  a 1.2, 1.5, ..., ..., 2.4
  b 7.5, 7.1, ..., ..., 5.9
  c 12.6, 13, ..., ..., 14.2

6 Work out
  a 4.6 + 2.7   **b** 1.2 + 3.2
  c 5.6 + 4.9   **d** 3.1 + 4.7 + 1.2
  e 4.5 − 3.2   **f** 6.8 − 2.9

Key point

In Q3 all the sequences follow a rule.

Q3a hint

What is being added on each time?

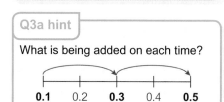

Q4 hint

Use the number line to help you.

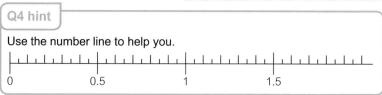

Q6 Strategy hint

First add or subtract the whole number, and then the tenths.

Q6a hint

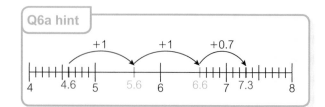

7 Problem-solving What is the total length of two pipes measuring 1.6 m and 2.5 m?

8 Problem-solving Ahmed lives 6.4 km away from school and Jenna lives 3.7 km away. How much further away does Ahmed live?

Worked example

Work out 75.9 + 56.3

$$\begin{array}{r} 75.9 \\ + 56.3 \\ \hline \end{array}$$

Set out the numbers so that they are in columns. Make sure the columns are lined up, tens with tens, units with units, tenths with tenths. Line up the decimal points.

$$\begin{array}{r} 75.9 \\ + 56.3 \\ \hline .2 \\ {\scriptstyle 1} \end{array}$$

Start in the tenths column. Add the numbers together. 9 + 3 = 12. Put the 2 below the tenths and carry the 1. Write the 1 underneath the units column.

$$\begin{array}{r} 75.9 \\ + 56.3 \\ \hline 132.2 \\ {\scriptstyle 1\ 1} \end{array}$$

Repeat for each column.
Put the decimal point in the answer.

9 Work out

  a 24.5 + 17.9   **b** 23.8 m + 18.7 m

  c 34.8 km + 26.4 km   **d** 8.4 + 26.9

  e 43.9 + 16   **f** 125.9 + 63.8

Q9a hint

Write as a column addition.

$$\begin{array}{r} 24.5 \\ + 17.9 \\ \hline \end{array}$$

Q9e hint

Line up the tens and units.

$$\begin{array}{r} 43.9 \\ + 16 \\ \hline \end{array}$$

10 Work out

  a 26.7 − 12.5   **b** 34.6 − 21.8

  c 45.2 − 28.9   **d** 123.4 − 87.6

  e 164.9 − 85   **f** 45 − 23.4

Q10a hint

Line up the tens, units, tenths and the decimal points.

$$\begin{array}{r} 26.7 \\ - 12.5 \\ \hline \end{array}$$

11 Problem-solving What is the total length of two cables measuring 10.8 metres each?

12 Problem-solving How much heavier is 12.5 kg than 8.9 kg?

13 Problem-solving A chef has a 15 litre drum of oil.
He has used 8.2 litres. How much does he have left?

Q10e hint

85 is the same as 85.0

14 Problem-solving A farmer buys 24 m of wire for fencing.
He uses 8.5 m in one area and 12.8 m in another.
How much does he have left?

15 Explore What is the total distance around a sports field?
Is it easier to explore this question now you have completed the lesson? What further information do you need to be able to answer this?

16 Reflect Look back at the hints with Q9 and Q10.
Discuss with a classmate, why the hints for questions:
  a Q9a and Q10a suggest you set out the calculations in columns
  b Q9e and Q10e suggest you wrote 16.0 and 85.0.

Q16 hint

How did these hints help you to answer the questions?

Explore

Reflect

6.5 Rounding

You will learn to:
- Round decimals to the nearest whole number and nearest tenth
- Use a calculator and interpret the display in different contexts (decimals).

CONFIDENCE

Why learn this?
You can estimate how much your shopping will cost by rounding prices to the nearest pound.

Fluency
What is the value of the 3 in these numbers?
- 327
- 7.38
- 0.03
- 14.93
- 23.5
- 30.9

Explore
Approximately how much will it cost to buy a new laptop computer and accessories?

Exercise 6.5

Warm up

1 a Round these numbers to the nearest 10.
  i 56   **ii** 92   **iii** 45

b Round these numbers to the nearest 100.
  i 367   **ii** 409   **iii** 250

2 Write these decimals in order, smallest first.
   4.1, 4.3, 4.02, 4.49, 4.36, 4.58, 4.5

> **Key point**
> For rounding to the nearest whole number, look at the tenths.
> - 0.5 and above round up.
> - 0.4 and below round down.
>
>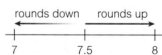

3 Round these measurements to the nearest whole centimetre.
   Use the ruler to help you.

a 6.2 cm
b 2.8 cm
c 9.6 cm
d 7.5 cm

4 Round each quantity to the nearest whole number.
   a 16.4 ml
   b 9.8 kg
   c 21.19 km
   d £2.80

> **Q4c hint**
> Look at the tenths.

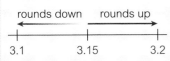

Key point

For rounding to 1 decimal place, look at the hundredths.
- 0.05 and above round up.
- 0.04 and below round down.

rounds down | rounds up

3.1   3.15   3.2

Key point

Write the first decimal place, even if it is 0, to show you have rounded to 1 decimal place and not the nearest whole number.

5 For each measurement
  i write the measurement in metres
  ii round to 1 decimal place.

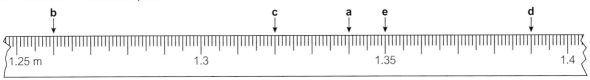

b   c   a   e   d

1.25 m   1.3   1.35   1.4

6 Reasoning Which of these numbers are written to 1 decimal place?
  3.13   13.9   1.8   14.32   6   2.0   91.49   5.1

Worked example

Round 4.97 to 1 decimal place.

4.97= 5.0 to 1 d.p.

> 4.97 rounds up to 5.
> Write 5.0 so there is 1 decimal place.

Literacy hint

d.p. stands for 'decimal place'.

7 Round these decimals to the nearest tenth (1 decimal place).
  a 3.67   **b** 4.22
  c 5.13   **d** 8.28
  e 5.36   **f** 2.91
  g 4.82   **h** 7.96

8 Work out each calculation. Write the answer on the calculator display.
  Then round to 1 decimal place.
  a 413 ÷ 4
  b 726 ÷ 25
  c 622 ÷ 8

9 Problem-solving / Reasoning Sally rounds to the nearest whole number and gets 8. Write 3 decimals that round to 8.

10 Finance Round each price to the nearest £.
   Add them up to estimate the total cost.

£5.99
£6.99
£3.75
£2.50
£10.49

11 **Explore** Approximately how much will it cost to buy a new laptop computer and accessories?
   Is it easier to explore this question now you have completed the lesson? What further information do you need to be able to answer this?

12 **Reflect** Discuss with a classmate why it can be useful to round numbers in everyday life.

Q12 hint

Look back at some of the questions in this lesson.

6.6 Multiplying and dividing decimals

You will learn to:

• Consolidate and extend mental calculation methods, including decimals
• Multiply and divide decimal numbers.

CONFIDENCE

Why learn this?
Car drivers use division to work out how many kilometres they get for each litre of petrol.

Fluency
Round to the nearest whole number
• 5.6
• 2.4
• 10.5
Does 3 × 5 = 5 × 3?

Explore
How many buses could you park on your school football pitch?

Exercise 6.6

Warm up

1 Copy and complete.

a 30 ÷ 6 = ☐
   ☐ × 6 = 30

b 56 ÷ 8 = ☐
   ☐ × 8 = 56

c 63 ÷ 9 = ☐
   ☐ × 9 = 63

d 42 ÷ 7 = ☐
   ☐ × 7 = 42

2 Work out

a 36
    × 5
   ―――

b 92
    × 7
   ―――

3 Work out

a 5)385   **b** 4)112   **c** 7)315   **d** 6)558

Investigation   Reasoning / Problem-solving

1 a Work out 6 × 4
   b Work out 0.6 × 4
   c What is the same about the two answers? What is different? Can you explain why?
2 Repeat for
   b 7 × 8 and 0.7 × 8
   c 4 × 3 and 0.4 × 3
3 Write the answer to 0.3 × 9. Check your answer on your calculator.

---

4 Work out

a 0.3 × 2

b 0.7 × 5

c 0.5 × 9

d 8 × 0.2

e 7 × 0.4

f 5 × 0.6

┌─────────────────────────┐
│ **Q4d hint** │
│ 8 × 0.2 is the same as 0.2 × 8 │
└─────────────────────────┘

Worked example

Work out 8.7 × 6
Use an estimate to check your answer.

```
  8 7
×   6
─────
5 2 2
    4
```

87 × 6 = 522
8.7 × 6 = 52.2

> Ignore the decimal point and work out 87 × 6.
> 87 ÷ 10 = 8.7, so work out 522 ÷ 10 to get the final answer.

Check: 8.7 ≈ 9, 9 × 6 = 54
52.2 is close to 54

5 Work out

  a 6.1 × 3

  b 4.4 × 6

  c 8 × 7.4

  d 2.9 × 9

  e 7 × 2.8

  f 4 × 9.5

> **Q5c hint**
> 8 × 7.4 is the same as 7.4 × 8

6 **Problem-solving** A recipe for a fruit cake needs 0.3 kg flour.
How much flour is needed for 4 cakes?

7 **Problem-solving** Ruth needs 4 pieces of 9.6 cm long string for her
DT project. How much string does she need altogether?

  Discussion How did you decide which calculation to do?

8 Work out

  a 1.8 ÷ 6

  b 8.1 ÷ 9

  c 1.6 ÷ 4

  d 2.1 ÷ 7

  e 5.6 ÷ 8

  f 4.5 ÷ 5

> **Q8a hint**
> ☐ × 6 = 1.8

Worked example

Work out 97.3 ÷ 7

> Look at the digits in 97.3, starting on the left.
> 7 goes into 9 once so write a 1 in the tens column above.
> The difference between 9 and 7 is 2, so write these
> 2 tens in the units column, to make 27.

> 7 goes into 27 3 times with remainder 6 so write a 3 in the units
> column above. Write 6 units in the tenths column, to make
> 63 tenths. Write a decimal point in the answer.

```
  1 3. 9
7)9²7.⁶3
```

> 7 goes into 63 9 times so write a 9 in the tenths column above.

9 Work out

  a $85.5 \div 5$

  b $98.4 \div 3$

  c $69.2 \div 4$

  d $89.4 \div 6$

  e $99.2 \div 8$

  f $38.5 \div 7$

Q9a hint

$5\overline{)8\,5\,.\,5}$

10 Problem-solving Keiran makes 9 equal length tree stakes from a 2.7 m piece of wood. How long is each tree stake?

11 STEM In a science experiment, Katrina needs to know the mass of a seed pod. She measures the mass of 8 seed pods as 10.4 g. What is the mass of 1 seed pod?

  Discussion How did you decide which calculation to do?

12 Explore How many buses could you park on your school football pitch?

  Is it easier to explore this question now you have completed the lesson? What further information do you need to be able to answer this?

13 Reflect The first worked example in this lesson shows how to multiply decimals.

  The second worked example in this lesson shows how to divide decimals.

  Choose **a** or **b** below:

  a Write a new worked example that shows how to work out 5.6×2

  b Write a new worked example that shows how to work out $57.2 \div 4$

  Add any new instructions to your worked example that you think may help others to understand what to do.

Q13a hint

Look at the first worked example. Begin with 'Work out 5.6×2', then Estimate: 5.6×2

Q13b hint

Look at the second worked example. Begin with 'Work out $57.2 \div 4$, then check by estimating.

6.7 FINANCE: Calculating with money

You will learn to:
- Use a calculator to solve word problems involving money
- Round amounts on a calculator to 2 decimal places.

Why learn this?
When you hire a rowing boat, you can use a calculator to share the cost equally between friends.

Fluency
How many more pence do you need to make £1?
- 64p
- 25p
- 37p
- 48p
- 81p

Explore
How do you fill in a bank paying-in slip?

Exercise 6.7: Money calculations

1 Round these prices to the nearest £1.

a £34.71

b £7.86

c £11.25

d £54.92

e £21.50

2 Write these amounts in pounds.

a 63p = £0.6☐

b 57p

c 8p = £0.0☐

d 2p

e 10p

f 152p = £1. ☐☐

g 327p

3 Real Work out the change from £10 for each amount?

a £8.25

b £5.50

c £4.99

d £2.75

e £3.95

f £7.99

Q3a hint

Count up to the next pound. Then count up to £10.

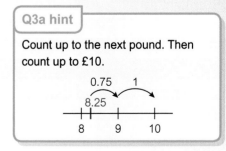

4 Problem-solving Charles has been selling books online.
He sells books for £1.50 each. He has made £54.
How many books has he sold?

Warm up

5 Reasoning Suzanne has 240 5p coins.
She works out 240 × 5 = 1200.
Ben works out 240 × 0.05 = 12.
Which answer is in pounds and which is in pence?
Discussion Which is the better method?

6 Real 356 students paid 50p each to wear their own clothes for a charity day. How much was raised? Give your answer in pounds.

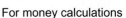

Q6 hint

Enter amounts in £.
50p = £☐.☐
Enter 50p as ☐.☐

7 Problem-solving The total cost for 30 cakes was £16.50.
How much was each cake? Give your answer in pence.

8 28 identical coins add up to £5.60.
Which type of coin are they?

Key point

For money calculations

5.7

means £5.70.

9 Work out these total amounts on a calculator.
- a 5 × £1.25
- b 4 × £3.50
- c £2.75 × 6
- d £2.50 ÷ 5
- e £7.20 ÷ 8
- f £4.55 + £12.95
- g £1.20 + £3.89 + £2.01
- h £45 − £23.90
- i £100 − £66.80

10 Work these out on a calculator. Write all the numbers on the display, then round to the nearest whole number.
- a 3654 ÷ 5
- b 2787 ÷ 4
- c 2745 ÷ 6
- d 6345 ÷ 4
- e 988 ÷ 8

Worked example

Round the amounts of money on the calculator display to the nearest penny.

a 3.426   b 7.22349   c 52.99642

a 3.4**2⑥**   £3.43 —— Look at the number after the pence: £3.426
It is 6, so round up. Write the £ sign.

b 7.22**③**49   £7.22 —— 3, so round down.

c 52.99**⑥**42   £53.00 —— 6, so round up (we don't have to write .00 in money).

11 Round these calculator values to the nearest penny (2 decimal places).
- a 13.231
- b 27.258
- c 23.8953
- d 89.0906
- e 72.999
- f 99.997

12 Work out the answer then round to the nearest penny.
- a £2679 ÷ 8
- b £1.75 ÷ 4
- c £5.98 ÷ 5
- d £6254 ÷ 9
- e £4690 ÷ 16

Discussion When you round to the nearest penny, how many decimal places are you rounding to?

13 Problem-solving Castle Hill School needs to raise £1250 in one year for a new school garden.
How much will they need to raise each month?
Give your answer to the nearest penny.

14 Problem-solving A holiday apartment for 6 people costs £830.
How much will each person need to pay?

Q14 hint

Will there be enough money to pay or do you need to round up?

15 Finance A restaurant bill for 3 people comes to £45.73.
How much does each person pay?
Discussion Why does rounding to the nearest pound or penny not always work?

 16 Real 16 people share a prize of £2550.
   a How much did each receive? Give your answer to the nearest penny.
   b Multiply your answer to part **a** by 16.
   c Is your answer more than £2550?
   d What amount should each person receive?

17 Explore How do you fill in a bank paying-in slip?
Is it easier to explore this question now you have completed the lesson? What further information do you need to be able to answer this?

18 Reflect A shop-keeper works out a customer's change (in pounds) on a calculator:
Which coins should the shop-keeper give the customer?

1.05

Explain your answer to a classmate.

6 Check up

Log how you did on your Student Progression Chart.

Decimal numbers

1 Write the number of units, tenths and hundredths in this number.
4.83 has … units … tenths … hundredths

2 What is the value of the 5 in each number?
a 4.56   **b** 6.25

3 Write the next 3 terms in each sequence.
a 2.3   2.7   3.1   ☐   ☐   ☐
b 7.8   7.5   7.2   ☐   ☐   ☐

4 Write these decimals in order, smallest first.
a 6.7   8.2   4.3   6.5   5.0
b 12.7   12.09   12.65   12.6

5 Round these numbers to 1 decimal place.
a 3.62   **b** 12.35   **c** 8.97

 6 Use a calculator to work these out.
Write the answers to the nearest whole number.
a 409 ÷ 4   **b** 383 ÷ 5

7 Work out mentally
a 24.8 + 32.7   **b** 64.5 − 29.8

8 Work out mentally
a 9 × 0.8   **c** 4.8 ÷ 6

9 Work out
a 6 × 3.7   **b** 69.2 ÷ 4

 10 Work these out on a calculator.
a 8 × £1.75   **b** £259.20 ÷ 4

 11 Yasmin, Robyn and Alan raised £300 in sponsorship money.
Yasmin raised £95 and Robyn £117.50. How much did Alan raise?

12 Three friends make £21.97 on a cake stall. How much does each friend get?

Measurements and scales

13 Which units would you use to measure
a the length of an eye lash   **b** the width of a classroom
c a dose of medicine   **d** the mass of a person?

14 Write the measurements shown by each letter.

15 Copy and complete these conversions.

  a 450 cm = ☐ m   **b** 6.25 m = ☐ cm   **c** 37 mm = ☐ cm

  d 6000 g = ☐ kg   **e** 2.5 km = ☐ m   **f** 3.25 litres = ☐ ml

16 Write these measurements in order, from smallest to largest.

  a 2.5 m   2.39 m   240 cm   25 cm

  b 6.5 litres   6.45 litres   6505 ml   6456 ml

17 Write the measurements shown on these scales

a 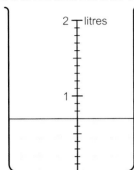   **b**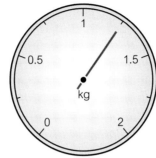

 18 345 cm has been cut from a 5 m ball of string. How much is left?

19 How sure are you of your answers? Were you mostly

  😞 Just guessing   😐 Feeling doubtful   🙂 Confident

  What next? Use your results to decide whether to strengthen or extend your learning.

Challenge

20 Problem-solving In these pyramids, each number is the sum of the two numbers below it.

  a Copy and complete each pyramid.

  i 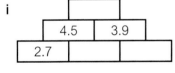   **ii**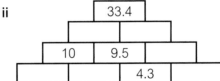

  iii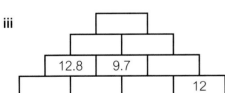

  b Is there more than one way to complete the third pyramid?

21 Here are the ingredients for a loaf of bread

  350 ml water

  20 ml oil

  2 teaspoon salt

  450 g wholemeal flour

  150 g strong white bread flour

  5 g dried yeast

  Sophie makes 2 loaves of bread.

  a How much wholemeal flour will be left from a 1.5 kg bag?

  b How much strong white bread flour will be left from a 1.5 kg bag?

  c She measure out 0.6 litres of water. Is that enough?

  d How many loaves could she make with 20 g of yeast?

  e Is 100 ml of oil enough for 5 loaves?

6 Strengthen

You will:

• Strengthen your understanding with practice.

Decimal numbers

1 a Copy the place-value table. Write these numbers in it.

i 3   **ii** 3.1   **iii** 3.06

T	U	.	t	h

b How many

    i tenths in 3.1   **ii** hundredths in 3.06?

2 Put each number into a place-value table.
What is the value of the 9 in each number?
The first one has been started for you.

a 8.93

U	.	t	h
8	.	9	3

b 9.51   **c** 4.09

3 Which of these numbers have the same value?
    6.3   6.03   6.30   66.30   6.3000

4 Compare these pairs of numbers. Write < or > between each pair.

a 4.83 ☐ 4.38

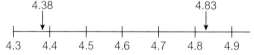

b 9.51 ☐ 9.58   **c** 4.31 ☐ 4.09   **d** 4.25 ☐ 4.9

5 Write these decimals in order, smallest first.

   a 8.9   5.5   6.7   8.3
   b 3.51   3.61   3.15   3.55
   c 7.7   7.69   7.39   7.03

6 Round these numbers to the nearest whole number.

   a 2.7
   b 3.2
   c 5.5
   d 8.13
   e 12.45

Q2a hint

Which column is the 9 in?

Q3 hint

Write them in a place-value table.

Q4a hint

Write both numbers in a place-value table.

U	.	t	h
4	.	8	3
4	.	3	8

Work from the left.
They both have 4 units, but 4.83 has more tenths than 4.38.

Q5 hint

Compare the digits, starting with the units.

Q6a hint

Use a number line.
Which whole number is it closer to?

7 Round these numbers to 1 decimal place.
a 5.84
b 1.89
c 11.55
d 5.11

Q7a hint

Which number to 1 decimal place is it closer to?

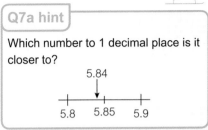

8 Round these calculator displays to
i the nearest whole number
ii 1 decimal place.
a [93.75]
b [3.52]
c [16.66]

Q9a and b hint

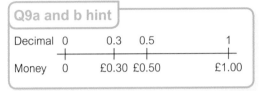

9 These are the answers to money calculations.
Write them in £ . p.
a 0.5
b 0.3
c 6.5
d 1.3
e 2.7

Q10a hint

You need to give your answer in pounds and pence. For example, when the calculator display shows

[9.5]   the answer is £9.50.

10 Work out
a £6.25 × 6
b 5 × £93.10
c £61.20 ÷ 9
d £500 ÷ 40

11 Real / Finance Terry earns £9.50 an hour.
How much does he earn for 7 hours' work?

Q11 hint

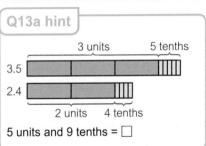

12 Real / Finance Anna earned £100 for 8 hours' work.
How much is that for each hour?

13 Work out
a 3.5 + 2.4
b 2.2 + 0.6
c 1.8 + 5.3
d 3.5 + 3.8

Q13a hint

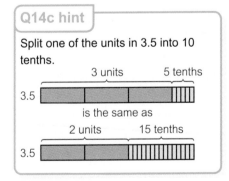

5 units and 9 tenths = ☐

14 Work out
a 7.9 − 5.3
b 8.5 − 2.4
c 3.5 − 1.7
d 5.3 − 3.8

15 Work out
a 33.5 + 46.3
b 25.5 + 53.8
c 38.9 + 47.6
d 147.3 + 39.2

16 Work out these subtractions.
a 78.3 − 35.9
b 64.3 − 27.6
c 52.7 − 39.4
d 153.2 − 38.9

Q14c hint

Split one of the units in 3.5 into 10 tenths.

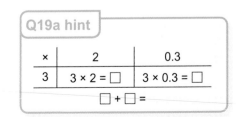

is the same as

17 a Work out 3 × 6 and 3 × 0.6.
    What do you notice?
  b 4 × 8 = 32. Work out 4 × 0.8.
  c 5 × 7 = 35. Work out 0.5 × 7.

18 Work out these multiplications.
a 15 × 0.1
b 10 × 1.7

19 Work out these multiplications.
a 3 × 2.3
b 8 × 4.1

Q19a hint

×	2	0.3
3	3 × 2 = ☐	3 × 0.3 = ☐
	☐ + ☐ =	

20 a Work out 49 ÷ 7 and 4.9 ÷ 7.
    What do you notice?
  b 27 ÷ 9 = 3. Work out 2.7 ÷ 9.

21 Work out these divisions.

  a 3.5 ÷ 5   **b** 2.4 ÷ 2

  c 7.2 ÷ 9   **d** 4.4 ÷ 4

Measurements and scales

1 Write the number shown by each arrow.

a    **b**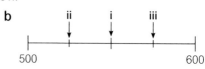

Q1a hint

Try counting up in different steps.
What size step takes you to 400?

2 Write these measurements. Write the number and the units.

a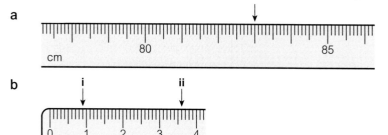

b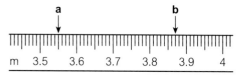

Q2b hint

What measurement do the small marks represent?

3 Write these measurements to 2 decimal places.

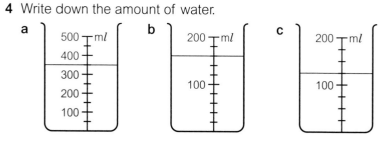

4 Write down the amount of water.

Q4a hint

What is halfway between 300 and 400?

a   **b**   **c**

5 Estimate the mass shown on these dials.

a 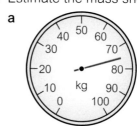   **b**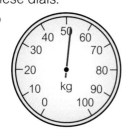

Q5a hint

What number is halfway between 70 and 80?

Q5b hint

Is the mass closer to 50 or 60?

6 Write the mass shown for each letter.

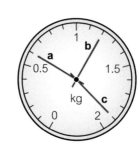

7 Compare these units. Write < or > between each pair.

   a 1 cm ☐ 1 m   **b** 1 cm ☐ 1 mm

   c 1 kg ☐ 1 g   **d** 1 ml ☐ 1 litre

Q7 Literacy hint

'cent' means 100 in several languages.

'kilo' (Greek) and 'milli' (Latin) mean 1000.

8 Write the missing numbers or units.

   a ☐ mm = 1 cm   **b** 100 cm = 1 ☐

   c ☐ g = 1 kg   **d** 1000 ☐ = 1 litre

9 Use a double number line to convert between centimetres and millimetres.

   a 2 cm = ☐ × 10 = ☐ mm   **b** 6.5 cm = ☐ mm

   c 40 mm = ☐ ÷ 10 = ☐ cm   **d** 48 mm = ☐ cm

×10

cm	1	2	3	4	5
mm	10	20	30	☐	☐

÷10

10 Use a double number line to convert between centimetres and metres.

   a 8 m = ☐ × 100 = ☐ cm   **b** 6.13 m = ☐ cm

   c 400 cm = ☐ ÷ 100 = ☐ m   **d** 720 cm = ☐ m

×100

metres	1	2	3	4
cm	100	200	300	☐

÷100

11 Use the double number lines to work out these conversions.

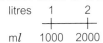
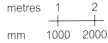

   a 2 m = ☐ × 1000 = ☐ mm   **b** 3.5 kg = ☐ g

   c 9.83 litres = ☐ ml   **d** 4000 ml = ☐ ÷ 1000 = ☐ litres

   e 1500 g = ☐ kg   **f** 5700 mm = ☐ m

12 Work out these conversions.

   a 1360 g = ☐ kg   **b** 4.5 cm = ☐ mm

   c 8.9 km = ☐ m   **d** 4330 ml = ☐ litres

13 Compare these measurements. Write < or > between each pair.

   a 350 cm ☐ 4 m   **b** 45 mm ☐ 3 cm

   c 4.5 litres ☐ 4200 ml   **d** 7200 g ☐ 7.3 kg

Q13 hint

Convert each set to the same units.

14 Write each set of measurements in order, from smallest to largest.

   a 78 mm   6.9 cm   96 mm   7 cm

   b 12.3 kg   1190 g   1200 g   1.02 kg

Q14 hint

Convert one of the measurements to the same unit as the other measurement.

Enrichment

1 a Write down the number exactly halfway between 3 and 4.

   b Write down the number exactly halfway between 3 and your number from part **a**.

   c Write down the number exactly halfway between your numbers from part **b** and part **a**.

   d Continue to find the number that is exactly halfway between your last two numbers.

   e Will it ever be impossible to write the number exactly halfway between two numbers?

Q1 hint

3   4

2 Reflect

Write down one thing when working with decimals and measures that you are good at.

Find someone in your class whose answer to Q1 is different to yours. Ask them to explain it to you.

6 Extend

You will:
- Extend your understanding with problem-solving.

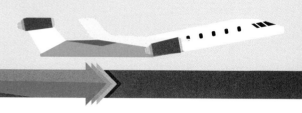

1 **Reasoning** Write three pairs of numbers with 2 decimal places, one starting 12.☐ and one starting 13.☐
Choose numbers that have a difference of
a 0.3   b 0.06

2 **Reasoning** Work out the missing numbers in these sequences.
a 4.5   5.0   ☐   ☐   6.5
b 5.6   4.8   ☐   ☐   2.4

Q2 hint
The same amount is added or subtracted each time.

3 **Reasoning** Work out the missing numbers in these sequences.
a 1.2   ☐   ☐   ☐   3.6
b 2.2   ☐   ☐   ☐   6.6

4 a Write all the numbers in the grid that have
    i 4 tenths   ii 7 hundredths.
  b Round each number in the grid to the nearest
    i tenth   ii whole number.
  c Write the numbers in the top row in order, smallest first.
  d Write the numbers in the bottom row, largest first.

35.37	35.43	35.77	35.47	35.74
126.57	126.7	126.47	126.07	126.4

Q4b hint
A tenth is rounding to 1 d.p.

5 Round these prices to the nearest 10p.
a £4.78   b £6.25   c £5.53   d £3.99

6 Round these lengths to the nearest mm.
a 5.73 cm   b 15.461 cm   c 19.0155 cm   d 0.97 cm

Q6a hint
How many decimal places do you need to show mm?

7 **Reasoning** Here are two calculations that Kay did for homework. Explain the mistake she has made in each calculation.
Do each calculation correctly.

a
    46.7
  + 5.3
    ‾‾‾‾
    99.7

b
    74.2
  − 57.9
    ‾‾‾‾
    23.7

8 **Reasoning** These athletics results have been measured in different units.
  a Who won each event?

	LONG JUMP	HIGH JUMP	SHOT PUT	DISCUS
R ANDERSON	470 CM	162 CM	16 M	4765 CM
C KUMAR	4.68 M	1.6 M	1590 CM	47.8 M
M LEE	4.73 M	161.5 CM	16.09 M	47.79 M
J JONES	471 CM	1.58 M	1602 CM	4770 CM
S SIMON	4.59 M	160.9 CM	16.1 M	47.72 M

Q8 hint
Make sure they are in the same units so you can compare them.

  b What is the range of the results for each event?

9 Convert between these measures.
  a 7.4 kg = ☐ g
  b 345 cm = ☐ m
  c 56 mm = ☐ cm
  d 0.9 km = ☐ m
  e 0.45 kg = ☐ g
  f 250 m*l* = ☐ litre

Q9 hint

Do you need to multiply or divide?

10 **Problem-solving**
  a Convert 1.25 km to m. Convert your answer in m to cm.
    Convert your answer in cm to mm.
  b Convert 63 000 cm to km.

11 How much water is there?
  a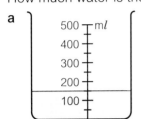
  b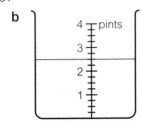
  c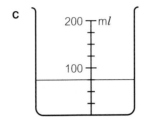

12 **Problem-solving** Kaz has 3 flavours of juice.
  How much does she have altogether?

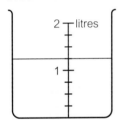 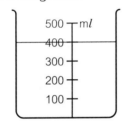 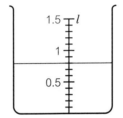

13 Write the masses shown on these scales.

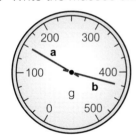 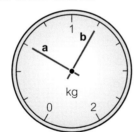

14 Estimate the readings shown on these scales.
  a
  b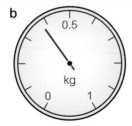
  c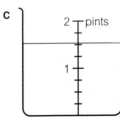

Q14 hint

Which two values is it in between?
Which is it closer to?

Q14a Literacy hint

km/h means kilometres per hour.

15 Use the scales on the graph to convert
  between grams and kilograms.
  a 1 kg = ☐ g   b 200 g = ☐ kg
  c 2.5 kg = ☐ g   d 1.5 kg = ☐ g
  e 0.5 kg = ☐ g   f 1400 g = ☐ kg

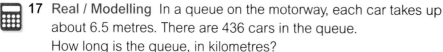

16 Write these measurements in order, smallest first.
   a 0.04 kg   425 g   0.41 kg   3.1 kg
   b 7503 m   7.2 km   0.8 km   8053 m
   c 2340 mm   2400 cm   0.233 m   23.45 cm

17 **Real / Modelling** In a queue on the motorway, each car takes up about 6.5 metres. There are 436 cars in the queue. How long is the queue, in kilometres?

18 **Problem-solving**
   a Use the digits 3, 5 and 8 to make two 3-digit numbers with 2 decimal places, e.g. 5.38.
      i Write the numbers with < or > between them.
      ii Work out the difference between the numbers.
   b Find the pair of numbers that give
      i the largest difference   **ii** the smallest difference.

Q18 Strategy hint
How would you work out the difference between two 3-digit numbers?

19 Work out
   a 4.25 + 3.71   **b** 9.68 − 4.23
   c 12.5 − 7.24   **d** 17.83 + 32.6

Q19a hint
```
    4 . 2 5
 +  3 . 7 1
 ---------
```

20 Work out
   a 127.861 + 39.033   **b** 45.895 + 45.893
   c 24.561 − 11.934   **d** 78.653 − 35.87

21 **Real** Di is travelling from Barcelona to Valencia, and then to Madrid.

   348.1 km   372.1 km

   Barcelona   Valencia   Madrid

   a What is the total distance between Barcelona and Madrid?
   b Round the two distances to the nearest km and add them.
   c What is the difference between the rounded distance and the actual distance?
   d The shortest distance between Barcelona and Madrid is 600.7 km. How many more kilometres is the journey going via Valencia?

22 **Real / Problem-solving** An athlete took 27.47 seconds to complete the 200 m run and 55.74 seconds to complete the 400 m run. Did it take her twice as long to run twice the distance?

23 Work out
   a 45.3 × 7   **b** 9 × 162.9   **c** 736.8 ÷ 6   **d** 160.98 ÷ 3

24 A chemistry experiment needs 3.4 g of magnesium. There are 8 groups in the class. How much magnesium is needed in total?

25 **Real** A square field is surrounded by a fence that is 75.2 metres long. How long is the fence along one of its sides?

26 A team won the 4 × 100 m relay in a time of 48.28 seconds. What was the mean time for each runner?

Q26 hint
4 runners took 48.28 seconds between them.

27 Use a calculator. Write down all the numbers on the display, then round to the nearest pound.
   a £1234 ÷ 5   **b** £1233 ÷ 4   **c** £6254 ÷ 9
   d £2985 ÷ 12   **e** £4736 ÷ 3   **f** £2680 ÷ 9
   Discussion What do you notice about the numbers after the decimal point in parts **e** and **f**?

Q27 Literacy hint
Decimals where the digits repeat are called recurring decimals.

Topic links: Sequences, Mean, Range, Shapes (square)

28 Problem-solving 1 litre ≈ 1.75 pints

a Copy and complete the double number line.

b How many pints is the same as 5 litres?

c A milk carton holds 4 pints. How many litres is this?

d Which is more, 6 litres or 10 pints?

29 Reasoning Simon is rounding to 1 decimal place. Which of these recurring decimals will he round up and which will he round down?

a 0.333333...   b 0.555555...   c 0.111111...

d 0.888888...   e 0.444444...   f 0.99999...

30 Round each calculator display to give an answer in pounds and pence.

a ┌──────────┐
   │ 42.5678 │
   └──────────┘

b ┌──────────┐
   │ 35.09123 │
   └──────────┘

c ┌──────────┐
   │ 15.6734 │
   └──────────┘

d ┌──────────┐
   │ 42.525252│
   └──────────┘

e ┌──────────┐
   │ 27.566666│
   └──────────┘

f ┌──────────┐
   │ 24.999999│
   └──────────┘

31 Batteries come in packs of 6 for £2.99 or 8 for £4.25. Which is the better buy? Work out your answers to the nearest pence.

32 15 m of cable costs £77.80. How much is that per metre, to the nearest penny?

33 Eight friends share a prize of £2355. How much, to the nearest penny, do they each receive?

34 Reasoning The total hotel bill for three friends is £631.
Lynn says that they each need to pay £210.50.
Jan says it should be £210.33.
Maya says that they need to pay £210.34.
Who is right? Explain your answer.

> **Q28 Literacy hint**
>
> ≈ means 'is approximately equal to'

> **Q29 hint**
>
> Look at the digit in the hundredths column. Is it greater than or less than 5?

> **Q30 hint**
>
> Look at the third decimal place – does it make the second decimal place round up or down?

Investigation   Reasoning / Problem-solving

1 Divide £10 by 3, 4, 5, 6, 7, 8 and 9. Give each answer to the nearest pence.

2 Repeat step 1 for
   a £20   b £30   c £40   d £50

3 Which amount has the most whole pound answers?

4 Which of the divisors, 4, 5, 6, 7, 8 and 9, produce the most recurring decimals?

5 Do any divisors always give an answer that does not need rounding?

35 Reflect

Look back at Q3a in these Extend lessons.
Sophie says, 'My first step was to work out 3.6 – 1.2.'
Jamie says, 'My first step was to try adding 1 each time, and seeing if I got to 3.6.'
What was your first step?
Discuss the first steps with a classmate. Which one is best? Why?

Reflect

6 Unit test

Log how you did on your Student Progression Chart.

1 Write down these measurements.

a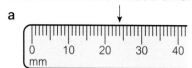

b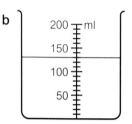

2 Estimate the mass shown on the scale.

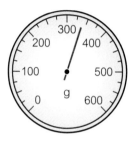

3 Measure this line.

_____

4 What is the value of the 8 in each of these numbers?
   a 24.86
   b 58.05
   c 83.99
   d 17.38

5 What is the change from £10 for each amount?
   a £7.15
   b £4.95

6 Write these in order, smallest first.
   8.1   7.46   7.6   8.15   1.7

7 Write these measurements to 2 decimal places.

8 Work out
   a 7.2 + 3.9
   b 9.6 − 6.7
   c 42.9 + 67.8
   d 120.6 − 84.7

9 How much lighter is 47.5 kg than 81.9 kg?

10 Convert these units.
   a 2.1 kg = ☐ g
   b 8360 ml = ☐ litres
   c 906 cm = ☐ m

11 Write these measures in order, smallest first.

4500 g   4.49 kg   4.55 kg

12 What is the total width of two pieces of paper measuring 15.8 cm and 72 mm?

13 Round each number to the nearest whole number.

    a 4.49   **b** 5.6

14 Round each number to 1 decimal place.

    a 2.37   **b** 4.81   **c** 9.75

15 Work out

    a 0.6×5 **b** 3×0.8

    c 8×7.4 **d** $4.8 \div 6$

    e $3.5 \div 7$ **f** $74.7 \div 9$

 16 A cake stall raised £29.60 selling cakes for 20p each.
How many cakes did they sell?

 17 Work out the total amount.

    a $6 \times £2.25$

    b £100 − £43.20

    c £412 ÷ 8

 18 Tickets to the cinema cost £8.75 for adults and £4.25 for children.
How much does it cost to buy 4 adults and 6 children's tickets?

 19 How many 330 m*l* bottles can be filled from a 5 litre container?

 20 A pack of 12 key rings costs £57.80. How much does one key ring cost, to the nearest penny?

Challenge

21 **Real / Reasoning** Sue is trying to work out how many kitchen cupboards she can fit across a 3 m wall.
The cupboards come in these widths: 300 mm, 400 mm, 500 mm and 600 mm.

    a Work out how many 300 mm cupboards would fit along the wall. Repeat for the other cupboard widths.

    b Find different combinations that leave either no space or as little space as possible.

    c Discuss which combination you would choose for a kitchen. Explain why.

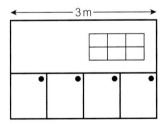

22 **Reflect** Think back to all the work you have done in this Unit. Discuss with a classmate how decimals and measure could help you in:

    • other school subjects

    • everyday life.

Reflect

7.1 Right angles and lines

You will learn to:
- Know a right angle is 90 degrees
- Recognise quarter, half and three-quarter turns
- Recognise parallel and perpendicular lines
- Use compass points.

CONFIDENCE

Why learn this?
Right angles in buildings must be exact.

Fluency
What is:
- 9 + 9
- 90 + 90
- 9 + 9 + 9
- 90 + 90 + 90?

Explore
How do computer-game designers program characters to move and face different directions?

Exercise 7.1

Warm up

1 What fraction of each circle is shaded?

a 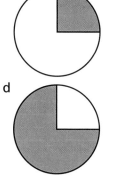 b 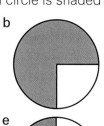 c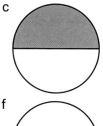

d 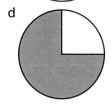 e 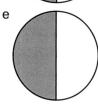 f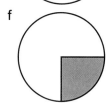

2 Are these **angles** all **right angles**?

a b c

d e

Key point

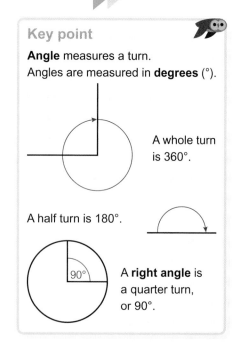

Angle measures a turn.
Angles are measured in **degrees** (°).

A whole turn is 360°.

A half turn is 180°.

90° A **right angle** is a quarter turn, or 90°.

Key point

This symbol means an angle is a right angle.

3 Copy these shapes onto squared paper.
Mark any right angles using the right-angle symbol.

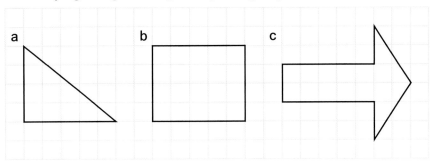

a   b   c

Q3 hint

A corner of a piece of paper is a right angle. To check an angle, see if the corner fits it exactly..

4 Are these turns **clockwise** or **anticlockwise**?

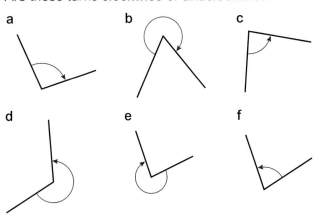

a   b   c

d   e   f

Key point

The direction of a turn is either **clockwise** or **anticlockwise**.

clockwise   anticlockwise

Q4 hint

Think of the numbers on a clock face. As you move clockwise the numbers increase.

5 Look at each turn. Is it clockwise or anticlockwise?
Is it a $\frac{1}{4}$, $\frac{1}{2}$ or $\frac{3}{4}$ turn?

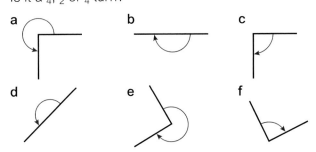

a   b   c

d   e   f

Q5 hint

Look back at Q4 to help you.

Discussion What is the angle on a straight line?

6 **Real** Skateboarders perform tricks called 180s and 360s.
180 and 360 is the number of degrees the skateboard turns in the air.
  a What fraction of a turn is 180°?
  b What fraction of a turn is 360°?

7 **Real** Look at the map.
What is
  a north of the lighthouse
  b south-east of the ship
  c west of the lighthouse
  d north-west of the swimmer
  e south of the coastguard?

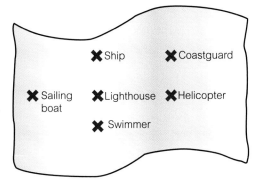

✖ Ship   ✖ Coastguard

✖ Sailing   ✖ Lighthouse ✖ Helicopter
boat

✖ Swimmer

Key point

You can use a compass to give directions.

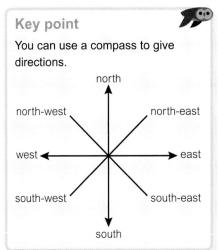

north
north-west   north-east
west   east
south-west   south-east
south

8 a Copy and complete this compass.
Use the angles 90°, 180° and 270°.

b Imagine following these instructions.
Which direction are you facing afterwards:
north, east, south or west?

   i Start facing N and turn clockwise through 90°

   ii Start facing W and turn clockwise through 180°

   iii Start facing S and turn anti-clockwise through 90°

   iv Start facing E and turn anti-clockwise through 180°

   v Start facing N and turn clockwise through 270°

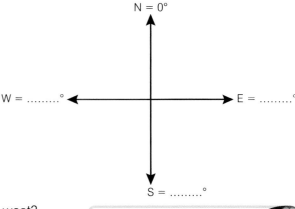

Discussion How could you describe a turn from north to west?
Is there more than one way?

9 Look at these pairs of lines. Are they **perpendicular**, **parallel** or neither?

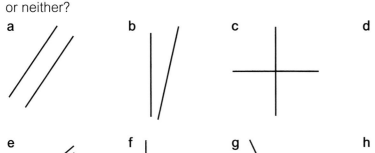

> **Key point**
>
> Angles on a compass are measured clockwise from north.

> **Key point**
>
> **Perpendicular** lines meet at right angles (90°).
> **Parallel** lines are always the same distance apart and never meet.

10 Look at these shapes.

a Write down the number of pairs of parallel lines in each shape.

b Write down the number of right angles in each shape.

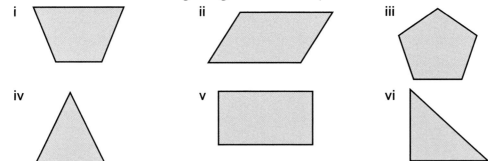

11 Explore How do computer-game designers program characters to move and face different directions?
Look back at the maths you have learned in this lesson.
How can you use it to answer this question?

12 Reflect In this lesson you have learned how two lines can make:
a right angle   points of a compass   perpendicular lines   parallel lines
Describe one of these to a classmate. Begin 'I am thinking of two lines. They ...'
Ask your classmate to listen carefully and then decide what you are describing.
Swap over, so your classmate does the describing.

7.2 Measuring angles 1

You will learn to:
- Recognise acute and obtuse angles
- Measure acute angles
- Label lines and angles.

Why learn this?
Sailors need to consider the angle of the wind when plotting a course.

Fluency

What does mean?

Explore
How can you be sure an access ramp is at the correct angle?

Exercise 7.2

1 Which of these angles are larger than a right angle?

a   b   c   d

2 What is the size of the angle measured on this protractor?

3 What angles do these diagrams show?

a
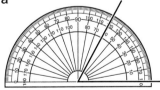

b
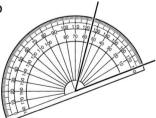

> **Q3 hint**
> Read up from 0 (on the inner scale).

4 What angles do these diagrams show?

a
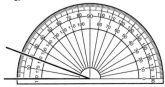

b
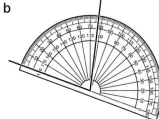

> **Q4 hint**
> Read up from 0 (on the outer scale).

Warm up

Worked example

Measure the angle.

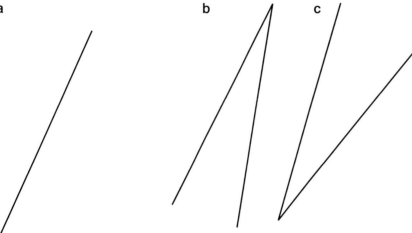

34°

Place the protractor on the point of the angle. Line up the zero line with one line of the angle. Read up from 0.

5 Measure each angle.

a   b   c

Q5 hint

Decide which scale to use by reading up from 0 each time.

6 **Real** What angle is the arrow being fired at?

Q6 hint

Measure the angle between the arrow and the horizontal line.

Key point

An **acute** angle is smaller than 90°. An **obtuse** angle is between 90° and 180°.

7 For each angle write '**acute**' or '**obtuse**'.

a   b   c   d

Q7 hint

Decide if the angle is smaller than a right angle (acute) or bigger (obtuse).

Topic links: Measuring lines to nearest mm, Reading scales, Properties of shapes

8 The thick red line is AB.
Write the names for the
a blue line   **b** green line
c orange line   **d** purple line.

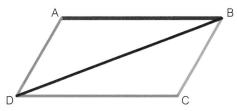

Q8 hint
Line AB joins A and B.

9 Write down the name of each of these angles.

a   **b**   **c**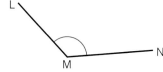

Discussion Is there more than one name for each angle?

Key point

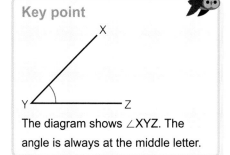

The diagram shows ∠XYZ. The angle is always at the middle letter.

10 Name the angle where
a line AB meets line BD
b line BD meets line AD
c line AD meets line AB.

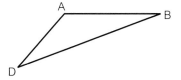

11 **Problem-solving** The diagram shows an isosceles triangle.

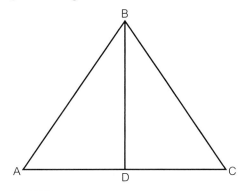

a Measure angle ABD.
b How big do you think angle ABC is? Measure to check your answer.

12 Measure these angles.

a ∠BAC   **b** angle CBA   **c** XŶZ   **d** PQ̂R   **e** QR̂P

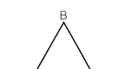 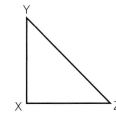 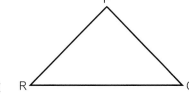

Q12a hint
Put your finger on B then move along the line to A and on to C. This is the angle to measure.

13 **Explore** How can you be sure an access ramp is at the correct angle?
Look back at the maths you have learned in this lesson.
How can you use it to answer the question?

14 **Reflect** Here are four angles.
Which angle(s) are

a a right angle   **b** acute   **c** obtuse?

Compare your answers with a classmate.
Explain why you chose each angle.

7.3 Measuring angles 2

You will learn to:
- Recognise acute, obtuse and reflex angles
- Measure obtuse angles.

Why learn this?
The angle of an aeroplane's wings affects how high it flies.

Fluency
Which angle is:
- 360°
- 180°
- 90°?

a 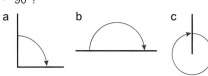 b c

Explore
What angles can you see in a wind turbine?

Exercise 7.3

1 Measure these angles.

a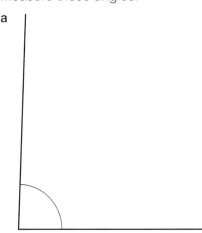

b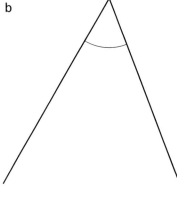

Key point
A **reflex** angle is more than 180°, but less than 360°.

2 For each angle write 'acute', 'obtuse' or 'right angle'.

a 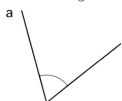 b 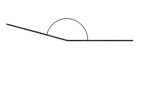 c d

3 For each angle write 'acute', 'obtuse' or '**reflex**'.

a b c   d

Q3 hint

The angle on a straight line is 180°. An angle larger than 180° is a reflex angle.

180°

Topic links: Measuring lines to nearest mm, Reading scales

4 What angles do these diagrams show?

a

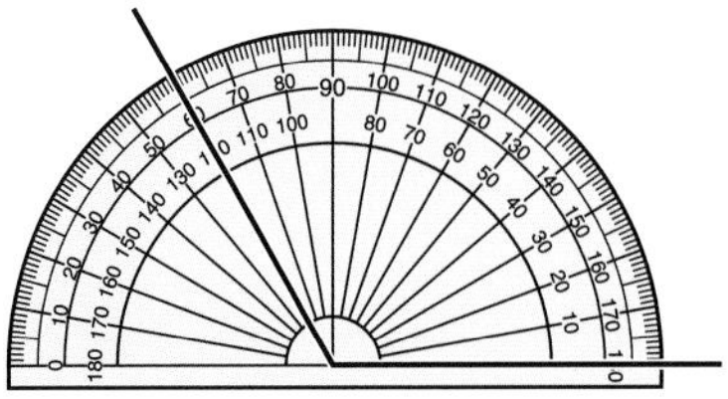

b

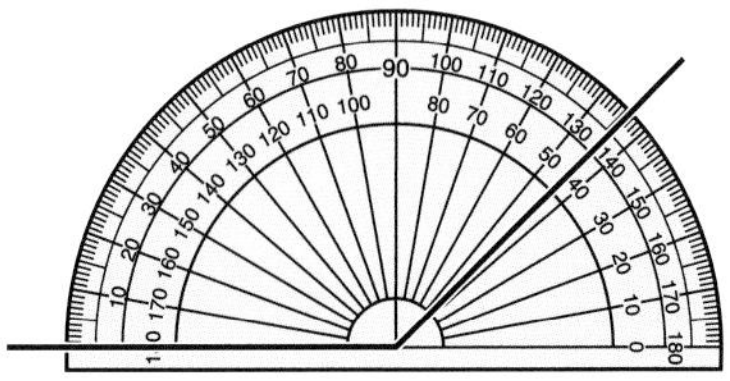

Q4 hint

Read up from 0 each time you measure an angle.

5 Measure these angles.

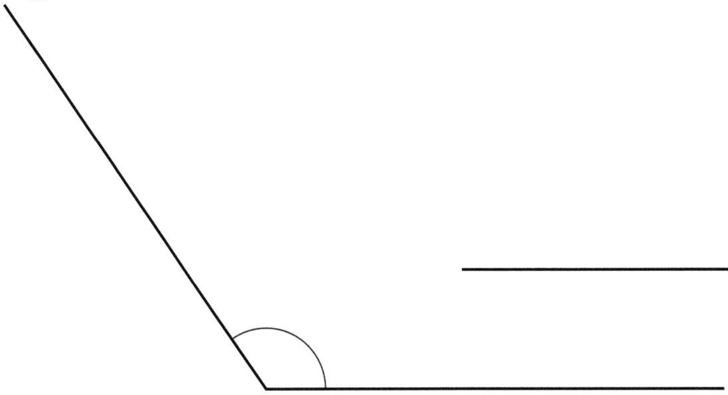

b

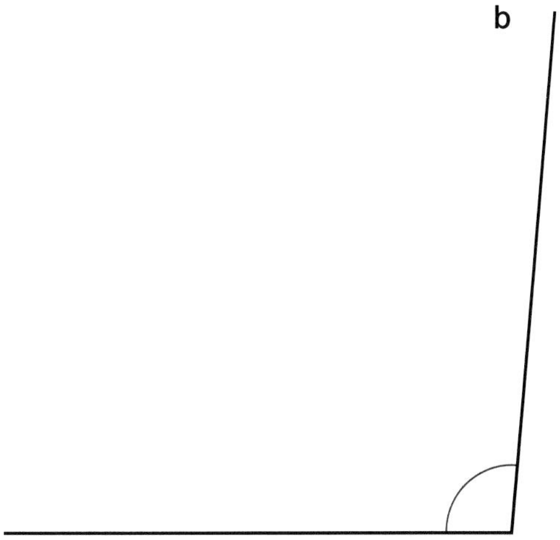

c

a

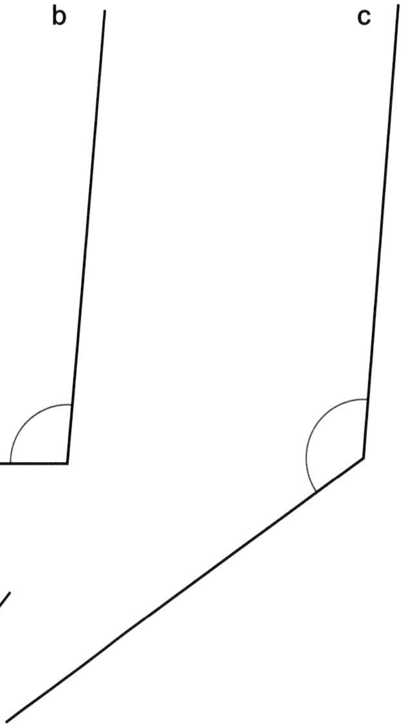

d

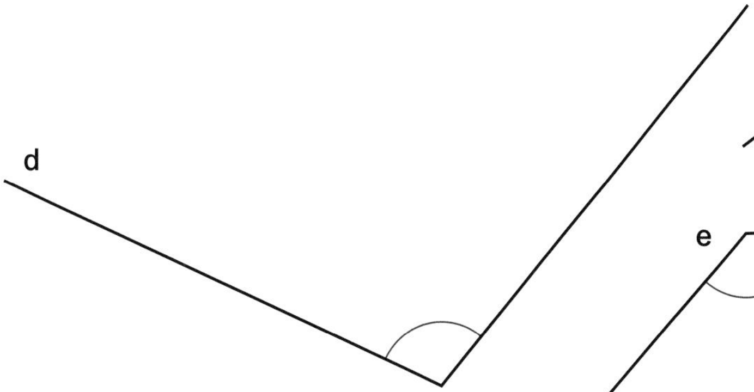

e

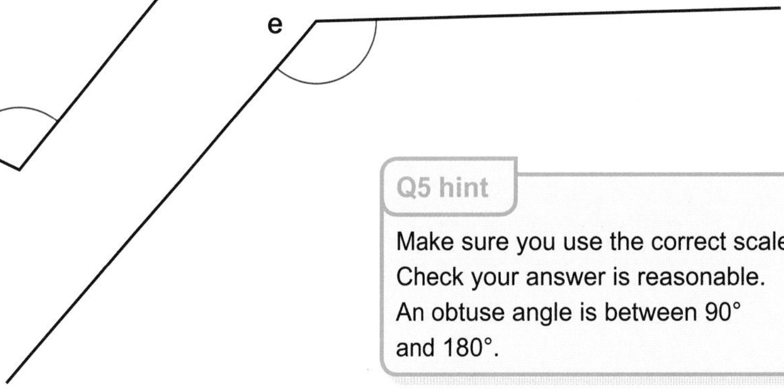

Q5 hint

Make sure you use the correct scale. Check your answer is reasonable. An obtuse angle is between 90° and 180°.

6 a Measure (to the nearest degree)
  a ∠ABC
  b angle BAC
  c A$\hat{C}$B

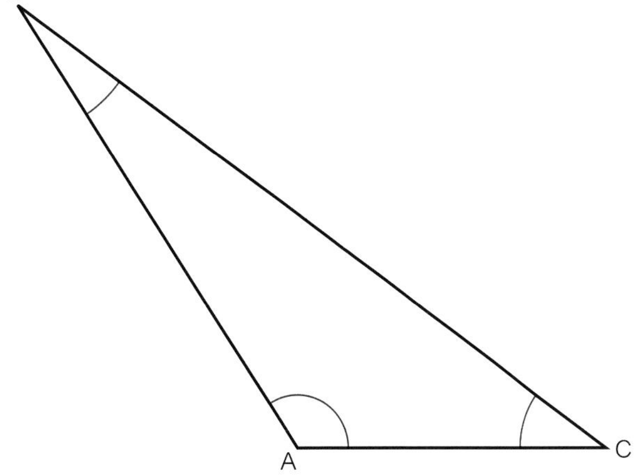

B

A

C

7 Problem-solving The diagram shows a regular octagon.
  a Measure angle ABC.
  b How big do you think angle DEF is?
    Measure to check your answer.

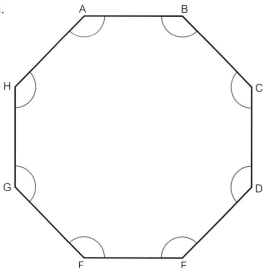

8 Real A sun lounger has three
  different positions for the back support:
  a Measure the three different angles.
  b The advert for the sun lounger says:
    Choose from three positions.
    Reading position
    Sleeping position
    Sitting position
  Match each position to one of the diagrams.

A

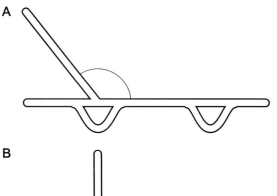

B

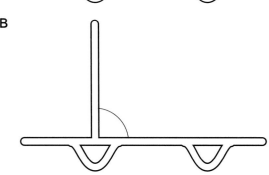

C

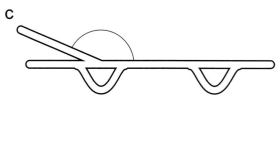

Investigation   **Problem-solving**

Can a triangle have
  i one obtuse angle
  ii two obtuse angles
  iii three obtuse angles?

If you think it can, draw the triangle. If you think it isn't possible, explain why.

9 Explore What angles can you see in a wind turbine?
  Look back at the maths you have learned in this lesson.
  How can you use it to answer this question?

10 Reflect Discuss with a classmate what is the same and what is
  different about using a ruler and protractor..

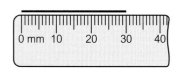
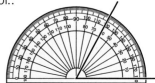

> **Q10 hint**
> • What are they used for?
> • What units do they measure in?
> • What is the same/different about their scales?
> • Where do you put them when measuring?

Active Learn   Pi 1, Section 7.3

7.4 Drawing and estimating angles

You will learn to:
- Estimate the size of angles
- Draw acute angles.

Why learn this?
Estimating angles can help you to make shots in snooker.

Fluency
Work out
- 90 × 2
- 90 ÷ 2
- 9 ÷ 3
- 90 ÷ 3

Explore
Is the angle of the back of a chair the same on all chairs?

Exercise 7.4

1 How many degrees are there in:

  a a right angle   **b** $\frac{1}{2}$ a right angle

  c $\frac{1}{3}$ of a right angle   **d** 3 right angles?

2 Measure these angles.

  a

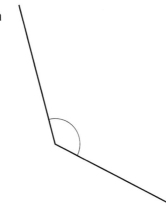

  b

> **Q3 hint**
>
> Think about whether the angle is more or less than 90°.

3 Match the measurements to the angles without measuring.

  a   **b**   **c**   **d**   **e**

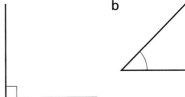 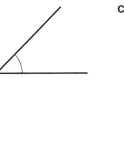 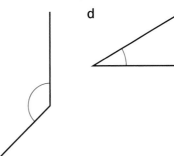 

   30°   45°   90°   135°   180°

Warm up

4 Estimate the size of each angle.

a 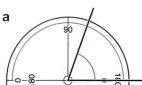 **b** 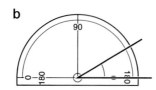 **c**  **d**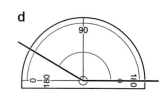

5 Estimate the size of each angle.
Check your answers by measuring.

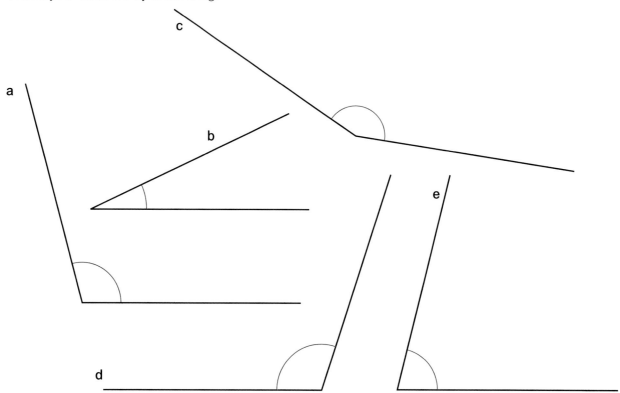

6 Estimate the size of the angle x in each of the triangles.
Check your answers by measuring.

a 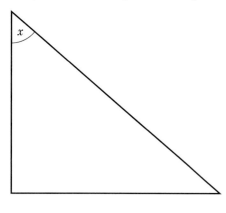 **b**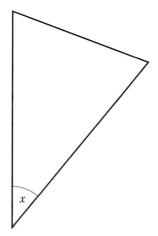

7 Real This diagram shows a starting block used in athletics.
Estimate the angle shown.
Check your answer by measuring.

Topic links: Drawing lines to nearest mm

Worked example

Use a protractor to draw an angle of 65°.

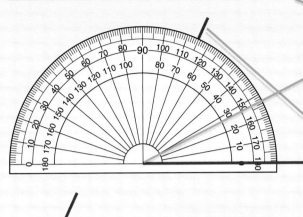

Use a ruler to draw a straight line.

Place the protractor on the line with the cross exactly on one end.
Start at 0 and read up to 65°.

Mark this point with a pencil.

Use a ruler to join up the point to the end of the line.
Label the angle 65°.

65°

8 Use a ruler and a protractor to draw these angles accurately.

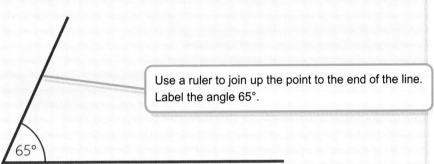

a
5 cm
35°
4 cm

b
2.5 cm 85° 5.5 cm

c
42°
7 cm   7 cm

9 a Are these angles acute or obtuse?

   i ∠ABC = 70°   **ii** Angle DEF = 95°   **iii** GĤI = 160°

   iv Angle JKL = 85°   **v** GĤI = 165°   **vi** angle PQR = 15°

  b Use a protractor to draw each angle in part **a**.

> **Q9b hint**
>
> Make sure you read the protractor properly. Use your answers to part **a** to check.

Investigation   **Problem-solving**

a The angle between the hour and minute hand on a clock face is 90°.
Both hands are pointing at a number.
What time could it be?

b What if the angle is 60°?

> **Strategy hint**
>
> Sketch or use a clock face.

10 Explore Is the angle of the back of a chair the same on all chairs?
Look back at the maths you have learned in this lesson.
How can you use it to answer this question?

11 Reflect Look back at Q5.
First you estimated the size of angles, and then you measured them accurately.
Discuss with a classmate why estimating first is a good thing to do.
Write down other maths topics where it helps to estimate first.

Explore

Reflect

7.5 Putting angles together

You will learn to:

* Find missing angles on a straight line
* Find missing angles round a point.

Why learn this?
Navigators measure angles clockwise from north to give directions.

Fluency
Estimate the size of each angle:

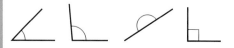

Explore
What is the angle between the bars on a playground roundabout?

Exercise 7.5

1 Work out:

  a $140 + \square = 360$ **b** $\square + 20 = 180$

  c $\square + 180 + 90 = 360$ **d** $360 - \square = 120$

  e $180 - 55 = \square$ **f** $180 - \square = 45$

  g $120 + \square + 5 = 180$ **h** $45 + 35 + \square = 360$

Investigation   **Problem-solving**

1 Measure the angles a and b.

2 Work out $a + b$.

3 Draw another straight line and draw a line to make two different angles, c and d.

4 Measure the angles and work out $c + d$.

5 What do you notice?

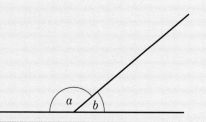

---

2 Work out the size of the unknown angles.

Key point

The angles on a straight line add up to 180°.

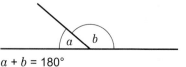

$a + b = 180°$

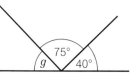

3 Problem-solving / Reasoning Work out the size of angle a.

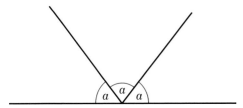

Q3 hint

All the angles are labelled with the same letter. This tells you they are all equal.

Discussion Can you make a straight line from two acute angles? Can you have two obtuse angles on a straight line?

4 Problem-solving / Reasoning
a Work out the size of angle a.

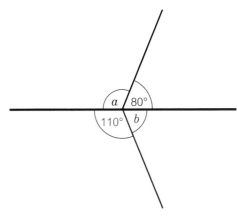

Q4a hint

$a + 80 = \square$

b Work out the size of angle b.
c Work out the sum of angles round a point.

5 Work out the size of the unknown angles.

a

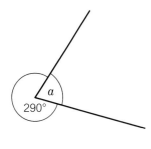

b

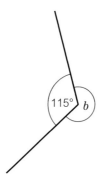

Key point

The angles round a point add up to 360°.

$a + b = 360°$.

6 Work out the size of $\angle ABC$.

a A

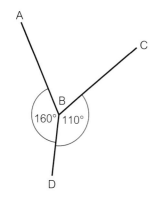

b A

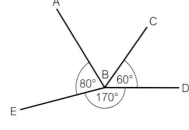

7 Problem-solving / Reasoning

a What is the acute angle between the hands of the clock?

b It is 8 o'clock. What is the obtuse angle between the hands now?

8 Problem-solving All the angles in a regular hexagon are equal.

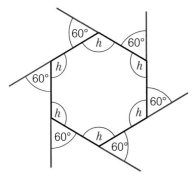

Q8 hint

$h + 60 = 180°$

a Work out the size of angle h.

b Work out the sum of the angles in a hexagon.

9 Problem-solving Mike broke three plates into pieces. Work out which pieces belong together.

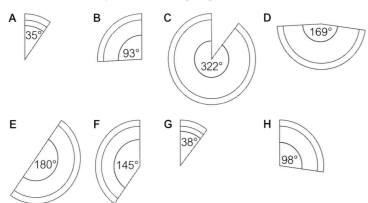

A 35°   B 93°   C 322°   D 169°

E 180°   F 145°   G 38°   H 98°

10 Explore What is the angle between the bars on a playground roundabout?

Look back at the maths you have learned in this lesson.

How can you use it to answer this question?

11 Reflect Match each angle to a description.

a 19°   A Obtuse angle
b 90°   B Reflex angle
c 98°   C Right angle
d 180°   D Round a point
e 198°   E Acute angle
f 360°   F Straight line

Master
P169

CHECK

Strengthen
P186

Extend
P190

Test
P194

7 Check up

Log how you did on your
Student Progression Chart.

Types of angles and lines

1 Which of these shapes have a right angle?

 A  B C 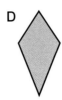 D

For each shape write down the number of right angles.

2 Which pair of lines is

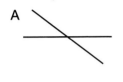 A B C  D

a parallel
b perpendicular?

3 Write 'acute', 'obtuse', 'reflex' or 'right angle' for each angle.

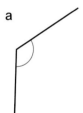 a b  c 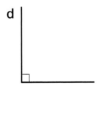 d

Estimating, measuring and drawing angles

4 Which turn is clockwise?

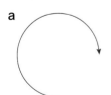 a 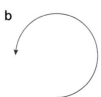 b

5 Write the fraction of a complete turn shown in each diagram.

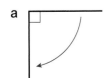 a 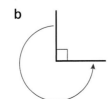 b 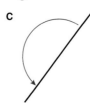 c

6 Estimate the size of angles

   a ABC   **b** EAB

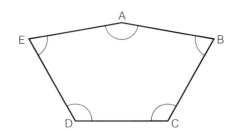

7 Use a protractor and ruler to
draw this angle accurately.

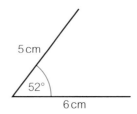

8 Measure the angle ACB.

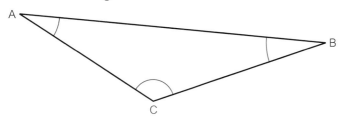

Calculating angles

9 Work out the size of

   a ∠BCD   **b** ∠AFB   **c** angle c **d** angle x

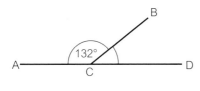 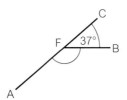 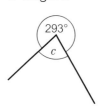 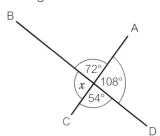

10 How sure are you of your answers? Were you mostly

   😣 Just guessing   😐 Feeling doubtful   🙂 Confident

   **What next? Use your results to decide whether to strengthen or
extend your learning.**

Challenge

11 Work out the size of angles d.

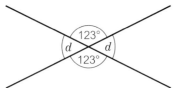

   What do you notice?

7 Strengthen

You will:

- Strengthen your understanding with practice.

Types of angles and lines

1 Fold a paper circle in half and half again. What angle does it make?

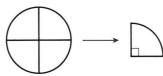

2 Angle a is a right angle. Which one of the other angles is *not* a right angle?

a   b   c   d   e

3 Which of these angles are acute?

a   b   c   d   e

4 Which of the angles in Q3 are obtuse?

5 Which of these pairs of lines are parallel?

a   b   c   d

6 Which of these pairs of lines are perpendicular?

a 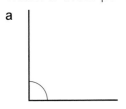   b   c

d    e   f

7 One of these angles is *not* a reflex angle. Which one?

a    b   c   d

Estimating, measuring and drawing angles

1 The hands on a clock move clockwise.

Q1 hint

Trace your finger round the arrow and keep going. Is this the same way as a clock hand?

Are these arrows pointing clockwise or anticlockwise?

a   **b**   **c**   **d**   **e**

2 a How many right angles make this one whole turn?

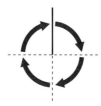

Q2 hint

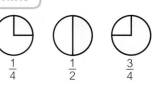

$\frac{1}{4}$ $\frac{1}{2}$ $\frac{3}{4}$

b Describe these angles as $\frac{1}{4}$, $\frac{1}{2}$ or $\frac{3}{4}$ of a whole turn.

A   B   C   D   E   F

3 Caroline measures an angle.
She says, 'This angle measures 115°.'
Andrew says, 'It can't be.
It is smaller than a right angle.'
What has Caroline done wrong?

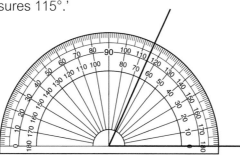

Q4 hint

Are the angles larger or smaller than 90°?

4 Choose the correct measurement for each of these angles.

a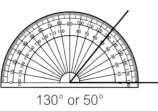

130° or 50°

b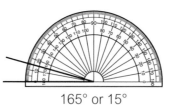

165° or 15°

c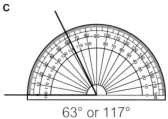

63° or 117°

d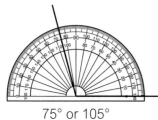

75° or 105°

e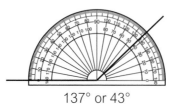

137° or 43°

f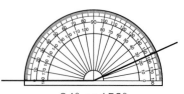

24° or 156°

5 Measure these angles.

a   **b** **c**

6 Copy and complete the names for these angles.
The first one is done for you.

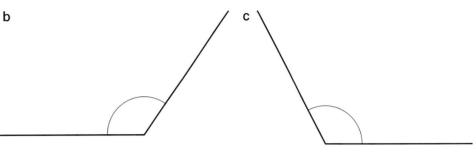

a ∠ABC **b** ∠D...... **c** ∠......... **d** ∠.........

7 Which 3 angles in the cloud match the angle shown here?

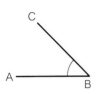

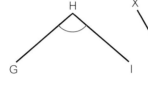

PR̂Q   angle PQR
∠PRQ
        ∠PQR   PQ̂R
∠QPR
        angle QPR

8 Choose the best estimate for each angle.

a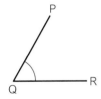

80°
100°
170°

b

70°   95°   130°

c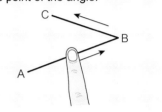

30°
70°   110°

d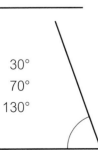

30°
70°
130°

e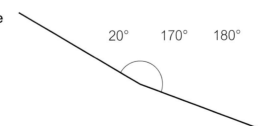

20°   170°   180°

f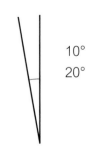

10°
20°

9 a Dawn is drawing an angle of 60°.
She draws a line and places the cross of the protractor at one end of the line.
She marks a dot at 60°.
Use a ruler and protractor to copy and complete the angle.

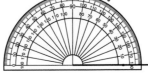

b Use the same method to draw an angle of 85°.

Calculating angles

1 Jacob is calculating the size
of a missing angle.
Copy and complete his working.

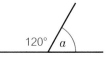

Angles on a straight line add up to ☐°.

120° + ☐ = 180°

a = ☐°

Q1 hint

☐

120 130 140 150 160 70 180

2 Work out the missing angles. Explain your reason.

a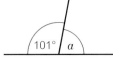

b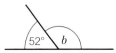

c

3 Copy and complete the calculation for the first angle.
Work out the next two in the same way.

a

b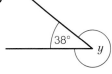

c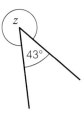

Q3a hint

295 300   360

295° + ☐ = 360°

x = ☐

Angles at a point add up to ☐°.

Enrichment

1 On squared paper plot the points
A = (2, 3), B = (0, 5) and C = (4, 5).
Join A to B to C.
What kind of angle is $A\hat{B}C$?

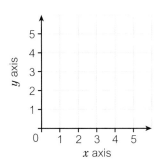

2 Reasoning / Problem-solving Six friends share a circular pizza equally.
What angle is each slice?

3 How many pairs of parallel sides does a regular
hexagon have?
Does it have any perpendicular sides?

4 **Reflect** Which of these tasks is the easiest?
Which of these tasks is the hardest?
A Naming angles (like in Types of angles and lines, Q1, Q2 and Q3).
B Measuring angles (like in Estimating, measuring and drawing angles, Q5).
C Drawing angles (like in Estimating, measuring and drawing angles, Q9).
D Working out missing angles (like in Calculating angles, Q2 and Q3).
Discuss with a classmate the thing you found hardest. Why is it hard?
Ask your classmate for tips on how to make this task easier.

Reflect

7 Extend

You will:
- Extend your understanding with problem-solving.

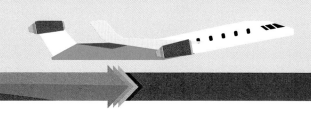

1 Sam is facing the door. Describe two ways he could turn to face
  a the window
  b the table
  c the chair.

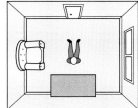

Q1 hint

$\frac{1}{4}$ turn clockwise or □ turn anticlockwise.

2 a Look at the compass.
     Write the angle between
      i north and south
      ii south and west
      iii north-east and south-east
      iv south-east and north-west.

  Discussion Is there more than one possible answer for each?
  b List all the pairs of directions which are perpendicular to each other.

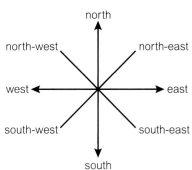

Q2a hint

Give your answer in degrees.

3 **Real** A soldier started her journey facing north.
  She walked 12 miles and then turned through 135° clockwise before continuing her journey.
  What direction is she now travelling?

4 **Reasoning / Modelling** Copy and complete these statements.

acute
$0° < x < □°$

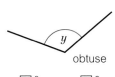
obtuse
$□° < y < □°$

reflex
$□° < z < 360°$

5 For each shape, write down the number of:
  a right angles
  b pairs of parallel sides
  c pairs of perpendicular sides.

  i

  ii

  iii

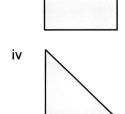

  iv

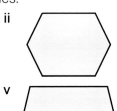

  v

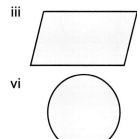

  vi

6 a Measure

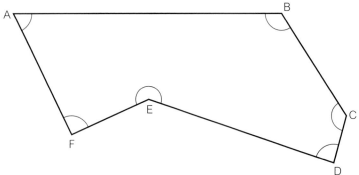

    i line AB   **ii** angle ABC   **iii** line EF   **iv** CD̂E

b Write down the number of each type of angle in the shape.
    i acute angles   **ii** obtuse angles   **iii** reflex angles

7 Draw a shape with four sides, one pair of parallel lines and two pairs of perpendicular lines.
How many right angles are in the shape?

8 Reasoning Work out the size of these angles.

a angle b is twice the size of angle a

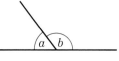

b angle d is three times the size of angle c

c angle f is five times the size of angle e

9 Real Swinging a yo-yo through 360° is called a 'Round the world'. Eddie completes 2 round the worlds. What angle has he spun the yo-yo through?

10 Jan cuts a pizza in half.
2 and 180° are factors of 360°.

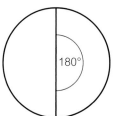

> **Q10 hint**
> A factor is a whole number.

Write the angle and factors of 360° for each pizza slice.

a   **b**   **c**   **d**   **e**

11 Real In diving competitions there are four types of back dives.
How many degrees does the diver turn through for each back dive?
    a Back dive in the straight position
    b Back $1\frac{1}{2}$ somersaults
    c Back $2\frac{1}{2}$ somersaults
    d Back $3\frac{1}{2}$ somersaults

Topic links: Coordinates, Measuring and drawing lines to the nearest millimetre, Units of time

Subject links: Sport (Q11)

12 Real / Reasoning

a What angle does the minute hand of a clock turn through in
i 15 minutes   ii $\frac{3}{4}$ hour   iii 20 minutes?

b What angle does the second hand of a clock turn through in
i 1 minute   ii 30 seconds   iii 10 seconds?

c What angle does the hour hand of a clock turn through in
i 6 hours   ii 3 hours   iii 1 hour?

13 Reasoning Work out the size of these angles.

a angle b is twice the size of angle a

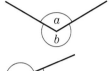

b angle d is 7 times the size of angle c

c angle f is 9 times the size of angle e.

14 a Draw the triangle accurately using a ruler and a protractor.

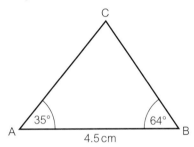

Q14 hint

Draw the line AB first. Next measure and draw the angles.

b Measure
i AC   ii BC   iii ∠ACB

15 Draw ∠XYZ = 47°

16 Copy these axes.
a Plot these points and join them in order: (1, 5) (3, 4) (3, 2)
(2, 0) (−2, 0) (−3, 2) (−3, 4) (−1, 5).
b How many of each type of angle are there in the shape?
i acute angles   ii obtuse angles   iii reflex angles

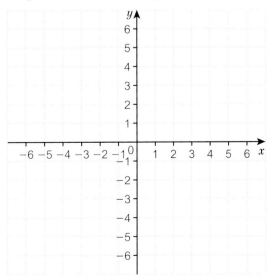

17 Problem-solving / Reasoning

The diagram shows two of the corners of a right-angled triangle.
List as many different coordinates for the third corner of the
triangle as possible.

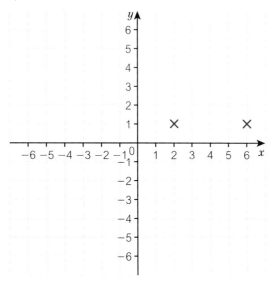

Investigation   Problem-solving

1 Draw any four-sided shape and measure each of the angles.
2 Find the sum of the angles.
3 Repeat for at least 3 other four-sided shapes.
What do you notice?

18 **Reflect** Mathematics uses a lot of **notation**.
Write down the notation for
a degrees in an angle
b a right angle
c less than
d more than
e equals.
Write down some more mathematics notation you know.
Discuss with a classmate other subjects that use notation.

Literacy hint

Notation means symbols.

Q18 hint

Look at the symbols at the end of
sentences.

Reflect

7 Unit test

Log how you did on your Student Progression Chart.

1 Which of these are right angles?

a 　b 　c 　d

2 Look at each turn. Is it clockwise or anticlockwise? Is it a $\frac{1}{4}$, $\frac{1}{2}$ or $\frac{3}{4}$ turn?

a 　b 　c

3 a How many acute angles are in triangle ABC?

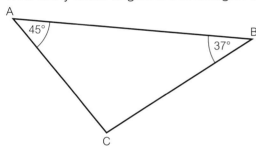

b Measure the length of the line AB.

4 The diagram shows a quadrilateral.

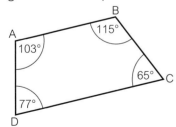

a What is the size of angle DAB?

b Is ∠ABC acute or obtuse?

5 Look at these pairs of lines. Are they parallel, perpendicular or neither?

a 　b 　c 　d

6 Look at the diagram.

  a For each angle, A–E, write down if it is acute, obtuse or reflex.

  b Measure

  i ∠ABC

  ii angle BCD

  iii AÊD

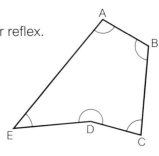

7 Work out the size of angle a.

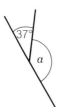

8 Estimate the size of each angle.

  a   **b** 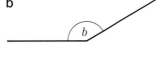 **c**

9 Draw these angles accurately.

  a   **b**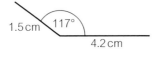

10 Work out the size of each lettered angle.

  a   **b**  **c**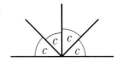

Challenge

11 You can draw a triangle with three acute angles.
Can you draw a triangle with

  a 2 acute angles and 1 obtuse angle

  b 2 obtuse angles

  c 1 right angle

  d 2 right angles

  e 1 reflex angle?

Draw sketches and explain how you decided.

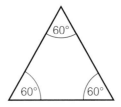

12 **Reflect** Look back at the questions you answered in this test.
Which question made you think the hardest?
Discuss with a classmate:

  • how you felt while working on this question

  • did you keep trying until you had an answer? Did you give up
    before reaching an answer, and move on to the next question?

  • did you think you would get the answer correct or incorrect?

What can you do to stay calm when answering tricky maths
questions?

MASTER

| Check P211 | Strengthen P213 | Extend P218 | Test P222 |

8.1 Shapes

You will learn to:
- Identify triangles, squares and rectangles
- Recognise the properties of triangles, squares and rectangles.

Why learn this?
Timber frames can be described using different shapes.

Fluency
- What does this mean?

- What are the names of these shapes?

Explore
Which shapes were used in the building of your home or school?

Exercise 8.1

1 Measure each line.
  Write your answer in
  i millimetres
  ii centimetres.

  a ——————————

  b ————————————————

  c ——

2 Measure each angle to the nearest degree.

a

b

3 Measure the sides and angles of each **triangle**.
Write down if it is **scalene, isosceles** or **equilateral**.

a

b

c

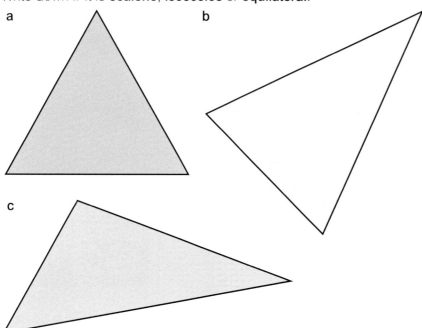

4 For each triangle write down if it is scalene, isosceles or equilateral.

a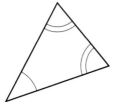

b

c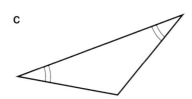

d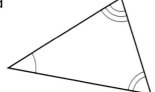

Discussion For each triangle, which sides are equal?

5 For each triangle write down if it is scalene, isosceles or equilateral.

a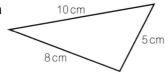

b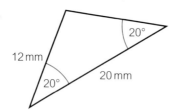

c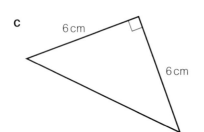

d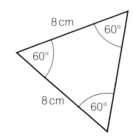

6 Which shapes are **quadrilaterals**?

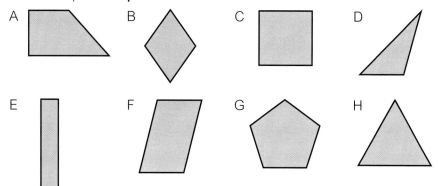

Key point

* A **quadrilateral** is a flat shape with four straight sides.
* **Squares** and **rectangles** are special quadrilaterals. All their corners are right angles.

square   rectangle

all sides   opposite sides
equal   equal

7 **a** On squared paper, draw a **square** with 5 cm sides.
   Mark the equal sides using dashes. Mark the four right angles.

b Join two opposite corners to make a **diagonal**.

c Measure the diagonal to the nearest millimetre.

d Draw and measure the other diagonal. What do you notice?

e Copy and complete.
   The diagonals of a square are _____

Q7b hint

8 **a** Draw a **rectangle** with sides 8 cm and 5 cm on squared paper.

b Draw its diagonals and measure them.

c Copy and complete
   The diagonals of a rectangle are _____

d Measure the angles between the diagonals. Use arcs to mark any that are equal.

Investigation   **Reasoning**

1 Use triangular dotted paper to draw each shape.
   i equilateral triangle   **ii** isosceles triangle   **iii** scalene triangle   **iv** rectangle
   a Write the name of the shape beneath it.
   b Mark the equal sides using dashes.
   c Mark information about the angles.
2 Can you join the dots to make a square? Try it and see.

---

9 **Explore** Which shapes were used in the building of your home or school?
   Is it easier to explore this question now you have completed the lesson? What further information do you need to be able to answer this?

10 **Reflect** **a** Close your book and write
   • three facts about triangles
   • three facts about quadrilaterals.
   Then open your book again.
   b Look back at this lesson to check your facts are correct.
   c Compare your facts with others in your class.

Q10b hint

Check your spelling too.

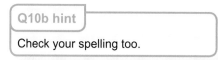

8.2 Symmetry in shapes

You will learn to:
* Describe the line symmetry of triangles, quadrilaterals and other shapes.

CONFIDENCE

Why learn this?
Aeroplanes have line symmetry to make them fly straight.

Fluency
* Name these triangles.

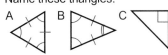

A   B   C

* What do you know about a rectangle?

Explore
What is the line symmetry of a sports playing area?

Exercise 8.2

Warm up

1 a Copy the square and rectangle.
 b Use dashes to mark equal sides and lengths.
 c Use arcs to mark equal angles.

square   rectangle

2 a For each triangle write down if it is scalene, isosceles or equilateral.
 Give a reason for your answer.

i 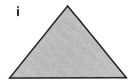 **ii** **iii**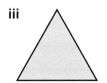

b Trace each triangle and cut it out.
 Try folding it in half in different ways.

c Copy and complete these sentences.
 An equilateral triangle has ☐ **lines of symmetry**.
 An isosceles triangle has ☐ lines of symmetry.
 A scalene triangle has ☐ lines of symmetry.

> **Key point**
> * A shape has **line symmetry** if one half folds exactly on top of the other half.
>
>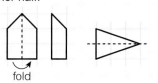
> fold
>
> * The dashed line is called a **line of symmetry**.

3 Reasoning Describe the **line symmetry** of each triangle.

a 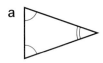 **b** **c** 60° 30° **d**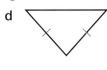

Explain your answer. The first one has been done for you.

a One line of symmetry because it is an isosceles triangle (two equal angles).

Discussion Do all right-angled triangles have line symmetry?

Subject links: PE (Q7)

4 How many lines of symmetry does each shape have?

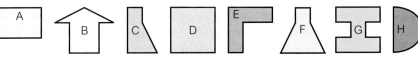

Q4 hint

Imagine folding the shape along a dotted line. How many ways can you fold it in half?

Discussion Does a person's face have line symmetry?

5 a Copy each quadrilateral onto squared paper.

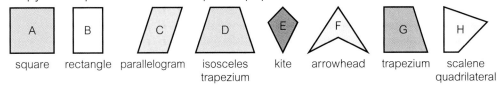

square   rectangle   parallelogram   isosceles trapezium   kite   arrowhead   trapezium   scalene quadrilateral

b Draw in the lines of symmetry.

c Describe the properties of each shape. The first one has been done for you.

A Four equal sides, four right angles, opposite sides are parallel.

6 A **rhombus** is a **parallelogram** with all sides equal. Opposite sides are parallel, as shown by the arrows.

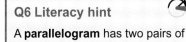

a Measure the corner angles. What do you notice?

b Measure the angles between the dotted diagonals. What do you notice?

c Copy the diagram and mark all the information you know.

d Does a rhombus have line symmetry?

Q6 Literacy hint

A **parallelogram** has two pairs of opposite parallel sides.

Discussion A rhombus is like a square without right angles. What is another difference between a square and a rhombus?

Investigation   Real / Modelling

1 Design your own paper aeroplane using squared paper. Cut it out and fold it up. Add some weight to the front (nose) using staples. Does it fly straight?

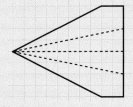   

2 Cut a piece off the tip of one wing. Does your plane still fly straight?

3 Cut the other wing to give the plane line symmetry again. Does it fly straight again?

4 Compare your design with a classmate's. Which flies furthest?

---

7 Explore What is the line symmetry of a sports playing area? Is it easier to explore this question now you have completed the lesson? What further information do you need to be able to answer this?

8 Reflect Antony says, 'I am thinking of a capital letter. It has only one line of symmetry.'

a List all the capital letters Antony could be thinking about.

b Compare your answer with a classmate.

c Discuss with a classmate how you made sure you listed *all* the capital letters.

Q8 hint

You could look at a computer keyboard to help you.

8.3 More symmetry

You will learn to:
- Solve problems using line symmetry
- Describe rotational symmetry.

CONFIDENCE

Why learn this?
Boat engine propellers have rotational symmetry.

Fluency
Turn your exercise book through a full turn.

Explore
Does a propeller have both line and rotational symmetry?

Exercise 8.3

Warm up

1 Name each shape. Write down the number of lines of symmetry it has.

a

b

c

d

e

2 a Find the missing lengths and angles in these triangles.

i

5 cm
25°

ii

5 cm
40°
70°

iii

60°
15 cm   15 cm
60°

Q2a hint
The dashed lines are lines of symmetry. One half fits exactly on top of the other half.

b Name each triangle. Give a reason for your answer.

3 Problem-solving These are all isosceles triangles.
Find the missing sides and angles.

a
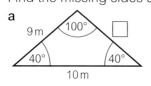
9 m
100°
40°   40°
10 m

b
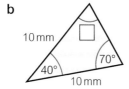
10 mm
70°
40°
10 mm

c
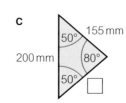
155 mm
50°
200 mm   80°
50°

Q3 hint
Where is the line of symmetry?

Topic links: Angles

4 Find the order of **rotational symmetry** for each shape.

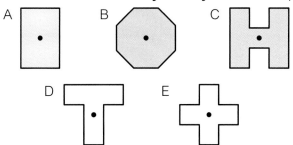

Discussion Which shapes have no rotational symmetry?

5 For each shape work out the
   a order of rotational symmetry   **b** number of lines of symmetry.

6 For each object work out the
   a order of rotational symmetry   **b** number of lines of symmetry.

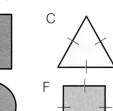

Discussion Can you think of any other real objects with symmetry?

Investigation   Reasoning

1 a How many lines of symmetry does the letter H have?
   b What is the order of rotational symmetry of the letter H?
2 Investigate the line and rotational symmetry of
   a your name written using capital letters
   b the digits 0 to 9.
3 The word MUM has 1 line of symmetry.
   Write some more words that have line **MUM**
   symmetry.
4 The number **916** has rotational symmetry.
   Find two more numbers that have rotational symmetry.
5 Find a word that has rotational symmetry.

---

7 Explore Does a propeller have both line and rotational symmetry?
Is it easier to explore this question now you have completed the lesson?
What further information do you need to be able to answer this?

8 Reflect Show which of these statements are true by drawing a sketch.
A shape can have both a line of symmetry **and** rotational symmetry.
A shape can have rotational symmetry **and no** line of symmetry.
A shape can have a line of symmetry **and no** rotational symmetry.

Explore

Reflect

8.4 Regular polygons

You will learn to:
- Identify polygons
- Understand the line and rotational symmetry of regular polygons.

Why learn this?
Polygons are used in construction.

Fluency
Name each shape.

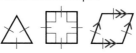

Explore
Which flat shapes are used to make domes?

Exercise 8.4

1 A △ B ▭ C ▷ D ▢ E ▱

 a How many lines of symmetry does each shape have?
 b What is the order of rotational symmetry for each shape?

2 Match the names to the descriptions.

A Pentagon	i 10-sided shape
B Hexagon	ii 5-sided shape
C Heptagon	iii 9-sided shape
D Octagon	iv 6-sided shape
E Nonagon	v 7-sided shape
F Decagon	vi 8-sided shape

3 The diagram shows the ends of some pencils.

A B C D E F ⬤

 a Name the shape of each end.
 b Which ends are not **regular polygons**? Why not?

Key point

A **polygon** is a 2D shape with straight sides. A **regular polygon** has equal sides and equal angles.

Q4b hint

Are all of the sides and angles equal?

4 Look at each shape.

    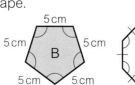 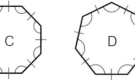 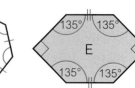 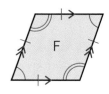

 a Name each one.
 b Is it a regular polygon?

Worked example

a How many lines of symmetry does a regular octagon have?

> Rotate the octagon a full turn. In how many positions does it look the same?

A regular octagon has 8 lines of symmetry.

> How many ways can you fold an octagon in half?

b What is the order of rotational symmetry of a regular octagon?

An octagon has rotational symmetry of order 8.

5 **Reasoning** **a** Draw this hexagon on triangular grid paper.
   b Explain why this is a regular hexagon.
   c Draw the lines of symmetry using dashed lines.
      How many does it have?

> **Q5d hint**
> Only count the starting position once.

   d Rotate the hexagon a full turn about the centre.
      In how many positions does it look the same?
   e Copy and complete the table.

Regular polygon	pentagon	hexagon	heptagon	octagon	nonagon	decagon
Lines of symmetry						
Order of rotational symmetry						

   Discussion What is the rule for the number of lines of symmetry for a regular polygon? What is the rule for the order of rotational symmetry?

6 **Problem-solving / Reasoning** Sketch a polygon with
   a 2 lines of symmetry and 6 sides   **b** 1 line of symmetry and 5 sides
   c no lines of symmetry and 6 sides.

> **Q6 hint**
> Is it a regular polygon?

7 **STEM** These satellites are covered with identical solar panels.
   a **i** How many lines of symmetry has
       Satellite A?
    ii What is its order of rotational symmetry?
Satellite B has control boxes fitted to two panels.
   b **i** How many lines of symmetry does it have?
    ii What is its order of rotational symmetry?

8 **Explore** Which flat shapes are used to make domes?
Is it easier to explore this question now you have completed the lesson?
What further information do you need to be able to answer this?

9 **Reflect** Which of these shapes is a hexagon?

> **Q9 hint**
> Is there more than one?

  A   B   C   D

Explain to a classmate how you decided.
Draw a pentagon. Compare your pentagon with others in your class.

Explore

Reflect

8.5 Perimeter

You will learn to:
- Find the perimeter of squares, rectangles and regular polygons
- Calculate the perimeter of shapes made from rectangles
- Solve problems involving the perimeter of squares and rectangles.

Why learn this?
To replace the gutter around a house you need to know its perimeter.

Fluency
- What do you know about the sides of
  a a square
  b a rectangle?
- How many sides does a pentagon have?

Explore
How can you find the length of gutter using a plan of a building?

Exercise 8.5

1 Work out
 a 4 cm + 6 cm + 4 cm + 6 cm
 b 20 cm + 20 cm + 20 cm + 20 cm
 c 8 × 7 cm

2 Work out
 a 4.2 m + 3.6 m + 4.2 m + 3.6 m
 b 5.7 cm + 9.3 cm + 5.7 cm + 9.3 cm
 c 6 × 4.6 cm

3 Measure the sides of each quadrilateral in millimetres (mm).
 Copy and complete the table.

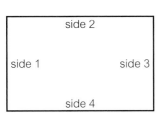

rectangle   square

	Rectangle	Square
Side 1		
Side 2		
Side 3		
Side 4		

Discussion Did you need to measure every side?

Topic links: Square roots

4 Work out the **perimeter** of both shapes in Q3.

5 a What are the other side lengths of this square?
  b Work out the perimeter.

  8 cm

  Discussion What is a quick way to work out the
  perimeter of a square?

6 A square jacuzzi has a side of 4.7 m. Work out its perimeter.

7 a What are the other side lengths of this rectangle?
  b Work out the perimeter.

  5 cm

  3 cm

  Discussion What is a quick way to work out the
  perimeter of a rectangle?

8 A baking tray is 46.5 cm by 33.2 cm. Work out its perimeter.

9 These shapes are drawn on centimetre squared paper.
  Work out the perimeter of each shape.

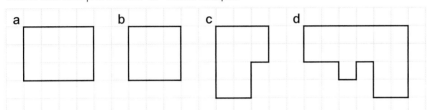

a   b   c   d

10 a Find the other side lengths of this regular pentagon.
   b Work out the perimeter.

   Discussion What is a quick way to work out the perimeter
   of a regular polygon?

2 cm

11 Work out the perimeter of
   a a regular hexagon with a side of 4 cm
   b a regular octagon with a side of 10 mm
   c a regular nonagon with a side of 50 cm.

12 A 50p coin has the shape of a heptagon.
   Each edge is 1.2 cm long.
   Find its perimeter.

13 These shapes have been made by joining rectangles together.

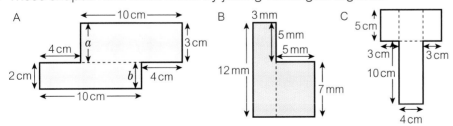

A   B   C

  a For shape A, write down the length of
    i side a
    ii side b.
  b Work out the perimeter of shape A.
  c Work out the missing lengths and the perimeter of the other
    two shapes.

14 Real This room is going to be laid with carpet. Carpet gripper is put around the perimeter of the room first.

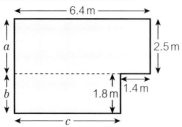

    a Work out the lengths a, b and c.
    b Work out the total length of carpet gripper needed.

Q14a hint

$c = \square - \square$

15 Problem-solving A safety fence surrounds a hole in the road.
The fence is 8 m long. It makes a square.
Work out the length of a side of the square.

Q15 hint

Four sides add up to 8 m.

16 Problem-solving a The perimeter of this rectangle is 22 cm.

    i Work out the sum of the two lengths.

7 cm

    ii Work out the sum of the two widths.
    iii Work out the width of the rectangle.
  b The perimeter of this rectangle is 30 cm.
    Work out the width of the rectangle.

9 cm

Q16a ii hint

Subtract the two lengths from the perimeter.

Investigation   **Problem-solving**

The diagram shows a square drawn on a centimetre square grid.
1 Copy the square.
2 Work out the perimeter of the square.

3 Chomper eats a square at the edge of the shape.

  Work out the perimeter of the new shape.

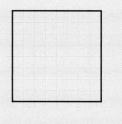

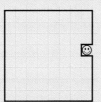

4 How has the perimeter changed?
5 Chomper eats an **adjacent** square along the shape's edge.
  How has the perimeter changed?
6 What will be the perimeter if Chomper eats two more adjacent squares on the edge?
7 Get Chomper to eat more squares. Work out the new perimeter each time.

Literacy hint

Adjacent means 'next to' or 'touching'.

---

17 Explore How can you find the length of gutter using a plan of a building?
Is it easier to explore this question now you have completed the lesson?
What further information do you need to be able to answer this?

18 Reflect Write down the information you need to find the perimeter of a shape.

Q18 hint

Look back at some of the questions you answered in this lesson. What did you need to know?

Active Learn   Pi 1, Section 8.5

8.6 Area

You will learn to:

- Use metric units to measure area
- Calculate the area of squares and rectangles.

Why learn this?
Decorators need to know the area of the walls to work out the amount of paint to buy.

Fluency
Work out
- 2 × 3
- 3 × 4

Explore
How much carpet would you need for your classroom?

Exercise 8.6

1 Work out

   a 8 × 4   **b** 10 × 7   **c** 9 × 3   **d** 6 × 6

2 Write the square of

   a 4   **b** 9   **c** 10   **d** 8

Literacy hint
Read cm^2 as **centimetre squared**.

3 Each square of **centimetre squared** paper has an **area** of $1\,cm^2$.

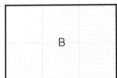

A

$1\,cm^2$

B

C

D

   a Find the area of each shape.

   b Copy and complete the table.

Shape	Length (cm)	Width (cm)	Area (cm²)
A			

Key point
Area is the space inside a shape. Area is measured using **square units**.

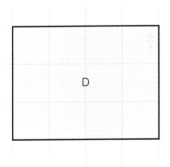

1 cm

1 cm

one square centimetre = $1\,cm^2$

   c Look at your table. How can you find the area from the length and width?

   d i Draw a different rectangle D and a square E on squared paper.

      ii Add them to your table.

Q3a hint

Count the squares.

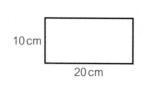

Worked example

Work out the area of the rectangle.

area of a rectangle = length × width
= 20 cm × 10 cm
= 200 cm²

Key point

area of a rectangle = length × width

4 Work out the area of each rectangle.

a 2 cm ↕ ←8 cm→

b 10 cm ↕ ←30 cm→

c 12 cm ↕ ↔ 2 cm

Q4 hint

area = ☐ × ☐ = ☐ cm²

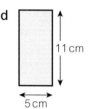

d 11 cm, 5 cm

e 4 cm, ←4 cm→

5 a Estimate the length and width of the front cover of this book in centimetres.

b Use your calculator to work out the area from your estimates.

c Measure the length and width with a ruler.

d Use your calculator to calculate the area of the front cover from your measurements.

6 a Reasoning Which square units are best to describe the areas of these objects: cm² or mm²?

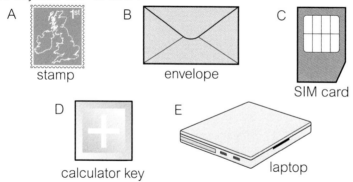

A — stamp
B — envelope
C — SIM card
D — calculator key
E — laptop

Key point

A square millimetre (mm²) is the area of a square of side 1 mm.

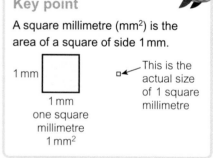

1 mm, 1 mm, one square millimetre 1 mm²

This is the actual size of 1 square millimetre

b Estimate the area of each object.

7 Problem-solving Draw a rectangle on squared paper with an area of

a 10 cm²　　**b** 14 cm²　　**c** 5 cm²

Q7a Strategy hint

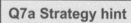

Think of two numbers that multiply to give 10.

8 a Work out the area of each square.

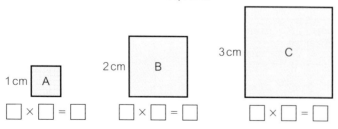

1 cm A
2 cm B
3 cm C

☐ × ☐ = ☐　　☐ × ☐ = ☐　　☐ × ☐ = ☐

b Work out the area of the next square in the pattern.

c Look at the areas you have calculated. What kind of numbers are they?

Discussion What is a quick way to work out the area of a square?

　Topic links: Square numbers

9 Problem-solving Work out the area of a square of side
   a 9 cm   **b** 25 mm   **c** 0.7 cm   **d** 2.4 mm

10 Problem-solving A square has a side of 6 cm.
A rectangle has a width of 4 cm and length of 8 cm.
Which shape has the greater area?

11 These shapes are made by joining two rectangles together.

a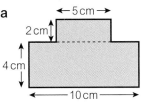

b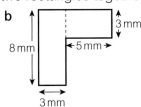

c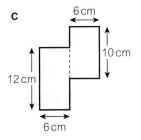

Work out the area of each shape.

Q9 hint

Write your answer using the correct square units.

Q10 Strategy hint

You can draw a sketch to help you.

Q11 hint

Work out the area of each rectangle. Add the answers together.

Investigation   **Problem-solving / Reasoning**

Use centimetre squared paper.
1 a Draw some rectangles with an area of 4 cm^2.
  b Work out the perimeter of each rectangle.
  c Which rectangle has the smallest perimeter? What shape is it?
2 Repeat Q1 for rectangles with area 9 cm^2 and 16 cm^2. What do you notice?
3 Which rectangle of area 36 cm^2 do you think will have the smallest perimeter?
    Test your answer by drawing a few rectangles.

12 Explore How much carpet would you need for your classroom?
Is it easier to explore this question now you have completed the lesson? What further information do you need to be able to answer this?

13 Reflect Write a list of three new words you have learned in this unit.
Compare your list with a classmate.
Take it in turns to define what each word means. Help each other to improve your definitions.

Q13 hint

Look back at the lessons to help you remember them.

Explore

Reflect

Master
P196

CHECK

Strengthen
P213

Extend
P218

Test
P222

8 Check up

Log how you did on your
Student Progression Chart.

Shapes

1 a Which one of these shapes is not a quadrilateral?

A   B    C    D

b Write the name of each shape.

2 Look at this polygon.

a What is its name?

b Is it a regular polygon?
Give a reason for your answer.

3 For each triangle write down if it is isosceles, scalene or equilateral.
Give a reason for your answer.

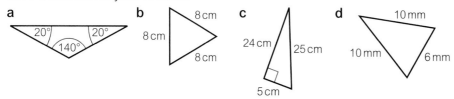

a 20° 20° 140°   **b** 8 cm 8 cm 8 cm   **c** 24 cm 25 cm 5 cm   **d** 10 mm 10 mm 6 mm

4 Sketch a rectangle. Mark equal sides using dashes.
Mark all of the angles correctly.

Symmetry

5 Sketch these shapes. Draw the lines of symmetry on each shape.

a   **b**   **c**

6 Trace this triangle.

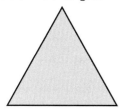

a What kind of triangle is it?

b Draw any lines of symmetry.

7 How many lines of symmetry does a kite have?

8 What is the order of rotational symmetry for each shape in Q5?

211

9 a How many lines of symmetry does this regular octagon have?

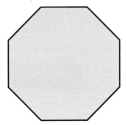

b What is the order of rotational symmetry?

Perimeter and area

10 Work out the perimeter of this rectangle.

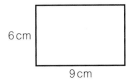

6 cm

9 cm

11 This shape is drawn on centimetre squared paper.
   a Work out the perimeter of the shape.
   b Work out the area.

12 Work out the area of the rectangle in Q11.

13 A square has a side of 7 cm.
   a Work out the perimeter.
   b Work out the area.

14 A safety fence is put around a small pool.
   The fence is 12 m long. It makes a square.
   How long is one side of the fence?

15 How sure are you of your answers? Were you mostly
   😦 **Just guessing**   😐 **Feeling doubtful**   🙂 **Confident**
   What next? Use your results to decide whether to strengthen or extend your learning.

Challenge

16 Draw these shapes on centimetre squared paper.
   Mark your shapes to show equal angles, equal sides and parallel sides.
   a A square with area 16 cm^2.
   b A rectangle with area 20 cm^2.
   c A rhombus with area 9 cm^2.
   d A trapezium with area 6 cm^2.
   e A regular octagon with area 7 cm^2.

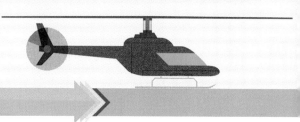

8 Strengthen

You will:
- Strengthen your understanding with practice.

Shapes

1 Link the **prefixes** to the numbers.

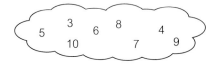

Q1 Literacy hint

A **prefix** is the beginning part of a word.

2 a Match each shape to its name.

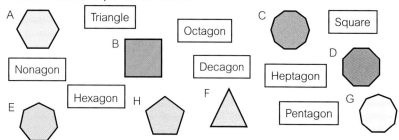

A — Triangle, Octagon
B — Nonagon
C — Square
D — Decagon, Heptagon
E — Hexagon, H
F — Pentagon
G

Q2 hint

Count the sides.

b Which one is a quadrilateral?

3 Measure the sides and angles of both polygons.
   a Which shape is regular?
   b What are the missing words?
   For a regular polygon the sides are _____ and the angles are _____

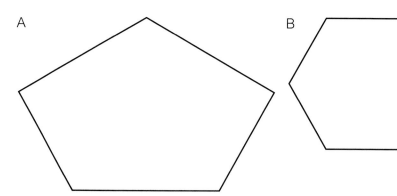

A

B

4 The diagram shows two equilateral triangles, two isosceles triangles and two scalene triangles.

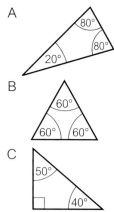

A — 80°, 80°, 20°

B — 60°, 60°, 60°

C — 50°, 40°

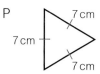

P — 7 cm, 7 cm, 7 cm

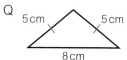

Q — 5 cm, 5 cm, 8 cm

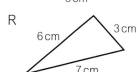

R — 6 cm, 3 cm, 7 cm

Q4 hint

Look at the first four letters.
- equi – like 'equal' – all angles and sides equal.
- **isos** – two letters the same – two angles and sides the same
- scal – all letters different – all angles and sides different

Match each triangle on the left with the same type of triangle on the right.

5 a Work out the red angles.

i

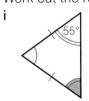

isosceles triangle

ii

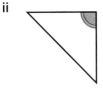

right-angled triangle

iii

equilateral triangle

Q5a hint

Look back at Q4 to help you.
Remember same arcs show same angles.

b Work out the red side lengths.

i

3 cm

isosceles triangle

ii

2 cm

equilateral triangle

iii

14 mm

10 mm

right-angled isosceles

Symmetry

1 Which shapes have line symmetry?

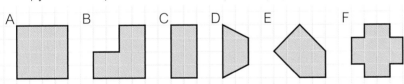

A   B   C   D   E

Q1 hint

Check using a mirror. Are the two halves the same?

2 Trace and cut out each quadrilateral.

A	B	C	D	E
rectangle	square	parallelogram	rhombus	isosceles trapezium

  a Fold the shape so that the two halves fit on top of each other.
  b Draw a dotted line along the crease.
  c Do this as many ways as possible. How many lines of symmetry does each shape have?

3 a Copy each shape on centimetre squared paper.

A   B   C   D   E   F

  b Draw a line of symmetry. Check your line using a mirror.
  c Draw any other lines of symmetry for each shape.
  d Write the number of lines of symmetry beneath each shape.

Q3b hint

Place a mirror upright along your line. Do you see the original shape?

4 a Trace each shape, including the dot and arrow. For E and F draw your own dot in the middle of the shape.

A   B   C

D   E   F

  b Hold your pencil on the dot. Rotate the traced shape a full turn. How many times does it look the same?
  c Write down the order of rotational symmetry.

Q4b hint

When rotating, count the number of times the traced shape fits the original.
Only count the starting position once.

5 a Trace each regular polygon.

A
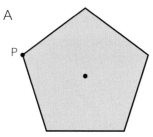

B
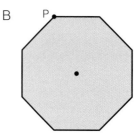

Mark the centre dot and the corner P.

b Find the order of rotational symmetry.

c Find the number of lines of symmetry.

Q5c hint

Cut out the polygon and fold it in half.

d What can you say about the number of sides, lines of symmetry and order of rotational symmetry?

Perimeter and area

1 These rectangles are drawn on centimetre squared paper.

A
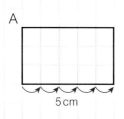
5 cm

B
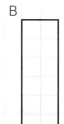

C
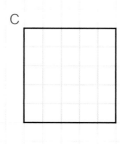

a Find the perimeter by counting squares all the way round each shape.

b Write the lengths of each side. What do you notice about opposite sides?

c Add the lengths together to find the perimeter. Is it the same as in part **a**?

2 a Sketch each rectangle.

A
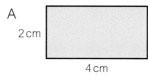
2 cm
4 cm

B
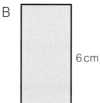
6 cm
3 cm

C
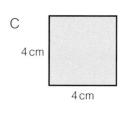
4 cm
4 cm

b Write the lengths of the other two sides on your diagram.

c Work out the perimeter of the rectangle.

3 The perimeter of each rectangle is given. Work out the width.

a
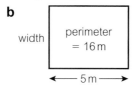
width | perimeter = 10 m
4 m

b
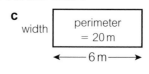
width | perimeter = 16 m
5 m

c
width | perimeter = 20 m
6 m

Q3 hint

Sketch each rectangle.
Label the sides you know.

4 These shapes are drawn on centimetre squared paper.

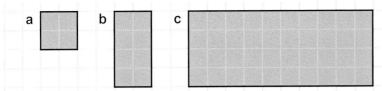

a   b   c

Q4 hint

Each square on centimetre squared paper has area 1 cm².

Find the area of each shape by counting squares.

5 These shapes are drawn on centimetre squared paper.

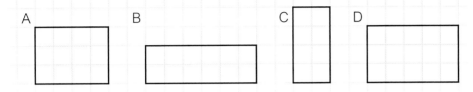

A   B   C   D

a For rectangle A
   i how many squares in the top row?
   ii how many rows?

Q5a iv hint

3 rows of 4 squares

3 × 4 = 12

   iii how many squares altogether?
   iv write down the area of the rectangle.
b Repeat for rectangles B–D.

6 Use the length and width to calculate the area of each rectangle.

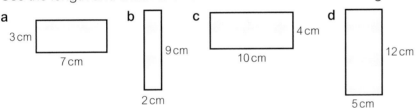

a   3 cm   7 cm
b   9 cm   2 cm
c   4 cm   10 cm
d   12 cm   5 cm

Q6a hint

3 rows of 7 squares

3 × 7 = ☐

7 a Copy these squares onto centimetre squared paper.
   Complete the area calculations.

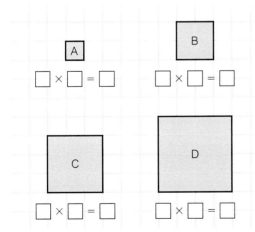

A   ☐ × ☐ = ☐

B   ☐ × ☐ = ☐

C   ☐ × ☐ = ☐

D   ☐ × ☐ = ☐

b Work out the area of the next square in the pattern.
c Look at the areas you have calculated.
   What kind of numbers are they?
d Work out the area of a square with side
   i 6 cm
   ii 10 cm.

8 These shapes are drawn on centimetre squared paper.
Each shape is made by joining two rectangles.

i 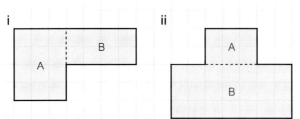 ii iii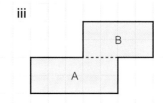

a Work out the perimeter of each shape.
b Find the total area of each shape.

9 Each shape is made by joining two rectangles.

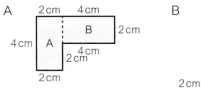 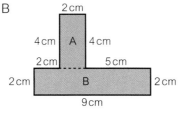

a Work out the perimeter of each shape.
b Work out the area of each shape.

Enrichment

1 a Cut out a large hexagon from triangle grid paper.
b Follow these steps to make a pattern.

FOLD   FOLD   CUT   OPEN

c How many lines of symmetry does your pattern have?
d What is the order of rotational symmetry?
e Fold the same hexagon a different way. Has the symmetry of your pattern changed?
f Cut out a large square from square centimetre paper. Make your own folded pattern.

2 Work in pairs. Do each activity for all the quadrilateral shapes.

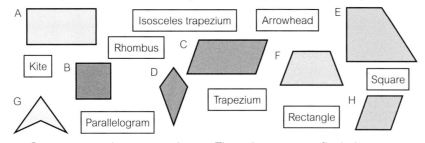

a One person chooses a shape. The other person finds its name.
b One person chooses a shape. The other person describes its properties.

3 Reflect Which action helps you to answer questions on:

Actions

a naming a shape
b finding the lines of symmetry of a shape
c finding the rotational symmetry of a shape
d working out the perimeter of a shape
e working out the area of a shape

A Add up the lengths of the sides
B Turn the page around
C Count the number of sides
D Count the squares inside
E Use a mirror

> **Q8a hint**
>
> For perimeter, count squares around the outside.

> **Q8b hint**
>
> Total area = area of rectangle A
>   + area of rectangle B

> **Q9b hint**
>
> Cover rectangle B.
> Find area of A = ☐ × ☐ = ☐.
> Cover rectangle A.
> Find area of B = ☐ × ☐ = ☐.
> total area = ☐ + ☐ = ☐

> **Q2b hint**
>
> Which sides are equal?
> Which angles are equal?
> Which sides are parallel?
> Are there any right angles?
> Are the diagonals equal?

> **Q3 hint**
>
> You only need to write the letters a–e and A–E.

Reflect

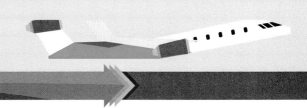

8 Extend

You will:
• Extend your understanding with problem-solving.

1 These triangles are made using matches.

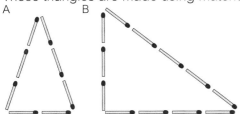 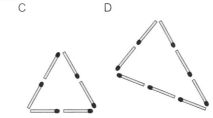

What is the name of each triangle?

Discussion Could you make an isosceles triangle using 10 matches?

2 Find as many polygons as you can in this image.
Name each one and say if it looks regular.

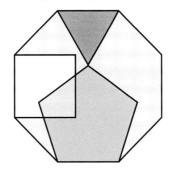

3 a Draw a triangle with three different sides and three acute angles.
Draw it big enough to measure the angles.

b What kind of triangle have you drawn?

c Measure the angles. What do you notice?

d Repeat for a scalene triangle with an obtuse angle.

e Repeat for another scalene triangle.

f Copy and complete the sentence.
The angles of a scalene triangle are _____

> **Q3a hint**
>
> An acute angle is less than ☐°.

> **Q3d hint**
>
> An obtuse angle lies between ☐° and ☐°.

4 Reasoning Using centimetre squared paper

a Draw a rectangle of length 3 cm and width 5 cm. Mark the equal sides using dashes.

b Repeat part **a** but use a width of 4 cm.

c Repeat using a width of 3 cm. What is another name for this rectangle?

d Copy and complete the sentence.
A square is also a _____

5 Problem-solving The diagram shows the two flaps on the top of a cardboard box.
Work out the perimeter of

a the top of the box

b one of the two flaps.

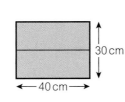

> **Q5b hint**
>
> The two flaps have the same length.

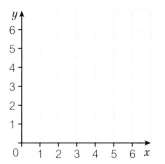

6 a Copy the coordinate grid on centimetre squared paper.
  b Plot these points on your grid.
   A(2, 2) B(3, 6) C(5, 4) D(6, 1)
  c Join the points in order, with straight lines.
   Join the last point to the first point.
   What shape have you drawn?
  d Use a ruler to measure the perimeter of the shape.

7 Problem-solving The diagram shows four regular polygons.

The sum of the perimeters of the triangle and hexagon is equal to the
sum of the perimeters of the pentagon and square.
Work out the side length of the square.

8 Problem-solving Each letter of this word is made using rectangles.

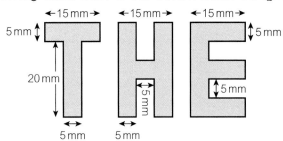

> **Q8 hint**
>
> Work out the height of the letters first.
> Split each letter into rectangles using
> dotted lines.

The rectangles have the same width. The letters have the same height.
Work out the perimeter of each letter.

9 A rectangular parking space has a width of 2.4 m and a perimeter
of 14.4 m. What is the length of the parking space?

> **Q9 Strategy hint**
>
> You may want to sketch a diagram
> to help you.

10 Problem-solving The diagram shows a rectangular
window frame.
The width of the window frame is 40 cm.
The perimeter of the window frame is 320 cm.
  a Work out the sum of the two widths.
  b Work out the sum of the two heights.
  c Work out the height of the window frame.

40 cm

> **Q10b hint**
>
> Subtract the two widths from the
> perimeter.

11 Problem-solving The police enclose a square crime scene
with 35 m of tape.

Work out the side lengths of the crime scene.

12 Only one kind of triangle has rotational symmetry. What is its name?
What is the order of rotational symmetry?

Topic links: Decimals, Coordinates   **Subject links:** Science (Q16)

13 The diagram shows some medical plasters.

  a Work out the area of the rectangular plaster A.

  b Work out the area of the square plaster B.

  c **Problem-solving** Plaster C is made by crossing two of plaster A at right angles. Work out the area of the shaded overlap.

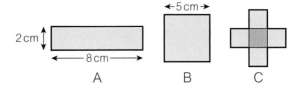

A   B   C

Q13c hint

What is the width of plaster A?

14 **Real / Problem-solving** Luda has 12 edging stones for a rectangular flowerbed. She puts 4 stones on side A.

  a How many edging stones will she need for side B?

  b How many stones are left to use?

  c How many stones will she use for side C?

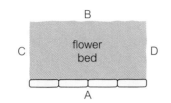

Q14b hint

There are 12 edging stones in total.

15 The diagram shows the steps to make a wooden gate.

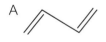 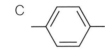 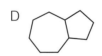

Step 1   Step 2   Step 3   Step 4   Step 5   Step 6

For each step

  a how many lines of symmetry are there?

  b what is the order of rotational symmetry?

16 **STEM** The diagram shows the chemistry symbols of some molecules. The symbols are made by joining lines of the same length. The polygons are regular.

A   B   C   D

Q16 hint

Lines are used to show bonds between atoms.
Two lines are used to show double bonds.

For each symbol

  a how many lines of symmetry are there?

  b what is the order of rotational symmetry?

17 Viewed from above, this building is a regular polygon.

  a How many walls could it have?

  b Sketch the view from above.

  c How many lines of symmetry does it have?

  d What is the order of rotational symmetry?

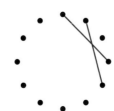

18 **a** Trace the circle of dots.

  b Join the rest of the dots as shown.

    i Describe the shape in the middle.

    ii How many lines of symmetry does it have?

    iii What is the order of rotational symmetry?

  c There are two regular 'stars'. For each star

    i how many lines of symmetry does it have

    ii what is the order of rotational symmetry?

19 Finance These pieces of carpet were cut to fit around corners.

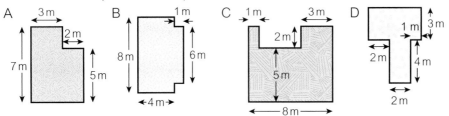

a Work out the area of each piece.

b A square metre of carpet costs £12.

   i Work out the total area of all the pieces of carpet.

   ii Work out the total cost of all the pieces of carpet.

Q19a hint

Use dotted lines to split each shape into rectangles.

20 Problem-solving This shape is made by joining two rectangles together.
Work out its area.

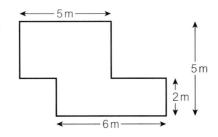

Q20 Strategy hint

width of top rectangle
= □ − □ = □ m

21 Work out the area of each set of steps in cm².

   a   **b**   **c**

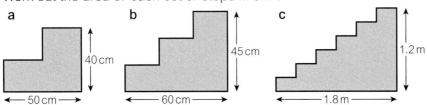

Q21a hint

height of a step = □ ÷ 2 = □
width of a step = □ ÷ 2 = □
Convert m to cm first.

Investigation   **Reasoning**

Look at these quadrilateral shapes.

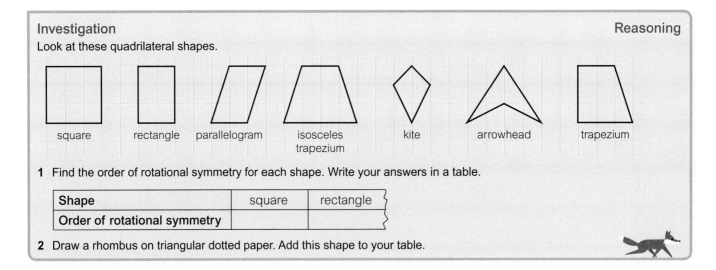

square   rectangle   parallelogram   isosceles   kite   arrowhead   trapezium
                                         trapezium

1 Find the order of rotational symmetry for each shape. Write your answers in a table.

Shape	square	rectangle
Order of rotational symmetry		

2 Draw a rhombus on triangular dotted paper. Add this shape to your table.

---

22 Reflect a Look again at Q9.
The hint suggests you sketch a diagram.
Discuss with a classmate how sketching a diagram helps when working out the perimeter.

   b Look again at Q10.
This question already has a diagram.
Discuss with a classmate how this diagram helped you to answer the question.

8 Unit test

Log how you did on your Student Progression Chart.

1 a Name each shape.

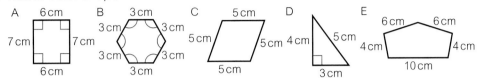

b Which shapes are quadrilaterals?

c Which shape is a regular polygon?

2 For each triangle, write down if it is isosceles, scalene or equilateral.

a   **b**   **c**   **d**

Give a reason for each answer.

3 Work out the perimeter of this rectangle.

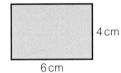

4 A regular nonagon has a side of 4 cm.
Work out its perimeter.

5 Answer these questions about each design.

A   B   C   D   E

a Does it have rotational symmetry?

b What is the order of rotational symmetry?

6 Work out the perimeter of this shape.

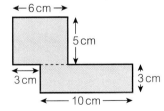

7 The dotted line is a line of symmetry.

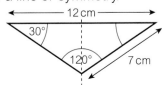

Find the missing length and angle.

8 a What is the name of this polygon?
  b Is it a regular polygon? Explain your answer.
  c Trace the shape.
  d Use dotted lines to draw any lines of symmetry.

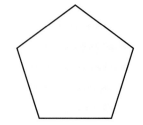

9 How many lines of symmetry does each quadrilateral have?

   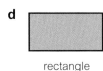

  a arrowhead   **b** square   **c** parallelogram   **d** rectangle

10 a How many lines of symmetry does this octagon have?
   b What is the order of rotational symmetry?

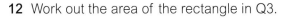

11 A square has a side of 6 cm.
  a Work out the perimeter.
  b Work out the area.

12 Work out the area of the rectangle in Q3.

13 The perimeter of this postcard is 50 cm.
Work out the width of the card.

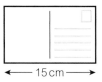

← 15 cm →

14 A regular decagon has a perimeter of 125 cm.
Work out the length of each side.

15 The diagram shows a swimming pool.
  a Work out the area of the pool.
  b Work out the perimeter of the pool.

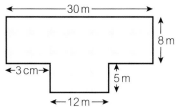

Challenge

16 a Draw a rectangle 6 cm by 4 cm on centimetre squared paper.
   b Use straight lines to split the rectangle into two different shapes.
     Name each shape. Draw dotted lines of symmetry, if possible.
     Describe the rotational symmetry.
   c Repeat parts **a** and **b**. This time, divide the rectangle into three
     different shapes.
   d Try dividing the rectangle into four or more different shapes.
     Try to include a polygon.

17 Reflect Put these topics in order, from easiest to hardest.
  A Naming triangles (like in lesson 8.1).
  B Naming quadrilaterals (like in lesson 8.1).
  C Naming polygons (like in lesson 8.4).
  D Line symmetry (like in lesson 8.2).
  E Rotational symmetry (like in lesson 8.3).
  F Perimeter (like in lesson 8.5).
  G Area (like in lesson 8.6).
  Think about the topic you said was hardest.
  Discuss with a classmate what made this topic hard.
  Write a hint to help you with this topic.

> **Q17 hint**
> You could just write the letters.

Reflect

9.1 Comparing fractions

You will learn to:

- Order fractions
- Use fractions to describe parts of shapes.

Why learn this?
You can compare fractions to find the best deals in the sales.

Fluency
- How many parts would you cut a shape into to make: halves, thirds, quarters, fifths?
- What fraction of each shape is shaded?

Explore
A piece of A5 paper is a fraction of a piece of A4 paper. What fraction is it?

Exercise 9.1

1 Which bar shows
  a $\frac{1}{2}$ b $\frac{1}{4}$?

A
B
C
D

2 a Match each **fraction** to the correct shaded bar.

$\frac{2}{5}$ A

$\frac{4}{5}$ B

$\frac{3}{5}$ C

Key point
A **fraction** is a part of a whole.

  b Now write the fractions $\frac{2}{5}$, $\frac{4}{5}$ and $\frac{3}{5}$ in order, smallest first.

  Discussion How could you order $\frac{7}{8}$, $\frac{1}{8}$ and $\frac{3}{8}$ without drawing bars?

3 Write each set of fractions in **ascending** order.
  a $\frac{3}{7}$ $\frac{1}{7}$ $\frac{6}{7}$ b $\frac{4}{9}$ $\frac{7}{9}$ $\frac{2}{9}$ c $\frac{1}{6}$ $\frac{4}{6}$ $\frac{3}{6}$
  d $\frac{4}{11}$ $\frac{5}{11}$ $\frac{10}{11}$ $\frac{3}{11}$ e $\frac{7}{15}$ $\frac{3}{15}$ $\frac{6}{15}$ $\frac{2}{15}$

Q3 Literacy hint
Numbers in **ascending** order go from smallest to largest.

4 Angie eats $\frac{2}{5}$ of a pizza. Ian eats $\frac{1}{5}$.
  Who eats more?

Q3 Strategy hint
Draw and shade a diagram to help.

5 Which is larger, $\frac{1}{2}$ or $\frac{1}{3}$?

6 a Copy this bar. Shade $\frac{1}{10}$.

   b Copy this bar. Shade $\frac{1}{8}$.

   c Which is smaller, $\frac{1}{10}$ or $\frac{1}{8}$?

7 a Draw bars the same length. Shade them to show these fractions.

    i $\frac{1}{5}$ **ii** $\frac{1}{3}$ **iii** $\frac{1}{7}$

   b Write the fractions $\frac{1}{3}$, $\frac{1}{5}$ and $\frac{1}{7}$ in ascending order.

   Discussion Two fractions have different **denominators** and a
numerator of 1. Can you decide which is larger without drawing bars?

8 Real Two shops are offering different discounts.

   Shop A – $\frac{1}{3}$ off all prices   Shop B – $\frac{1}{5}$ off all prices

   Which shop offers the better discount? Explain how you know.

Investigation   Reasoning / Modelling

Work with a partner to complete these statements using < or >.
Shade in squares on a copy of this grid to help explain your answers.

1 $\frac{1}{3}$ ... $\frac{1}{4}$ **2** $\frac{1}{6}$ ... $\frac{1}{12}$ **3** $\frac{1}{8}$ ... $\frac{1}{2}$ **4** $\frac{1}{2}$ ... $\frac{1}{3}$

---

9 What fraction of each bar is shaded?

   a   **b**

   c   **d**

10 What fraction of each shape is shaded?

   a   **b**   **c**   **d**   **e**

11 Explore A piece of A5 paper is a fraction of a piece of A4 paper.
What fraction is it?
Is it easier to explore this question now you have completed the lesson?
What further information do you need to be able to answer this?

12 Reflect Choose **A**, **B** or **C** to complete each statement.

In this lesson, I did...	**A** well	**B** OK	**C** not very well
So far, I think fractions are...	**A** easy	**B** OK	**C** hard
When I think about the next lesson, I feel...	**A** confident	**B** OK	**C** unsure

If you answered mostly As and Bs, did this surprise you? Why?
If you answered mostly Cs, write down one question in this lesson that you
found hard. Ask a friend or your teacher to explain this question to you again.

(Explore)   *(Reflect)*

9.2 Equivalent fractions

You will learn to:
- Identify equivalent fractions
- Simplify fractions by cancelling
- Change an improper fraction to a mixed number.

Why learn this?
Writing fractions in different ways can help when you are comparing amounts.

Fluency
In the fraction $\frac{3}{7}$, what is
- the denominator
- the numerator?

Explore
How many ways can you describe the shaded part of this shape?

Exercise 9.2

1 Work out the missing number.
  a $3 \times 7 = \square$ b $2 \times \square = 14$ c $\square \times 5 = 35$ d $6 \times \square = 18$

2 Work out
  a $24 \div 8$ b $99 \div 11$ c $18 \div 3$
  d $24 \div 6$ e $35 \div 5$ f $77 \div 7$

3 a How many thirds are there in one whole?
  b How many quarters are there in one whole?
  c How many fifths are there in one whole?

Q3a hint

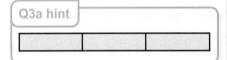

4 What fraction of each bar is shaded?

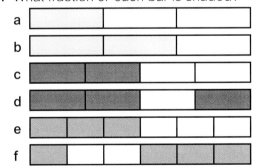

Worked example

Write the improper fraction $\frac{4}{3}$ as a mixed number.

$\frac{4}{3} = 1\frac{1}{3}$

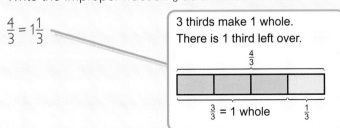

3 thirds make 1 whole.
There is 1 third left over.

$\frac{4}{3}$

$\frac{3}{3} = 1$ whole $\frac{1}{3}$

Key point

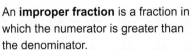

An **improper fraction** is a fraction in which the numerator is greater than the denominator.
A **mixed number** has a whole number part and a fraction part.
An improper fraction can be written as a mixed number.

Warm up

5 Write these **improper fractions** as **mixed numbers**.

  a $\frac{5}{4}$ **b** $\frac{6}{5}$ **c** $\frac{9}{7}$ **d** $\frac{12}{10}$

  e $\frac{7}{3}$ **f** $\frac{9}{4}$ **g** $\frac{11}{5}$ **h** $\frac{17}{6}$

6 Rectangular chocolate bars are divided into 10 pieces.

Ossian eats 17 pieces of chocolate.
Write the number of bars of chocolate he has eaten, as a mixed number.

7 For each bar write down the fraction that is shaded.

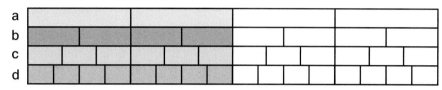

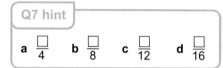

Q7 hint

a $\frac{\square}{4}$ **b** $\frac{\square}{8}$ **c** $\frac{\square}{12}$ **d** $\frac{\square}{16}$

Discussion What can you say about the size of these fractions?

8 Janet and Harrinda order a pancake each.
Janet cuts hers into two equal pieces and eats one piece.

Harrinda cuts his into four equal pieces and eats two of them.

  a Have they eaten the same amount of pancake?
  b Copy and complete this statement.
    $\frac{1}{2} = \frac{\square}{4}$

Worked example

Which of these fractions are equivalent?

$\frac{3}{4}$ $\frac{2}{3}$ $\frac{6}{8}$

> Draw the fractions as bars, all the same length.

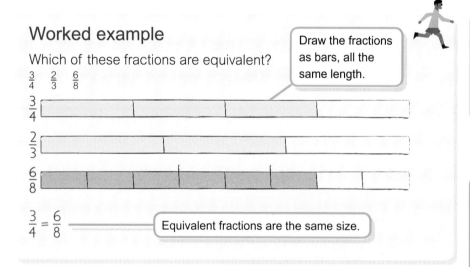

$\frac{3}{4}$

$\frac{2}{3}$

$\frac{6}{8}$

$\frac{3}{4} = \frac{6}{8}$ ——— Equivalent fractions are the same size.

Key point

Equivalent fractions are fractions that represent the same amount but use different numerators and denominators.

9 Which of these fractions are **equivalent**?

$\frac{2}{3}$ $\frac{4}{5}$ $\frac{3}{6}$ $\frac{8}{10}$

Q9 hint

$\frac{2}{3}$

$\frac{4}{5}$

$\frac{3}{6}$

$\frac{8}{10}$

Topic links: Multiples and factors, Sequences

10 Match the equivalent fractions in the diagram.

$\frac{9}{18}$

$\frac{1}{3}$

$\frac{2}{6}$

$\frac{3}{6}$

$\frac{4}{12}$

$\frac{1}{2}$

Q10 hint

Write $\frac{9}{18} = \square = \square$.

11 Use your answer to Q10 to copy and complete.

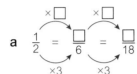

a $\frac{1}{2} = \frac{\square}{6} = \frac{\square}{18}$

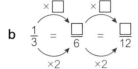

b $\frac{1}{3} = \frac{\square}{6} = \frac{\square}{12}$

Worked example

Simplify $\frac{5}{10}$

$\frac{5}{10} = \frac{1}{2}$ (÷5)

Both 5 and 10 can be divided by 5, so divide the numerator and denominator by 5.

Key point

Multiplying or dividing the numerator and denominator by the same number gives an equivalent fraction. When the numerator and denominator are as small as possible, the fraction is **simplified**. For example

$\frac{2}{6} = \frac{1}{3}$ (÷2)

12 Simplify these fractions.

Copy and complete **a** $\frac{10}{20} = \frac{\square}{\square}$ (÷10) **b** $\frac{50}{60} = \frac{\square}{\square}$ **c** $\frac{90}{110} = \frac{\square}{\square}$

13 Copy and complete **a** $\frac{5}{15} = \frac{\square}{\square}$ (÷5) **b** $\frac{25}{35} = \frac{\square}{\square}$ **c** $\frac{15}{55} = \frac{\square}{\square}$

14 Copy and complete **a** $\frac{2}{4} = \frac{\square}{\square}$ (÷2) **b** $\frac{6}{10} = \frac{\square}{\square}$ **c** $\frac{14}{20} = \frac{\square}{\square}$

15 Explore How many ways can you describe the shaded part of this shape?
Is it easier to explore this question now you have completed the lesson?
What further information do you need to be able to answer this?

Q16a hint

i Look back at Q4.
ii Look back at the first worked example.
iii Look back at Q7.

16 Reflect
  a This lesson used lots of pictures. Copy and complete these sentences.
    i 'Pictures help with understanding fractions because _____,'
    ii 'Pictures help with understanding improper fractions because _____,'
    iii 'Pictures help with understanding equivalent fractions because _____,'
  b Close your eyes and think of one third.
    What did you see, a fraction or a picture? Write or draw what you saw.

Explore

Reflect

9.3 Calculating with fractions

You will learn to:
- Calculate simple fractions of quantities.

CONFIDENCE

Why learn this?
Doctors calculate fractions of a dose of medicine depending on the weight and age of the patient.

Fluency
Work out
- 20 ÷ 5
- 30 ÷ 10
- 66 ÷ 6
- 49 ÷ 7
- 32 ÷ 10

Explore
How would a doctor work out how much of a dose would be required for different weight patients?

Exercise 9.3

Warm up

1 A game for 2 to 4 players has 12 counters.

How many counters does each player get when there are
a 2 players **b** 3 players **c** 4 players?

2 Sally loses $\frac{1}{4}$ of the counters for the game in Q1.
a How many are lost? **b** How many are left?

Worked example

Find $\frac{1}{3}$ of 18

> Draw a bar for 18.
> Divide it into 3 thirds.

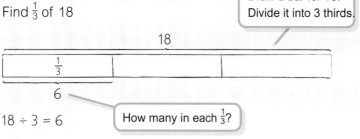

$18 \div 3 = 6$

> How many in each $\frac{1}{3}$?

3 Work out

a $\frac{1}{3}$ of 30 **b** $\frac{1}{2}$ of 10 **c** $\frac{1}{5}$ of 25 **d** $\frac{1}{7}$ of 14

e $\frac{1}{9}$ of 27 **f** $\frac{1}{4}$ of 24 **g** $\frac{1}{6}$ of 18 **h** $\frac{1}{10}$ of 50

Discussion How could you find $\frac{1}{100}$ of a number?

> **Q3 hint**
> Draw bars to help you.

4 Work out

a $\frac{1}{3}$ of 12 **b** $\frac{1}{4}$ of 24 **c** $\frac{1}{8}$ of 32 **d** $\frac{1}{7}$ of 21

e $\frac{1}{9}$ of 81 **f** $\frac{1}{10}$ of 40 **g** $\frac{1}{6}$ of 42 **h** $\frac{1}{5}$ of 50

> **Q4 hint**
> Use division to help you.

Topic links: Factors, Division, Dividing by 10

5 Find $\frac{1}{10}$ of

   a 40   **b** 700   **c** 80   **d** 55   **e** 99
   f 123   **g** 88   **h** 150   **i** 274   **j** 352

Q5 hint

Some of your answers will be decimal numbers.

6 Real / Finance The price of this bag is reduced by $\frac{1}{4}$ in a sale.

   a Work out $\frac{1}{4}$ of £20.

   b How much is the bag in the sale?

£20

Q6b hint

£20 − £☐ = £☐

7 Real / Finance Two shops sell MP3 players at the same original price. Both shops have a sale. Which MP3 player is cheaper? Explain how you know.

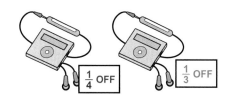

$\frac{1}{4}$ OFF $\frac{1}{3}$ OFF

8 Real / Finance All the prices in a clothes shop are reduced by $\frac{1}{3}$ in a sale. For each item work out

   a $\frac{1}{3}$ of the price

   b the sale price.

ALL PRICES REDUCED BY $\frac{1}{3}$

£33   £12   £45   £18

9 A shop sells jeans for £45. It reduces the price by $\frac{1}{10}$ in a sale.

   a Work out $\frac{1}{10}$ of £45

   b Copy and complete:
      Sale price of jeans = £45 − £☐ = £☐

   c Work out the sale price of
     i a jacket, original price £36
     ii a pair of trainers, original price £98
     iii a shirt, original price £29.50.

10 Real Two garages offer different deals on tyres. Which garage has the cheaper tyres?

USUALLY **£160** NOW $\frac{1}{10}$ **OFF**

Garage A

£180 REDUCED by $\frac{1}{5}$

Garage B

Investigation

1 Each of these tiles has a matching pair except one. Find the odd one out.

| $\frac{1}{6}$ of £30 | $\frac{1}{5}$ of £20 | $\frac{1}{8}$ of £40 | $\frac{1}{11}$ of £99 | $\frac{1}{7}$ of £21 | $\frac{1}{5}$ of £30 | $\frac{1}{4}$ of £16 | $\frac{1}{9}$ of £81 | $\frac{1}{3}$ of £9 |

Hint

Work out the answer for each tile.

2 Write a new tile to match the odd one out.

11 **Explore** How would a doctor work out how much of a dose would be required for different weight patients? Is it easier to explore this question now you have completed the lesson? What further information do you need to be able to answer this?

12 **Reflect** The final task in the investigation asked you to write a tile to match the odd one out. Write another tile to match the odd one out. Discuss with a classmate how you worked out what to write on your tile.

Q12 hint

What did you do first? Then what did you do?

Explore

Reflect

9.4 Adding and subtracting fractions

You will learn to:
- Add and subtract simple fractions.

Why learn this?
Distances and measurements are often given as fractions. To work out a total distance you need to add them.

Fluency
How many
- quarters
- fifths
- sevenths

are there in one whole?

Explore
How do builders decide how much mortar to use for different sized bricks?

Exercise 9.4

1 What fraction of each of these bars is shaded?

a    b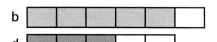

c   d

2 What fraction of each of these shapes is shaded? Write each fraction in its simplest form.

a 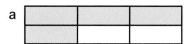   b   c

> **Q2 Literacy hint**
> 'To write a fraction in its simplest form' means to 'simplify' it.

3 Write these improper fractions as mixed numbers.

a $\frac{9}{5}$ b $\frac{8}{3}$ c $\frac{3}{2}$

d $\frac{9}{7}$ e $\frac{7}{4}$ f $\frac{11}{6}$

Worked example

Work out $\frac{1}{5} + \frac{2}{5}$

$$\frac{1}{5} + \frac{2}{5} = \frac{3}{5}$$

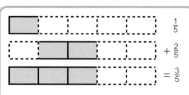

$\frac{1}{5}$

$+ \frac{2}{5}$

$= \frac{3}{5}$

The denominators are the same, so add the numerators.

4 Work out

a $\frac{1}{3} + \frac{1}{3}$ b $\frac{2}{7} + \frac{1}{7}$ c $\frac{2}{5} + \frac{2}{5}$ d $\frac{1}{9} + \frac{3}{9}$

e $\frac{2}{10} + \frac{1}{10}$ f $\frac{4}{11} + \frac{3}{11}$ g $\frac{5}{12} + \frac{2}{12}$ h $\frac{1}{15} + \frac{7}{15}$

Discussion What is a quick way of adding fractions with a **common denominator**?

> **Key point**
> Fractions with a **common denominator** have the same denominator. (They have that denominator 'in common'.)

Worked example

Work out $\frac{3}{5} - \frac{1}{5}$

$$\frac{3}{5} - \frac{1}{5} = \frac{2}{5}$$

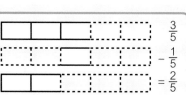

$$\frac{3}{5}$$
$$-\frac{1}{5}$$
$$=\frac{2}{5}$$

The denominators are the same, so subtract the numerators.

5 Work out

  a $\frac{2}{3} - \frac{1}{3}$ **b** $\frac{4}{7} - \frac{2}{7}$ **c** $\frac{5}{6} - \frac{4}{6}$ **d** $\frac{4}{5} - \frac{2}{5}$

  e $\frac{9}{10} - \frac{6}{10}$ **f** $\frac{6}{7} - \frac{2}{7}$ **g** $\frac{11}{15} - \frac{3}{15}$ **h** $\frac{10}{11} - \frac{9}{11}$

  Discussion What is a quick way of subtracting fractions with a common denominator?

6 Amy walks $\frac{1}{7}$ of a mile each day.

  a How far does she walk in two days?

  b How far does she walk in a week?

Q6a hint

You could draw a bar model to help you.

7 A recipe for a batch of biscuits uses $\frac{1}{4}$ of a cup of sugar. Hayden makes two batches of biscuits. How much sugar does he use?

8 Work out these additions. Write your answers as mixed numbers.

  a $\frac{7}{9} + \frac{3}{9} = \frac{\square}{9} = 1\frac{\square}{9}$ **b** $\frac{6}{9} + \frac{5}{9}$ **c** $\frac{6}{7} + \frac{3}{7}$

  d $\frac{3}{5} + \frac{2}{5}$ **e** $\frac{4}{9} + \frac{7}{9}$ **f** $\frac{7}{11} + \frac{7}{11}$ **g** $\frac{2}{3} + \frac{1}{3}$

9 a Work out the missing numbers in these calculations.

  $\frac{3}{5} + \frac{\square}{5} = \frac{5}{5} = \square$ $\frac{4}{7} + \frac{\square}{7} = \frac{7}{7} = \square$ $\frac{5}{11} + \frac{\square}{11} = 1$

  b Write five pairs of fractions which add to 1.

Key point

When the numerator and denominator are the same, the fraction equals one whole.

10 Copy and complete these subtractions.

  a $1 - \frac{11}{12} = \frac{12}{12} - \frac{11}{12} = \frac{\square}{12}$ **b** $1 - \frac{3}{7} = \frac{\square}{7} - \frac{3}{7} = \frac{\square}{\square}$

  c $1 - \frac{2}{5}$ **d** $1 - \frac{4}{9}$ **e** $1 - \frac{2}{3}$ **f** $1 - \frac{7}{8}$

11 Angharad cuts a pizza into 12 slices.
  She eats 4 slices and her friend Barney eats 3 slices.

  a What fraction of the pizza have they eaten altogether?

  b What fraction of the pizza is left?

Q11a hint

1 pizza $= \frac{\square}{12}$

12 $\frac{1}{9}$ of the guests at a party drink cola and $\frac{4}{9}$ drink lemonade. The rest drink tea.

  a What fraction drink cola or lemonade?

  b What fraction drink tea?

13 Explore How do builders decide how much mortar to use for different sized bricks?
  Is it easier to explore this question now you have completed the lesson? What further information do you need to be able to answer this?

14 Reflect

  a Write down two fractions that add to more than 1.

  b Copy and complete this sentence about your fractions.

  'I chose $\frac{\square}{\square}$ and $\frac{\square}{\square}$ because _____'

Q14 hint

Write why you chose the numerator and denominator of each fraction. Show that your fractions add to more than 1.
Write an addition calculation for your fractions and find the answer.

Explore

Reflect

9.5 Introducing percentages

You will learn to:

* Understand percentage as 'the number of parts per 100'
* Write a percentage as a fraction or decimal.

CONFIDENCE

Why learn this?
Companies use percentages to record how much profit they have made.

Fluency
Write these fractions as decimals.

* $\frac{23}{100}$
* $\frac{5}{10}$
* $\frac{9}{10}$
* $\frac{37}{100}$
* $\frac{99}{100}$

Explore
Which savings account gives you the best interest rate?

Exercise 9.5

Warm up

1 Simplify these fractions. Divide by 2, 5 or 10.

a $\frac{15}{40}$ b $\frac{30}{70}$ c $\frac{18}{22}$

d $\frac{70}{90}$ e $\frac{8}{10}$ f $\frac{25}{55}$

Q1a hint

$$\frac{15}{40} = \frac{\square}{\square}$$
$\div 5$ ... $\div 5$

2 What fraction of each of these grids is shaded?

a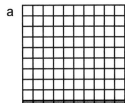

b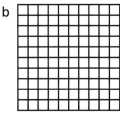

c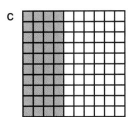

d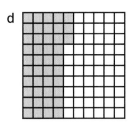

Worked example

What **percentage** of this grid is shaded?

There are 100 squares.
35 out of 100 squares are shaded.
So 35% is shaded.

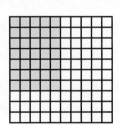

Key point
Per cent means 'out of 100'.
'%' stands for 'per cent'.

3 What percentage of each grid is shaded?

a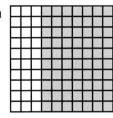

b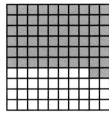

c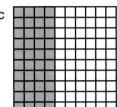

d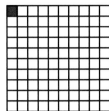

4 Write the fractions shown in Q2 as percentages.

Discussion How do you write a $\frac{\square}{100}$ fraction as a percentage?

How do you write a percentage as a fraction?

5 Finance For every £100 Tim earns, he pays £20 in tax.
What percentage does Tim pay in tax?

Q5 hint

£20 out of £100 = ☐%

6 Finance A bank account pays £2 interest on savings of £100.
What percentage is this?

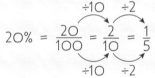

Worked example

Write 20% as a fraction.

$$\overset{\div 10 \qquad \div 2}{20\% = \frac{20}{100} = \frac{2}{10} = \frac{1}{5}}$$
$$\div 10 \qquad \div 2$$

First write 20% as a fraction of 100.

Then simplify the fraction by dividing the numerator and denominator by the same number. Keep doing this until the fraction is in its simplest form.

Key point

You can write percentages as fractions or decimals.

7 Write these percentages as fractions.

a $91\% = \frac{\square}{100}$

b $19\% = \frac{\square}{100}$

c $37\% = \frac{\square}{100}$

d 30%

e 70%

f 90%

Q7d hint

$$30\% = \frac{\square}{100} = \frac{\square}{10}$$
$$\div 10 \qquad \div 10$$

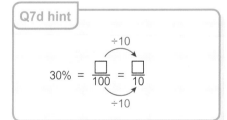

Worked example

Write 35% as a decimal.

$$35\% = \frac{35}{100} = 0.35$$

Write 35% as a fraction out of 100. Then divide 35 by 100 to write it as a decimal.

8 Write these percentages as decimals.

a 45%	b 67%	c 81%	d 42%	e 99%
f 94%	g 73%	h 87%	i 90%	j 37%
k 5%	l 7%	m 9%	n 3%	o 1%

Discussion What is a quick way of writing percentages as decimals?

9 Write these percentages as fractions and decimals.
The first one has been done for you.

a $50\% = \dfrac{50}{100} = \dfrac{1}{2}$ $50\% = 0.50 = 0.5$

b $10\% = \dfrac{\square}{100} = \dfrac{1}{10}$ $10\% = \square = \square$

c $1\% = \dfrac{\square}{100}$ $1\% = \square$

d $25\% = \dfrac{\square}{100} = \dfrac{\square}{20} = \dfrac{\square}{4}$ $25\% = \square$

e $75\% = \dfrac{75}{\square} = \dfrac{\square}{20} = \dfrac{\square}{4}$ $75\% = \square$

Q9 hint

You need to know these fraction, decimal and percentage conversions.

10 Write these percentages as fractions in their simplest form.

a $40\% = \dfrac{\square}{100} = \dfrac{\square}{10} = \dfrac{\square}{5}$

b $80\% = \dfrac{\square}{100} = \dfrac{\square}{10} = \dfrac{\square}{5}$

c $60\% = \dfrac{\square}{100} = \dfrac{\square}{10} = \dfrac{\square}{5}$

Q10a hint

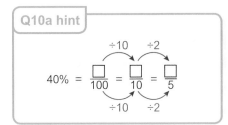

11 Write down each percentage and its equivalent fraction from the table.

70%	$\frac{21}{100}$
51%	$\frac{1}{10}$
80%	$\frac{39}{100}$
21%	$\frac{4}{5}$
10%	$\frac{7}{10}$
39%	$\frac{51}{100}$

12 **Finance** Two furniture warehouses offer different discounts.

Warehouse A   40% off all prices.   Warehouse B $\frac{1}{5}$ off all prices.

a Write 40% as a fraction.
b Which warehouse offers the better discount?

13 **a** Write 60% as a fraction.
    b Complete the statements below using < or >.
      i $\frac{1}{5} \square 60\%$
      ii $\frac{4}{5} \square 60\%$

14 **Explore** Which savings account gives you the best interest rate?
Is it easier to explore this question now you have completed the lesson?
What further information do you need to be able to answer this?

15 **Reflect** Which is easier
• writing a percentage as a fraction
• writing a percentage as a decimal?
Explain why.

Q15 hint

Write '_____ is easier, because _____.'

Explore

Reflect

9.6 FINANCE: Finding percentages

You will learn to:
* Calculate percentages.

Why learn this?
Price increases and decreases are often given in percentages. You can use them to work out whether you are getting a good deal.

Fluency
Work out $\frac{1}{2}$ of
* 30
* 50
* 25

Explore
Can you ever be 110% confident?
Can the price of something be 110% of the original?

Exercise 9.6: Real-life percentages

1 Work out

  a 20 ÷ 10   **b** 350 ÷ 10   **c** 840 ÷ 100

  d 240 ÷ 100   **e** 720 ÷ 10   **f** 55 ÷ 100

2 Find 50% of

  a 30   **b** 90   **c** 160

  d 54   **e** 18   **f** 19

3 Finance All prices are reduced by 50% in a sale.
How much is the reduction on each item?

> **Key point**
> 50% is the same as $\frac{1}{2}$.
> To find 50% of an amount you divide by 2.
>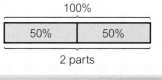
> 2 parts

4 Finance The price of petrol increases by 50%.
Before this it was £0.90 per litre.

  a How much does it increase by?

  b What is the price now?

5 Find 10% of

  a 400   **b** 30   **c** 250

  d 85   **e** 94   **f** 123

> **Key point**
> 10% ('ten per cent') is the same as $\frac{1}{10}$.
> To find 10% of an amount you divide by 10.
>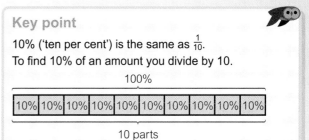
> 10 parts

6 Finance A bank pays 10% interest on all its accounts each year.
How much interest would each of these amounts earn in a year?

  a £3000   **b** £1200   **c** £180

  d £445   **e** £183   **f** £963

7 Finance Last year farmers were paid 30p per litre of milk. They are paid 10% less this year.
How much are they paid per litre this year?

8 Finance A freelance hairdresser charges £30 an hour. She has to pay 10% to the salon she works at.
a How much does she pay to the salon?
b How much does she earn per hour?
Discussion When you know 10% of £30, how can you use this to easily work out 20% of £30?

Worked example

Find 1% of 300

$300 \div 100 = 3$

$1\% = \frac{1}{100}$
So to find 1%, divide 300 by 100.

> **Key point**
> To find 1% of an amount you divide by 100.

9 Find 1% of
a 600	**b** 920	**c** 740	**d** 3000	**e** 9000
f 50	**g** 56	**h** 75	**i** 99	**j** 199

10 Finance A car showroom increases all its prices by 1%.
Work out the increase in price for each of these vehicles.
a Peugeot £10 000   **b** VW £12 000
c Toyota £13 000   **d** Vauxhall £15 000
e Audi £18 000   **f** Alfa Romeo £25 000
g BMW £35 000   **h** Porsche £51 000

11 Finance Jon receives a pay rise of 1%. Before this he earned £45 000 a year.
a How much is his pay rise?   **b** How much does he earn now?

Investigation   **Finance**

A savings account pays 1% interest each month.
At the beginning of January Shane put £10 000 into the account.
1 a How much interest will he receive at the end of January?
   b How much will he now have in his account?
2 a How much interest will he receive at the end of February?
   b How much will he now have in his account?
3 Work out how much he will have in his account at the end of March.

---

12 Explore Can you ever be 110% confident?
Can the price of something be 110% of the original?
Look back at the maths you have learned in this lesson.
How can you use it to answer this question?

13 Reflect Write down what you think is the most important thing to remember when working with percentages.
Compare what you have written with others in your class.
Have you written the same?
If no, then try to convince others that what you wrote is more important.

> **Q13 hint**
> Look back at everything you have learned in this lesson and lesson 9.5.

Topic links: Number system   *Active* Learn   Pi 1, Section 9.6

Explore

Reflect

Master
P224

CHECK

Strengthen
P240

Extend
P244

Test
P248

9 Check up

Log how you did on your
Student Progression Chart.

Fractions

1 a Match each fraction to a diagram.

$\frac{1}{2}$ $\frac{3}{6}$ $\frac{1}{6}$ $\frac{5}{6}$

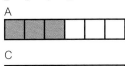

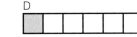

b Which pair of fractions are equivalent?

2 Which two of these fractions are equivalent?

$\frac{1}{2}$ $\frac{2}{3}$ $\frac{2}{4}$

3 Write these fractions in order from smallest to largest.

$\frac{3}{14}$ $\frac{1}{14}$ $\frac{7}{14}$

4 Copy and complete this statement using > or <.

$\frac{1}{3} \ldots \frac{1}{5}$

5 Work out $\frac{1}{3}$ of 36

6 A sale advertises $\frac{1}{4}$ off all prices. A pair of trousers costs £28 before the sale.

a Work out $\frac{1}{4}$ of £28

b What is the sale price of the trousers?

7 What fraction of each bar is shaded? Simplify your answers where possible.

a

b

c

8 Write these improper fractions as mixed numbers.

a $\frac{4}{3}$

b $\frac{9}{5}$

9 Work out $\frac{4}{13} + \frac{3}{13}$

10 Work out these calculations. Simplify your answers where possible.

a $\frac{4}{10} - \frac{3}{10}$

b $\frac{3}{8} + \frac{1}{8}$

c $\frac{19}{20} - \frac{4}{20}$

d $1 - \frac{2}{5}$

e $\frac{4}{9} + \frac{5}{9}$

f $\frac{5}{6} + \frac{2}{6}$

Equivalent fractions, decimals and percentages

11 Match each percentage to its equivalent fraction.

60%	81%	$\frac{1}{10}$	$\frac{1}{2}$
10%	50%	$\frac{1}{4}$	$\frac{1}{100}$
1%	25%	$\frac{6}{10}$	$\frac{81}{100}$

12 Write whether each statement is true or false.

a $10\% = 0.01$ **b** $0.23 = 23\%$ **c** $\frac{1}{2} = 50\%$

d $\frac{3}{10} = 0.03$ **e** $\frac{19}{100} = 1.9$ **f** $60\% = 0.6$

13 Write 30% as

a a decimal   **b** a fraction.

Finding percentages

14 Carys eats 17 sweets out of a packet of 100.
What percentage is this?

15 Find 50% of £36

16 Find 1% of 230

17 In a sale 10% is taken off all the prices.
a Work out 10% of £75
b What is the sale price of an item costing £75?

18 **How sure are you of your answers? Were you mostly**

🙁 **Just guessing**   😐 **Feeling doubtful**   🙂 **Confident**

What next? Use your results to decide whether to strengthen or extend your learning.

Challenge

19 $\frac{1}{4}$ of £24 = £6
Write down three different questions with fractions of amounts that have the answer £6

20 100 people were surveyed and asked which TV channel they were watching at 8 pm the previous evening.

a How many people were watching Channel 4?

b What percentage of the 100 people surveyed is this?

c What percentage were watching BBC1.

d What percentage were watching either Satellite TV or Channel 5?

e True or false?
$\frac{1}{4}$ of viewers were watching ITV.

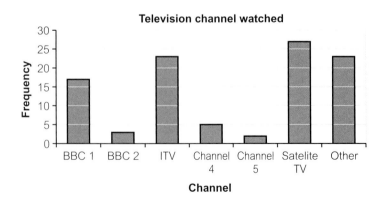

21 Describe how to find 90% of any number.

9 Strengthen

You will:

- Strengthen your understanding with practice.

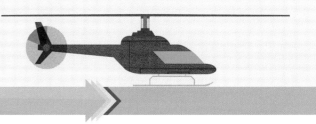

Fractions

1 Which is the largest fraction in each set of three bars?

a $\frac{3}{7}$

b $\frac{5}{12}$

$\frac{6}{7}$

$\frac{7}{12}$

$\frac{2}{7}$

$\frac{1}{12}$

Q1 hint

Which bar has the largest area shaded?

2 Which is larger

a three quarters or two quarters

b three fifths or two fifths

c $\frac{7}{9}$ or $\frac{2}{9}$

d $\frac{11}{12}$ or $\frac{6}{12}$

e $\frac{7}{15}$ or $\frac{11}{15}$?

Q2c hint

Read out loud, 'seven ninths or ....?'

3 Look at the bars. Which is larger, $\frac{1}{5}$ or $\frac{1}{12}$?

$\frac{1}{5}$

$\frac{1}{12}$

4 Which is larger

a $\frac{1}{2}$ or $\frac{1}{5}$

b $\frac{1}{9}$ or $\frac{1}{3}$

c $\frac{1}{7}$ or $\frac{1}{8}$?

Q4 hint

You could draw bars to help you. Make the two bars the same length.

5 Work out the number shown by the shaded part.

a 10 | $10 \div 2 = \square$

b 12 | $12 \div 3 = \square$

c 20 | $20 \div \square = \square$

d 15 | $15 \div \square = \square$

6 Find $\frac{1}{3}$ of 15

7 Find $\frac{1}{3}$ of

a 12

b 27

c 18

Q6 hint

Draw a bar to show $\frac{1}{3}$.

15

Work out how many in one part.

8 a Find $\frac{1}{4}$ of 20

b Find $\frac{1}{5}$ of 10

c Find $\frac{1}{6}$ of 12

d Find $\frac{1}{10}$ of 30

Q8a hint

Draw a bar to show $\frac{1}{4}$.

20

Work out how many in one part.

9 What should you divide by to find these fractions of an amount?

   a $\frac{1}{4}$ **b** $\frac{1}{5}$ **c** $\frac{1}{7}$ **d** $\frac{1}{9}$

Q9a hint

☐ parts

10 Four people have a bill for £48. They decide to split it into quarters. How much do they each pay?

11 A team of football players share their winnings of £66 between them. They take $\frac{1}{11}$ each.
   How much does each player get?

12 Copy and complete these simplified fractions.

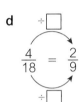 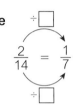 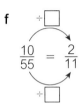

   a $\frac{4}{10} = \frac{2}{\square}$ (÷2, ÷2)
   b $\frac{5}{20} = \frac{\square}{4}$ (÷5, ÷5)
   c $\frac{30}{40} = \frac{\square}{4}$ (÷10, ÷10)

   d $\frac{4}{18} = \frac{2}{9}$ (÷☐, ÷☐)
   e $\frac{2}{14} = \frac{1}{7}$ (÷☐, ÷☐)
   f $\frac{10}{55} = \frac{2}{11}$ (÷☐, ÷☐)

13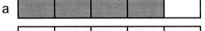

   a How many parts are shaded?
   b How many parts are in the whole bar?
   c What fraction of the bar is shaded?
   d What fraction of the bar is unshaded?

14 What fraction of each bar is shaded?

   a 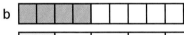   **b**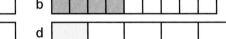

   c   **d**

Q14 hint

Use the steps in Q13.

15 A spinner is shaded red and blue.
   Gwennan says, 'The spinner has two colours and one of them is red. So half the spinner is red.'
   a Explain why she is wrong.
   b Draw a spinner with one half red.

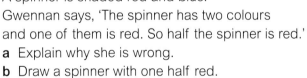
Red — Blue

16 **a** Three fifths add one fifth is ☐.
   b $\frac{2}{7} + \frac{3}{7}$
   c $\frac{5}{9} + \frac{2}{9}$

Q16a hint

When you add amounts of the same thing (whatever it is), just add the actual amounts. For example,
3 bananas + 1 banana = ☐ bananas.

Q16b hint

Read out loud, 'two sevenths add ...'.

17 Work out
   a $\frac{1}{12} + \frac{4}{12}$
   b $\frac{4}{7} + \frac{2}{7}$
   c $\frac{4}{9} + \frac{1}{9}$
   d $\frac{3}{11} + \frac{5}{11}$

Q17a hint

Draw a bar showing twelfths.
Colour in one twelfth and four twelfths.
How much is coloured altogether?

18 Complete these calculations.

   a $\frac{7}{9} - \frac{2}{9} = \frac{\square}{9}$ **b** $\frac{6}{11} - \frac{3}{11} = \frac{\square}{11}$ **c** $\frac{4}{5} - \frac{1}{5} = \frac{\square}{5}$

Q18a hint

Read out loud, 'seven ninths subtract two ninths is ☐.'

19 Work out

  a $1 - \frac{1}{5}$ **b** $1 - \frac{1}{7}$ **c** $1 - \frac{1}{3}$ **d** $1 - \frac{1}{4}$

20 Work out

  a $1 - \frac{3}{5}$ **b** $1 - \frac{5}{6}$ **c** $1 - \frac{2}{3}$ **d** $1 - \frac{7}{9}$

21 $\frac{5}{4}$ of these bars are shaded.

  a How many whole bars are shaded?

  b Copy and complete this statement.

    $\frac{5}{4} = 1\frac{\square}{4}$

22 **a** Draw bars to show $\frac{5}{3}$

  b Copy and complete this statement.

    $\frac{5}{3} = 1\frac{\square}{3}$

23 Copy and complete

  a $\frac{6}{5} = 1\frac{\square}{5}$ **b** $\frac{9}{7} = 1\frac{\square}{7}$ **c** $\frac{7}{6} = \square\frac{1}{6}$ **d** $\frac{8}{5} = \square\frac{\square}{5}$

  e $\frac{9}{8} = \square\frac{\square}{8}$ **f** $\frac{11}{9} = \square\frac{\square}{\square}$ **g** $\frac{13}{8} = \square\frac{\square}{\square}$ **h** $\frac{11}{6} = \square\frac{\square}{\square}$

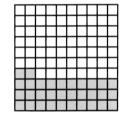

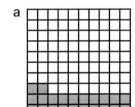

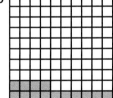

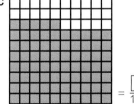

Equivalent fractions, decimals and percentages

1 **a** What fraction of this grid is *not* shaded?

  b What percentage of the grid is shaded?

2 Copy and complete these equivalent fractions and percentages.

  a $= \frac{22}{100} = \square\,\%$ **b** $= \frac{\square}{100} = \square\,\%$ **c** $= \frac{\square}{100} = \square\,\%$

3 Write these percentages as fractions.

  a $59\% = \frac{\square}{100}$ **b** $23\% = \frac{\square}{100}$ **c** $51\% = \frac{\square}{100}$

  d 19%   **e** 17%   **f** 93%

4 Write these percentages as fractions and then simplify the fraction.

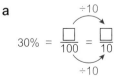

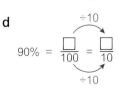

Hints

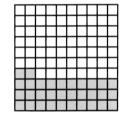

> **Q19a hint**
>
> $1 = \frac{5}{5}$
>
> | $\frac{1}{5}$ | $\frac{1}{5}$ | $\frac{1}{5}$ | $\frac{1}{5}$ | $\frac{1}{5}$ |

> **Q20a hint**
>
> Read out loud, 'five fifths subtract three fifths.'

> **Q1b hint**
>
> Remember that $\square\%$ is another way of saying '$\square$ out of 100'.

> **Q3 hint**
>
> How many squares out of 100 would you colour in?

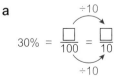

$30\% = \frac{\square}{100} = \frac{\square}{10}$ ($\div 10$)

$70\% = \frac{\square}{100} = \frac{\square}{10}$ ($\div 10$)

$10\% = \frac{\square}{100} = \frac{\square}{10}$ ($\div 10$)

$90\% = \frac{\square}{100} = \frac{\square}{10}$ ($\div 10$)

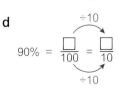

Finding percentages

1 a What do you divide by to find 10%?
b Work out 10% of £60

2 Find 10% of
a 30   **b** 500   **c** 420   **d** 88

3 a What do you divide by to find 50%?
b Work out 50% of 34

4 Find 50% of
a £60   **b** £320   **c** £450   **d** £17

5 Find 1% of
a 300   **b** 1400   **c** £1500
d 300 km   **e** 450 m   **f** 900 kg

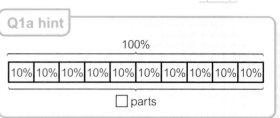

> **Q1a hint**
>
> 100%
>
> | 10% | 10% | 10% | 10% | 10% | 10% | 10% | 10% | 10% | 10% |
>
> ☐ parts

> **Q3a hint**
>
> 100%
>
> | 50% | 50% |
>
> ☐ parts

> **Q5 hint**
>
> To find 1% divide by 100.

Enrichment

1 The graph converts fractions to percentages.

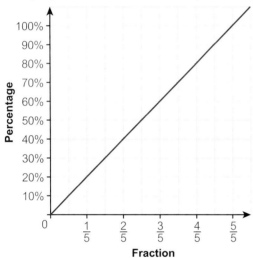

Fraction

Use the graph to copy and complete these conversions.

a $\frac{3}{5} = \square\%$ **b** $\frac{\square}{5} = 80\%$ **c** $\frac{1}{5} = \square\%$

2 a What fraction of each shape is shaded?
b Look at the fractions and use any patterns you notice to help you write three more equivalent fractions.

3 Write down the next three terms in each of these sequences.
a $\frac{1}{5}, \frac{2}{5}, \frac{3}{5}, \frac{4}{5}, \dots$ **b** $\frac{11}{11}, \frac{9}{11}, \frac{7}{11}, \dots$ **c** $1, \frac{11}{13}, \frac{9}{13}, \dots$

4 Reflect Tammy said, 'In this lesson, I am doing lots of dividing.'
Look back at your work in these Strengthen lessons.
Write down the numbers of three questions where you were dividing.
For each one, write whether you were working with fractions or percentages, or both.
Do you agree with Tammy?

Reflect

9 Extend

You will:
• Extend your understanding with problem-solving.

1 **Finance** A hospital records what fraction of its budget it spends on different departments.

$\frac{1}{8}$ Maternity $\frac{1}{5}$ Accident and Emergency

$\frac{1}{9}$ Children's wards $\frac{1}{15}$ Elderly Services

What does it spend the most on from this list?

2 The pictogram shows the favourite sports in a school.
   a Which is the most popular sport?
   b How many people chose swimming?
   c How many people chose hockey?
   d How many people were surveyed altogether?

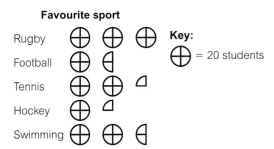

Favourite sport

Key: = 20 students

3 **Finance**
   a A shop sells shoes for £100. The price is reduced in a sale to £75.
     What percentage were the shoes reduced by?
   b Amit puts £100 into a savings account. He receives interest and after
     1 year has £102.
     What percentage interest does he get per year?

4 100 people were asked which type of restaurant is their favourite.

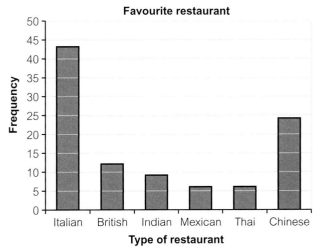

Favourite restaurant

   a What percentage of people preferred Thai restaurants?
   b What fraction of people preferred
      i Indian restaurants
      ii Italian restaurants
      iii Mexican or Thai restaurants?
     Give your answer as fractions in their simplest form.

5 **a** What is 10% of 721?

b What is 20% of 721?

6 Work out 20% of

a £321 **b** 189 cm **c** 194 m*l* **d** 265 km

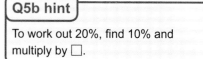

Q5b hint

To work out 20%, find 10% and multiply by ☐.

7 Work out

a 30% of 560 **b** 90% of 430 **c** 70% of 670

d 40% of 720 **e** 80% of 820 **f** 60% of 380

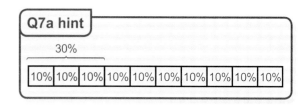

Q7a hint

30%

| 10% | 10% | 10% | 10% | 10% | 10% | 10% | 10% | 10% | 10% |

8 Scott works out 50% by working out 10% and then multiplying by 5. Caroline finds 50% by halving.
Use both methods to find 50% of 70.
Which method did you find easier?

9 **Finance** Computer prices are reduced by 30% in a sale. A tablet costs £520.

a Work out 30% of £520 **b** Work out the sale price of the tablet.

10 What fraction of each shape is shaded?
Write each answer in its simplest form.

a **b** **c**

d **e** 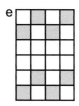 **f**

11 Work out

a 50% of 50 cm **b** 10% of £66 **c** 1% of 4 kg **d** 50% of 3 km

12 Work out these. Write your answers as mixed numbers.

a $\frac{3}{5} + \frac{3}{5} + \frac{2}{5}$ **b** $\frac{11}{15} + \frac{6}{15} + \frac{4}{15}$ **c** $\frac{19}{20} + \frac{13}{20} + \frac{11}{20}$

13 Prices are reduced by 10% in a sale. A TV costs £650.

a Work out 10% of £650 **b** What is the sale price?

14 Two cycle shops are having a sale. Each shop sells similar bikes.

Shop A: Original price £99 $\frac{1}{9}$ off all prices

Shop B: Original price £100   10% off all prices

a Work out the sale price of the bike in each shop.
b You want to buy the cheaper bike.
Which shop would you buy it from?

15 A competition offers these prizes.
- 50% of £120
- $\frac{1}{5}$ of £300
- $\frac{1}{9}$ of £900

Which prize is worth the most?

Topic links: Types of number, Bar charts, Proportion   **Subject links:** Science (Q23)

16 Write down the next two terms in each of these sequences.

a $\frac{1}{2}$, 1, 1$\frac{1}{2}$, 2, …

b $\frac{1}{4}$, $\frac{2}{4}$, $\frac{3}{4}$, 1, 1$\frac{1}{4}$, …

17 a Sort these cards into sets of three equivalent values.

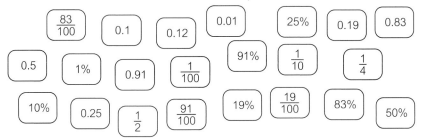

$\frac{83}{100}$ 0.1 0.12 0.01 25% 0.19 0.83	

0.5 1% 0.91 $\frac{1}{100}$ 91% $\frac{1}{10}$ $\frac{1}{4}$

10% 0.25 $\frac{1}{2}$ $\frac{91}{100}$ 19% $\frac{19}{100}$ 83% 50%

Q17a hint

Write 0.5 = ☐ = ☐

b Which card does not belong with a group?

c Write two other cards to complete the set for the odd one out.

18 Work out

a $\frac{1}{5}$ of 20 cm **b** $\frac{1}{3}$ of £33 **c** $\frac{1}{4}$ of 48 kg **d** $\frac{1}{9}$ of 27 inches

19 During a 10-hour flight a pilot spends

- $\frac{1}{10}$ of the flight in a holding pattern

- $\frac{1}{20}$ of the flight climbing

- $\frac{1}{20}$ of the flight descending

- $\frac{8}{10}$ of the flight cruising.

Work out how long she spends doing each.

20 A rectangle has a perimeter of 20 cm. One of the sides measures $\frac{1}{5}$ of the total perimeter.

a What is the length of this side?

b What are the lengths of the other sides?

c Calculate the area of the rectangle.

Q20 Strategy hint

Sketch the rectangle.
Label the measurements as you work them out.

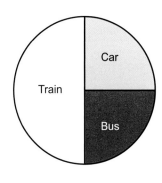

21 Match each value in column A with a value in column B.

A	B
$\frac{5}{6}$	1$\frac{5}{6}$
$\frac{11}{6}$	$\frac{7}{10}$
$\frac{17}{100}$	2$\frac{5}{6}$
$\frac{17}{6}$	$\frac{1}{4}$
70%	$\frac{10}{12}$
25%	$\frac{1}{10}$
10%	17%

Q21 hint

Write $\frac{5}{6}$ = ☐

22 Real The pie chart shows how students travel to school.

a What fraction travel by

i train

ii bus

iii car?

b What percentage travel by

i train

ii bus

iii car?

23 STEM A baby is expected to gain 50% of its birth weight after 3 months. A newly born baby weighs 8 lbs.
How much should she weigh after 3 months?

24 The marks in an exam are
50%, 65%, 70%, 70%, 95%, 60%, 63%, 72%, 70%, 75%
a What is the modal mark?
b What is the mean mark?
c What is the range of marks?

25 Finance For Christmas Chanelle is given £200. She spends $\frac{1}{5}$ on clothing and $\frac{2}{5}$ on an MP3 player. She saves the rest.
a How much does she spend on clothing?
b How much does she spend on an MP3 player?
c What fraction does she spend?
d What fraction does she save?
e How much does she save?

> **Q25 hint**
> To work out $\frac{2}{5}$, work out $\frac{1}{5}$ and multiply by □.

26 Which is greater, $\frac{1}{3}$ of £60 or $\frac{1}{5}$ of £200?

27 Finance Annie Matts leaves £48 000 in her will. She leaves
- $\frac{1}{5}$ to her son
- 10% to her granddaughter
- $\frac{1}{12}$ to her sister
- the rest to charity.
a Work out how much she leaves to each person.
b How much is left to charity?

> **Q28 hint**
> Work out how many of each type of number you need.
> 50% of 10 = □

28 Problem-solving Write a list of 10 numbers so that 50% of them are odd, $\frac{1}{10}$ are multiples of 5 and $\frac{1}{5}$ are larger than 60.

Investigation

A baby spends
- $\frac{1}{2}$ of the day sleeping
- $\frac{1}{4}$ of the day playing
- $\frac{1}{6}$ of the day crying
1 How many hours are left for eating?
2 Write a problem-solving question like this about your day.

---

29 Reflect Sarah and Jim are discussing Q17.
Here is what they said they did.
- Sarah says, 'First, I looked at each percentage and tried to find a matching decimal. Then, I looked at each decimal and tried to find a matching fraction. That's how I found the odd one out.'
- Jim says, 'First, I listed all the decimals in my book. Then, beside each decimal, I wrote its matching percentage and fraction. Then I compared my lists with the cards. That's how I found the odd one out.'

Write down what you did to answer Q17.
Which method is best, Sarah's, Jim's or yours? Explain why.

> **Q29 hint**
> Write '_____ method is best, because _____.'

9 Unit test

Log how you did on your Student Progression Chart.

1 Write these fractions in order from smallest to largest.
$\frac{7}{13}$, $\frac{9}{13}$, $\frac{2}{13}$, $\frac{5}{13}$, $\frac{12}{13}$

2 **a** What fraction of each shape is shaded?

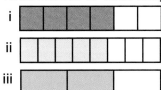

    b Which two fractions in part **a** are equivalent?

3 Which is the smallest fraction?

    A $\frac{1}{7}$ **B** $\frac{1}{9}$ **C** $\frac{1}{3}$

4 Work out

    a $\frac{1}{2}$ of 14   **b** $\frac{1}{3}$ of 18

5 70 dog owners completed a survey. $\frac{1}{7}$ of the dog owners said they visited the vet regularly.
How many is this?

6 Write down the number that makes these sentences correct.
    a If you cut a pizza into twelfths you cut it into ____ pieces.
    b To find $\frac{1}{8}$ you divide by ____.
    c Calculating $\frac{1}{5}$ is the same as dividing by ____.

7 In a test of 100 questions Chaitra correctly answered 53 questions.
What percentage did she get?

8 Work out
    a $\frac{1}{5}$ of £4   **b** $\frac{1}{7}$ of 35 metres

9 Match each question with the correct answer.

A 10% of 4000		**i** 40
B 1% of 400		**ii** 4
C 50% of 80		**iii** 400
D 10% of 80		**iv** 80
E 50% of 160		**v** 8

10 Everything is reduced by 10% in a sale.
The original price of a pair of trainers was £40.
    a Work out 10% of £40.
    b What is the sale price of the trainers?

11 Convert these percentages to fractions.

a $33\% = \dfrac{\square}{100}$
b $10\% = \dfrac{\square}{100} = \dfrac{\square}{10}$
c $50\% = \dfrac{\square}{100} = \dfrac{\square}{10} = \dfrac{\square}{2}$

12 What fraction of these shapes has been shaded?

a

b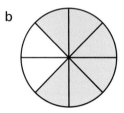

13 Work out

a $\dfrac{4}{9} + \dfrac{3}{9}$
b $\dfrac{1}{10} + \dfrac{3}{10} + \dfrac{3}{10}$
c $\dfrac{4}{5} - \dfrac{3}{5}$
d $1 - \dfrac{4}{7}$

14 Write these percentages as decimals.

a 45%
b 63%

15 Copy and complete

a $\dfrac{5}{4} = 1\dfrac{\square}{\square}$
b $\dfrac{7}{5} = \square\dfrac{\square}{\square}$

16 Work out

a $\dfrac{6}{7} + \dfrac{2}{7}$
b $\dfrac{1}{5} + \dfrac{4}{5} + \dfrac{3}{5}$

Give your answers as mixed numbers.

17 A savings account rewards savers with 1% interest on their savings each year. Ellie invests £450.
How much interest does she receive after 1 year?

18 Which is the odd one out in each of these lists? Explain why.

a 50% 0.05 $\dfrac{1}{2}$
b 10% 0.1 $\dfrac{1}{100}$
c 7% 0.7 $\dfrac{7}{10}$

19 Which is greater, $\dfrac{1}{4}$ of £1000 or $\dfrac{1}{3}$ of £900?

Challenge

19 Write these in order of size from smallest to largest by converting them to fractions.

0.25 $\dfrac{29}{100}$ 24% 30% 0.03

20 Work out

a $\dfrac{1}{2}$ of 600
b $\dfrac{1}{3}$ of the answer to part **a**
c $\dfrac{1}{4}$ of the answer to part **b**
d $\dfrac{1}{5}$ of the answer to part **c**

All your answers should be whole numbers.

e Find a number smaller than 600 for which this would also work.

f How many other numbers can you find for which this would work?

21 Reflect Which question in the unit test made you think the hardest? Explain why.

Q21 hint

Write, 'Question ___ made me think hardest, because _____.'

Reflect

10.1 Reflection

You will learn to:
- Reflect a shape in a mirror line.

Fluency
Wave your right hand at a mirror. Which hand does it look like is waving at you? Your left hand or your right hand?

Explore
Is one side of your face a reflection of the other?

Why learn this?
Designers use reflection to make symmetrical patterns.

Exercise 10.1

1 How many lines of symmetry does each shape have?

2 **a** Write down the coordinates of the points on the coordinate grid.
   b Copy the axes.
   Plot these points on your grid.
   E(5, 2) F(3, 4) G(2, 0) H(4, 1)

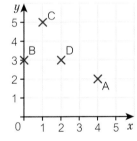

> **Key point**
> A **reflection** is a type of **transformation**.
> When a shape or object is reflected in a mirror the shape 'flips' over.

3 Which is the correct **reflection** of the shape?

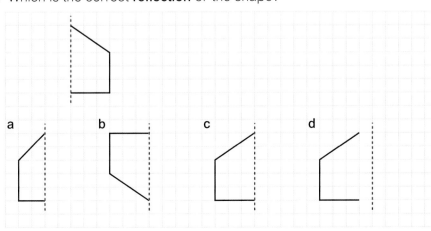

> **Q3 hint**
> You could use a mirror to help.

Warm up

4 Which is the correct reflection of the shape?

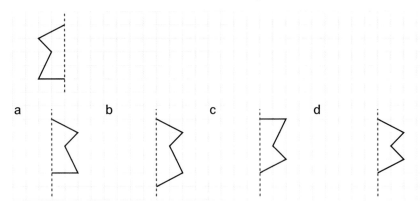

Discussion What is the same about a mirror line and a line of symmetry?

Investigation   Reasoning
1 If you look in a mirror what would happen to your reflection when you walk backwards?
2 Which is the correct reflection of the triangle: A, B or C?

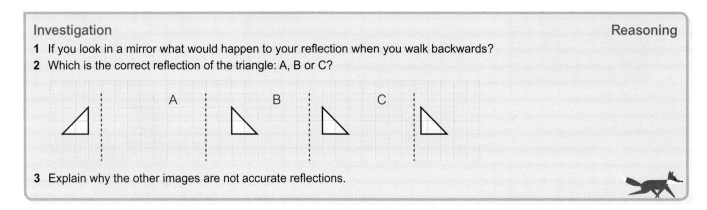

3 Explain why the other images are not accurate reflections.

5 Match each shape to its reflection in the **mirror line**.

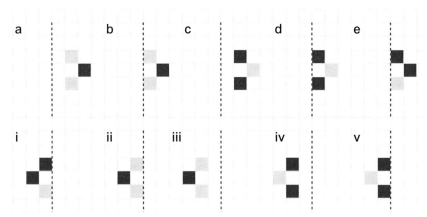

Key point

All points on an object are the same distance from a **mirror line** as the points on the image, but on the opposite side.

Literacy hint
A vertical mirror line is

A horizontal mirror line is - - - - - - - - - - -

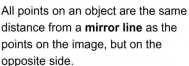

6 Copy and complete each picture to make an accurate reflection in the mirror line.

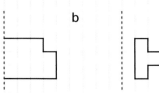

Reasoning If you reflect the capital letter A in a vertical mirror line it still looks the same.
Which other capital letters are the same when reflected in a vertical mirror line?
What about a horizontal mirror line?

A ⦙ A

Topic links: Symmetry of 2D shapes, Coordinates

7 This image shows part of a kaleidoscope design.

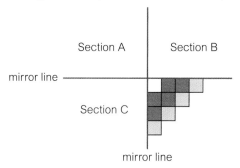

Choose which images should go into each section to reflect the design in the mirror lines shown.

a 　　**b** 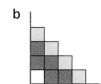　　**c**

8 a Copy each pair of shapes. Draw in the mirror line for each pair.

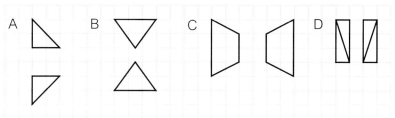

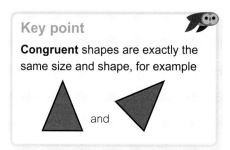

Key point

Congruent shapes are exactly the same size and shape, for example

and

b Are the shapes in each pair **congruent**?

Discussion When a shape is reflected in a mirror line what can you say about the perimeter of the shape and its reflection? What about the area of both?

9 The points A–E are reflected in the mirror line shown. Write down the coordinates of the reflection of each point.

Discussion How do you reflect a point on the mirror line?

10 Explore Is one side of your face a reflection of the other? Is it easier to explore this question now you have completed the lesson? What further information do you need to be able to answer this?

11 Reflect Sketch a shape that is easy to reflect in a mirror line. Copy and complete this sentence: This shape is easy to reflect, because _____. Sketch a shape that is difficult to reflect in a mirror line. Copy and complete this sentence: This shape is difficult to reflect, because _____. Compare your shapes and sentences with others in your class.

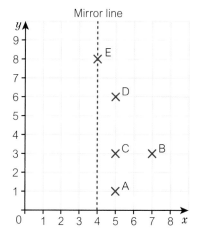

Q11 hint

Draw your shapes with pencil and ruler on squared paper.

Explore

Reflect

10.2 Translation

You will learn to:
• Translate a shape.

CONFIDENCE

Why learn this?
Fabrics often have a repeating pattern that is a translation of an original design.

Fluency
Draw an arrow that points
• left
• right.

Explore
How can you describe moves in chess?

Exercise 10.2

Warm up

1 a Write down the coordinates of the points A, B, C and D.

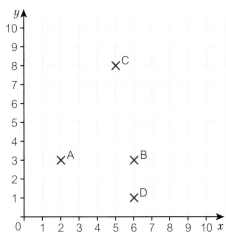

b To move from A to B, move 4 right. Describe how to move from

   i B to A   **ii** B to D   **iii** B to C   **iv** C to A.

2 Describe each move.
The first one is done for you.
a A to B
   4 squares left
b A to C
c A to D
d A to E

Q2 Strategy hint

Choose a corner of the green shape. Count how many squares you need to move that corner to the new position.

Topic links: Reading coordinates

3 Describe the **translation** that takes each black quadrilateral onto its red equivalent.

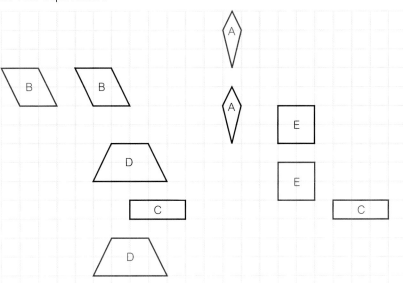

4 Describe each translation.

a A to B

b A to C

c A to D

d A to E

e A to F

f A to G

g A to H

Discussion When a shape is translated what can you say about the perimeter and area of both shapes? Are both shapes congruent?

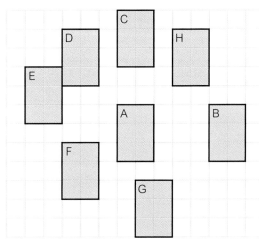

Q4 hint

First give moves left or right, then up or down.
A to B: ☐ squares right

Worked example

Translate the triangle 5 squares left and 3 squares down.

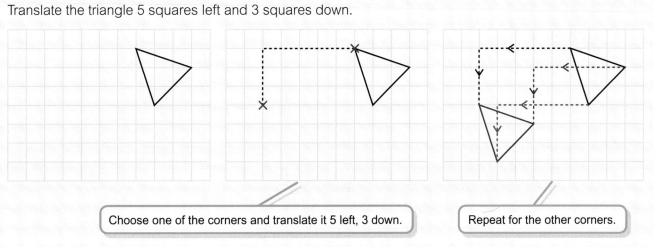

Choose one of the corners and translate it 5 left, 3 down.

Repeat for the other corners.

5 Copy each shape on to squared paper.
Translate the shape
  a 4 right
  b 2 up
  c 2 right 3 up
  d 3 left 6 down.

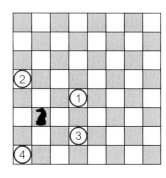

a   b   c   d

6 **Real** Here are some of the moves a knight can make on a chessboard.
  a Describe the four moves shown as translations.
  b Can this piece ever move to a black square?

  Discussion What is the rule for moving a knight?

7 Write down the coordinates of the red cross after each translation.
  a 4 left
  b 5 down
  c 3 left, 2 up
  d 4 right, 1 down
  e 3 left, 2 down
  f 2 right, 4 up
  g 6 left, 5 down

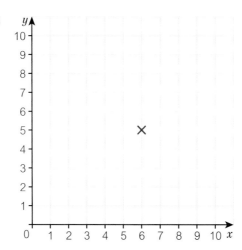

8 Copy this grid and shape X.
Translate shape X

  a 5 squares down.
  Label it A.
  b 3 squares right.
  Label it B.
  c 1 square right,
  2 squares down.
  Label it C.
  d 1 square left,
  7 squares down.
  Label it D.

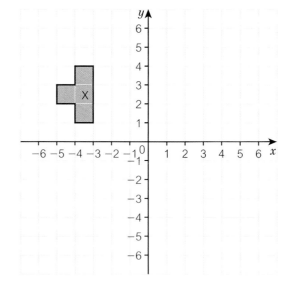

9 **Explore** How can you describe moves in chess?
Is it easier to explore this question now you have completed the lesson?
What further information do you need to be able to answer this?

10 **Reflect a** List any words that are useful for describing translations.
  b Write down what the numbers tell you when describing translations.

> **Q10 hint**
>
> Can you describe a translation without words or without numbers? Explain why.

Active Learn   Pi 1, Section 10.2

10.3 Rotation

You will learn to:

- Draw and describe rotations.

Why learn this?
Engineers need to understand rotation to help them design engines.

Fluency
Stand up and rotate through

- $\frac{1}{2}$ turn
- $\frac{1}{4}$ turn clockwise
- $\frac{3}{4}$ turn anticlockwise
- a complete turn.

Explore
Which shape looks the same no matter what angle you rotate it through?

Exercise 10.3

1 a Match each diagram to the correct description.

i 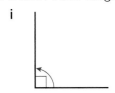   ii 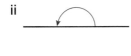   iii   iv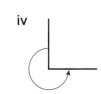

    A quarter turn

    B half turn

    C three-quarter turn

    D complete turn

b Match these angles to turns A–D.
    i 180°   **ii** 90°   **iii** 360°   **iv** 270°

2 Write down the order of **rotational** symmetry of

a   **b**   **c**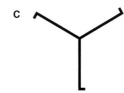

> **Key point**
>
> Turning a shape through an angle is called a **rotation**. A rotation is a type of transformation.

3 a Which shapes have been rotated through $\frac{1}{4}$ of a turn?

A   B   C

b Which of these shapes has been rotated through $\frac{1}{2}$ a turn?

D   E   F

4 Which shapes are rotations of shape A?

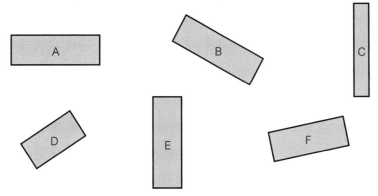

Q4 hint

Trace Shape A and see if it will fit exactly over the images.

Discussion Are shapes congruent after a rotation?

5 Real Which of these flags would look the same if they were hung upside down?

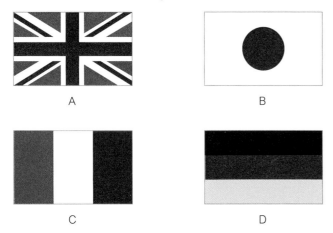

A

B

C

D

Discussion What angle are they rotated through to hang upside down?

Worked example

Rotate this shape through a $\frac{3}{4}$ turn clockwise.

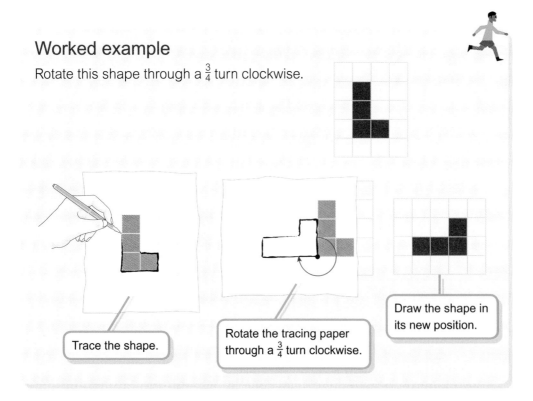

Trace the shape.

Rotate the tracing paper through a $\frac{3}{4}$ turn clockwise.

Draw the shape in its new position.

6 Copy each shape on to squared paper.
Draw the rotation for each shape.

a $\frac{1}{4}$ turn clockwise   **b** $\frac{1}{2}$ turn   **c** $\frac{1}{4}$ turn anticlockwise

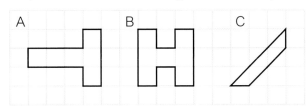

Discussion Does it matter in which direction you rotate part **b**?
How else could you have described the rotations for parts **a** and **c**?

Investigation   Reasoning

1 Investigate which of these rotations are the same.
   A $\frac{1}{2}$ turn anticlockwise
   B $\frac{1}{4}$ turn anticlockwise
   C 270° turn clockwise
   D 180° turn clockwise
2 Draw a shape and try the rotations.

---

7 Copy each shape onto squared paper.
Rotate it through the angle given about the **centre of rotation** marked ✕.

a

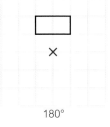

180°

b

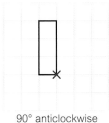

90° anticlockwise

c

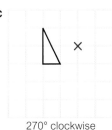

270° clockwise

d

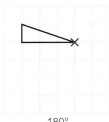

180°

e

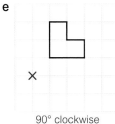

90° clockwise

f

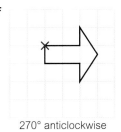

270° anticlockwise

Q7a hint

Use tracing paper to help you.

8 Each grey shape has been rotated about the centre of rotation ✕.
Describe each rotation.

Q8 hint

Give the angle and direction.

a   b   c

d   e   f

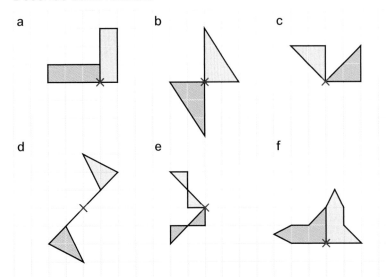

9 The shapes marked A have been rotated about the centre of
rotation ✕. Describe the rotations.

a   b   c

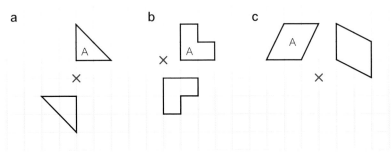

Discussion Which direction is the rotation in part **c**? Does it matter?

10 Explore Which shape looks the same no matter what angle you
rotate it through?
Look back at the maths you have learned in this lesson.
How can you use it to answer this question?

11 Reflect In lesson 10.1 you learned about reflection.
In this lesson you learned about rotation.
  a Sketch two pairs of shapes that show reflection **and** rotation.
  b Describe the rotation that also shows a reflection.
  c Does this rotation *always* show a reflection?

Q11 hint

Look back in this lesson at pairs of
shapes in Q4, and at your answer
to Q10.

Explore

Reflect

10.4 STEM: Congruency

You will learn to:

- Identify congruent shapes.

Why learn this?
Graphic designers use congruent shapes to design screen savers and computer wallpaper.

Fluency
Which shapes are congruent?

Explore
Which company logos are designed using transformations?

Exercise 10.4: Computer graphics

1 Draw a reflection of each shape in the mirror lines.

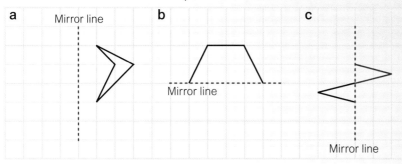

2 Describe the translation that takes shape A to
   a shape B   **b** shape C   **c** shape D.

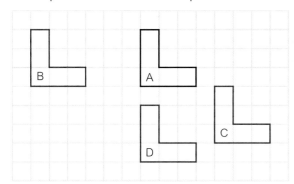

3 What fraction of a turn has each shape been rotated?
   Clockwise or anticlockwise?

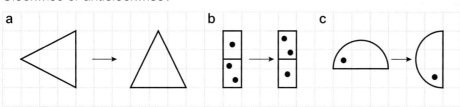

Warm up

A graphic designer draws two congruent trapeziums.

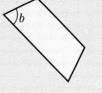

1 Trace the longest side of the blue trapezium. Lay this over the longest side of the green trapezium.
   Are they the same size?
2 Repeat for the other sides. Are they the same size?
3 Copy and complete this sentence.
   If two shapes are congruent the lengths of matching sides are _____.
4 Measure ∠a in the blue trapezium. Measure ∠b in the green trapezium. Are they the same size?
5 Repeat for the other angles. Are they the same size?
6 Copy and complete this sentence.
   If two shapes are congruent the matching angles are _____.

4 In a computer game, congruent shapes are worth the points shown.

Shapes that are not congruent are worth 0 points.
Here are the results. Write down the points for

a   b   c

d   e   f

5 Here is a wallpaper for a mobile phone.

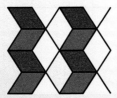

a What 2D shape has the designer used?
b Measure the sides and angles in each shape. Are all the shapes congruent?
c What type of transformation takes the red shape to the blue one?
d What type of transformation takes the yellow shape to the white one?

6 STEM A computer programmer is working on a game where shapes fit together. Which shapes are congruent?

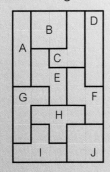

7 Reasoning Are these pairs of shapes congruent?
Give a reason for your answer.

a 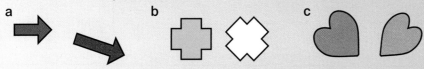 b   c

8 STEM / Reasoning Here is a design for tiling a kitchen.

Adrian thinks all the rectangles are congruent. Helena thinks only the red and green ones are.
Who is correct? Explain your answer.

9 This app logo

Q9 hint

Use tracing to make sure your shapes are congruent.

has three shapes that are congruent:
Design an app logo using at least thee shapes that are congruent.

10 Which two of these triangles are congruent? Explain how you know.

A    B 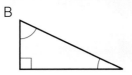   C

11 Is this translation correct?
Explain how you know.

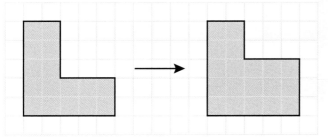

12 Explore Which company logos are designed using transformations?
Is it easier to explore this question now you have completed the lesson?
What further information do you need to be able to answer this?

13 Reflect In this unit you have learned about reflection, rotation, translation and congruent shapes.
Which is easiest? Explain why to your classmate.
Which is hardest? Explain why to your classmate.

STEM

Explore

Reflect

10 Check up

Log how you did on your Student Progression Chart.

Reflection

1 Which is the correct reflection of this shape?

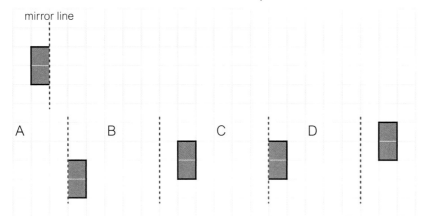

mirror line

A   B   C   D

2 This triangle has been reflected in a mirror line. Copy the diagram. Draw on the mirror line.

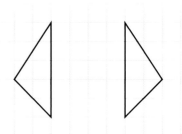

3 Copy this shape onto squared paper. Reflect it in the mirror line.

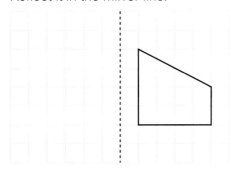

Translation

4 The blue shape is translated to make shapes A to D. Describe each translation.
   a blue shape to shape A
   b blue shape to shape B
   c blue shape to shape C
   d blue shape to shape D
   e blue shape to shape E
   f blue shape to shape F

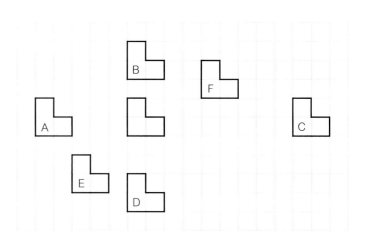

5 Copy the diagram on to squared paper.
Draw the triangle after each translation.
  a 3 down
  b 5 left, 3 up

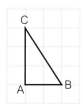

Rotation and congruency

6 A   B  C  D

  a Which show $\frac{1}{2}$ turns? **b** Which show $\frac{1}{4}$ turns?

7 Copy each shape onto squared paper. Draw the rotation.

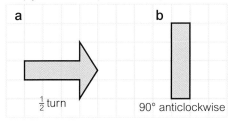

  a $\frac{1}{2}$ turn   **b** 90° anticlockwise

8 Are these rectangles congruent?
Explain how you know.

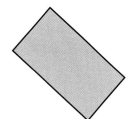

9 How sure are you of your answers? Were you mostly
  ☹ Just guessing 😐 Feeling doubtful ☺ Confident
  What next? Use your results to decide whether to strengthen or extend your learning.

Challenge

10 The point (3, 4) is plotted on a coordinate axis.
  What are the coordinates when the point is
  a reflected in the y-axis
  b reflected in the x-axis
  c translated 3 squares right, 4 squares down
  d translated 5 squares left, 7 squares up?

11 **a** Copy this rectangle on to squared
    paper.
  b How many shapes like this can you
    draw in your rectangle?

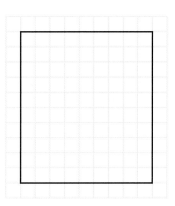

  c Did anyone in the class fit more in
    than you could?

Master
P250

Check
P263

STRENGTHEN

Extend
P270

Test
P274

10 Strengthen

You will:

• Strengthen your understanding with practice.

Reflection

1 Which is the correct reflection?

a

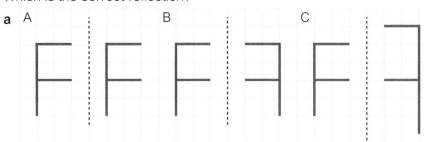

Q1a hint

Use a mirror to check.

b

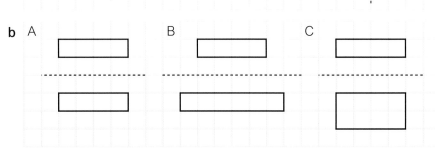

c

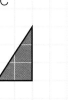

Q1c hint

Which one has both triangles the same distance from the mirror line?

2 a Copy this picture and mirror line on to squared paper.
Draw the reflection in the mirror line.
b What letter have you drawn?

Q2 hint

Count the squares.

3 Which reflections have the mirror line in the correct place?

a　　　　**b**　　　　**c**

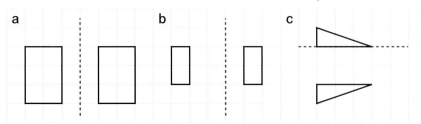

Q3 hint

Count the squares from each corner of the shape to the mirror line.

4 Reflect the shapes in the mirror lines. The first two parts have been started for you.

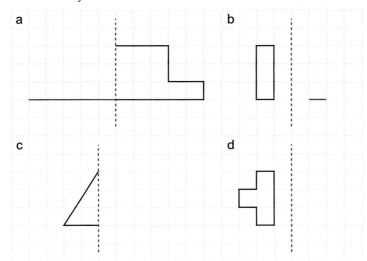

a

b

c

d

Q4 hint

The reflection must be the same size as the original shape.

Translation

1 In each diagram, shape A moves to shape B.

   a Copy this diagram on to squared paper.

Q1b hint

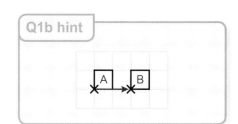

   b Draw an arrow from the corner marked with a cross on shape A to the corner marked with a cross on shape B.

   c Copy and complete the sentence to describe how shape A moves to make shape B.

   ☐ squares _____

   number ↑   ↖ left, right, up or down

2 In each diagram describe how shape A moves to shape B.

a

b

c

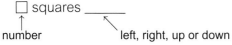
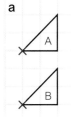
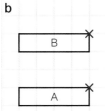
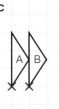

Q2 hint

Follow the steps in Q1.

3 For each diagram describe how point A moves to point B.

a

b

c

d

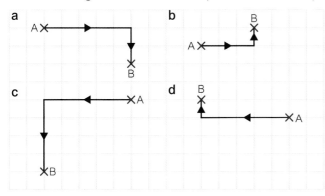

Q3 hint

☐ squares _____ ← left or right?
☐ squares _____ ← up or down?

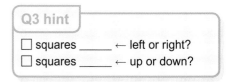

4 a Which two of triangles A–D are translations of the blue triangle?

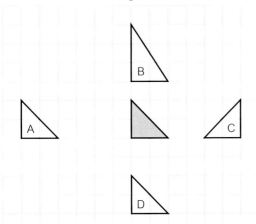

Q4a hint

A translation is a slide. A translated shape is exactly the same shape and size and is the same way round.

b Describe the two translations.

5 Describe the translation that moves shape
  a A to B
  b A to C
  c C to D
  d B to E.

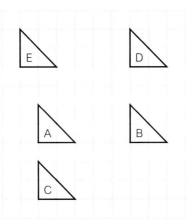

Q4b hint

Follow the steps in Q1.

Rotation

1 What fraction of a turn has the clock hand made?

a

b

c

2 Are these shapes rotated $\frac{1}{4}$ turn or $\frac{1}{2}$ turn?

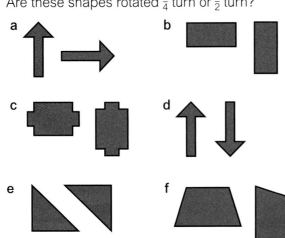

Q2 hint

Turning your book upside down would involve a $\frac{1}{2}$ turn.

Q2a and d hint

Look at Q1 for help.

3 All the blue shapes have been rotated $\frac{1}{4}$ turn. Write clockwise or anticlockwise for each one.

Q3 hint

anticlockwise   clockwise

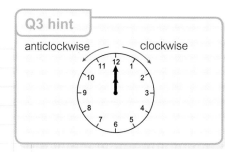

a

b

c

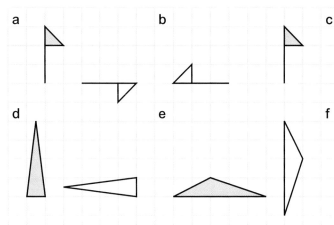

d

e

f

4 a Copy this triangle onto squared paper.

b Trace the shape. Turn the tracing a $\frac{1}{2}$ turn. Now draw the rotation.

c Repeat for $\frac{1}{4}$ turn clockwise.

d Repeat for $\frac{3}{4}$ turn anticlockwise.

e What do you notice about your drawing for parts **c** and **d**?

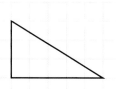

5 The shapes marked A have been rotated about a centre of rotation marked ✗.

Q5 hint

90°   180°   270°

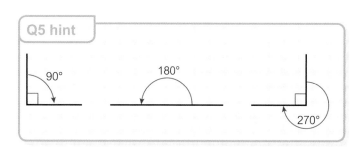

a

b

c

d

A

B

A

B

A

B

A

B

✗

✗

✗

✗

Copy and complete to describe each rotation.

☐° _____ ← clockwise or anticlockwise

Q5c and d hint

Visualise the dashed lines – picture them in your head.

6 The red shapes have been rotated from the black shapes about the centre of rotation marked ✕. Describe the rotations.

   a   **b**   **c**

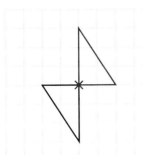 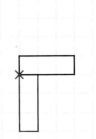 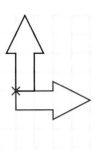

Congruency

Q6 hint

Write the angle and direction.

1 Which shapes are rotations of shape A?

A

Q1 hint

If a shape is rotated, its image is exactly the same shape and size.

B   C   D   E

2 Decide if these pairs of shapes are congruent.

   a   **b**   **c**

Q2 hint

Trace one of the pair. If the tracing fits exactly over the other shape, then they are congruent.

Enrichment

1 Copy this pentomino.
  a Reflect it in a vertical mirror line.
  b Reflect it in a horizontal mirror line.
  c Rotate it 90° clockwise or anticlockwise.
  d Translate it 2 right, 3 down.
  e Which of your shapes are congruent?
  f What is the missing word?
     Reflected, rotated and translated shapes are always _____.

2 Reflect Match each word to an action.

  A reflection   **1** slide
  B rotation   **2** same
  C translation   **3** flip
  D congruent   **4** turn

Reflect

10 Extend

You will:

• Extend your understanding with problem-solving.

1 Decide which transformation(s) (rotation, reflection or translation) could be used to form the image of each shape.
There may be more than one possible answer for any of the shapes.

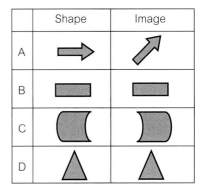

	Shape	Image
A		
B		
C		
D		

2 a Describe the translation that takes this shape from

  i A to B

  ii B to A.

 b What do you notice about your answers to part **a**?

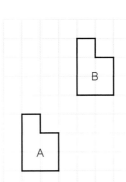

3 This shape is translated 3 squares right and 4 squares up.
It is then translated 2 squares left and 3 squares down.
 a Copy the shape onto squared paper and draw the image.
 b What translation takes the original shape to the final image?

4 Copy and complete the stained-glass window so that one side is a reflection of the other.

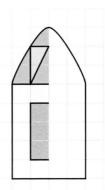

5 Each line is reflected in the mirror line.

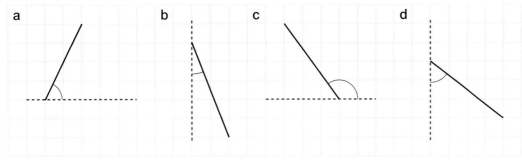

For each part decide whether the angle between the original line and its reflection is acute, obtuse or reflex.

6 Here is a company logo.
Copy the logo onto squared paper.
Colour the logo so that it looks exactly
the same when it is rotated through $\frac{1}{2}$ turn.

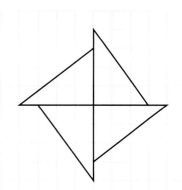

7 **Problem-solving** The number 808 reads the same when reflected in a
mirror. List as many other numbers as you can like this.

8 The aim of a computer game is to
use falling shapes to complete a
solid line.
Describe how to rotate the purple
shape to complete a line.

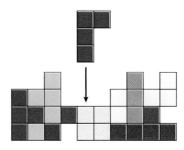

9 The diagram shows four triangles on a coordinate grid.
Are these statements true or false?
  a The translation from A to C is 1 left, 3 down.
  b The translation from D to C is 4 left, 1 up.
  c The translation from B to A is 4 right.
  d The translation from A to C is equivalent to the
    translation from C to D.
  e All the triangles have the same area.
  f The triangles do not have the same perimeter.

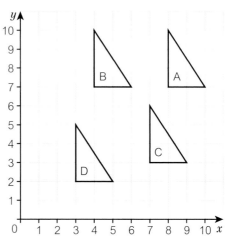

10 Each shape is reflected in the mirror line.
Write the name of the final shape.

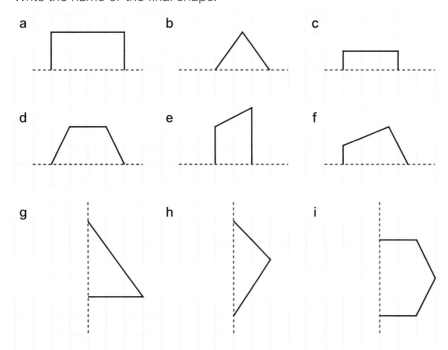

Topic links: Angles, 2D shapes, Area and perimeter, Coordinates

11 Which of these logos are exactly the same when
   a translated through 3 units right and 5 units down
   b rotated through $\frac{1}{4}$ turn clockwise
   c reflected in a **vertical** mirror line?

Q11 Literacy hint
A **vertical** line runs up and down the page.

A   B 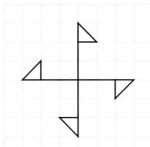   C    D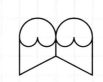

12 A counter on a board can move 1 square left, right, up or down.
   It can move 2 times in total. What combination of moves can it
   make? Two examples have been done for you.

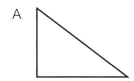   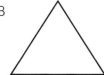

Q12 Strategy hint
List all the moves that start left,
_____. Then list all the moves that
start right, _____. That way, you
shouldn't miss any moves.
(You do not need to draw the grid
and counter each time.)

13 Which triangles are congruent?

A   B

C    D

14 Are these statements true or false?
   a When you rotate a shape the image is congruent.
   b When you translate a shape the image is *not* congruent.
   c When you reflect a shape the image is congruent.
   d The angles inside two congruent shapes are equal.
   e The perimeters of two congruent shapes are *not* equal.
   f When you reflect a quadrilateral in a mirror line, the image always
     looks identical to the original.
   g When you rotate a quadrilateral through a $\frac{1}{2}$ turn, the image always
     looks identical to the original.
   h When you translate a quadrilateral, the image always looks
     identical to the original.

15 The points A–G are reflected in the mirror line shown. Write the coordinates of the images of each point.

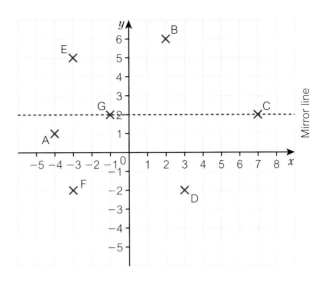

16 a Draw a coordinate grid like the one shown. Mark on the point A.
b Points B, C and D are translations of point A. Mark them on the grid.
  B 7 right
  C 5 right, 4 down
  D 2 left, 2 down
c Join the points in the order A, B, C, D, A.
d Name this shape.

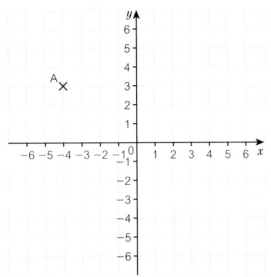

17 Sally plots the point (4, −2) on a coordinate axis. She then translates it 7 down, 2 left, then 3 up, 4 right.
  a What is the coordinate of the new point?
  b What transformation will take it back to (4, −2)?

Q17 Strategy hint

Draw out a coordinate grid and mark on the points.

18 a Make a copy of this diagram. Reflect the shape in the mirror line. Label the image B.
  b Translate shape B 4 right and 2 down. Label the image C.
  c Describe a translation that moves C to A.

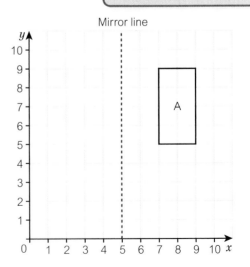

19 Reflect Sally says, 'This unit is all about transformations, but I am using lots of other maths.' Sally starts a list. She begins with:
Names of angles…
Look back at the questions you answered in these Extend lessons. Add at least two other maths topics to Sally's list that you have used.

Reflect

10 Unit test

Log how you did on your Student Progression Chart.

1 Describe the translation that takes shape A to shape B.

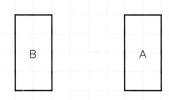

2 The blue arrow has been translated 3 right and 2 up. Which is the correct image?

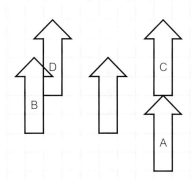

3

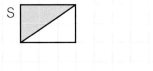

Which shape is shape S after

i $\frac{1}{2}$ turn

ii $\frac{1}{4}$ turn clockwise

iii $\frac{1}{4}$ turn anticlockwise?

4 Copy the pictures. Reflect the shapes in the mirror lines shown.

a

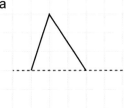

b

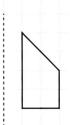

5 The shaded shapes have been rotated about the centre of rotation ✕.
Describe each rotation.

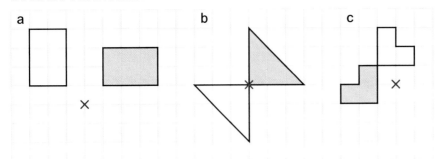

a   b   c

6 Which pairs of shapes are congruent?

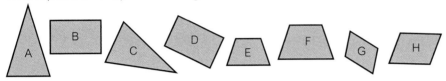

7 Explain why these two triangles are not congruent.

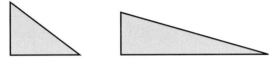

8 Copy this shape on to
squared paper. Use the
centre of rotation ✕
and rotate it
  a 90° anticlockwise. Label it A.
  b 90° clockwise. Label it B.
  c 180°. Label it C.

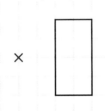

Challenge

9 Design a logo for a burger company. It must
  a look identical after a $\frac{1}{2}$ turn
  b have one line of symmetry.

10 a Make a copy of this diagram. Reflect the shape in the mirror line.
Label the image B.
  b Translate shape B 2 units right, 1 unit down. Label it C.
  c Reflect shape C in the mirror line. Label the image D.
  d Describe the translation that takes D to A.

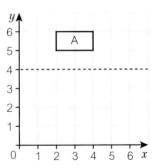

11 Reflect Discuss with your classmate if these statements are true.
  A Transform a shape and you move it to a new position.
  B Rotate a shape 180° clockwise.
     This is the same as rotating it 180° anticlockwise.
  C Draw a shape. Flip, turn or slide it (but keep it exactly the same
     size) and draw it again. Your two shapes are congruent.

> **Q11 hint**
>
> Look back at some questions you
> have answered in this unit to help
> you decide.

Reflect